ANIMALS AND PLANTS
OF THE
CENOZOIC ERA

ENGLAND: BUTTERWORTH & CO. (PUBLISHERS) LTD.
                  LONDON: 88 Kingsway, W.C.2

AUSTRALIA: BUTTERWORTH & CO. (AUSTRALIA) LTD.
                  SYDNEY: 6/8 O'Connell Street
                  MELBOURNE: 473 Bourke Street
                  BRISBANE: 240 Queen Street

CANADA: BUTTERWORTH & CO. (CANADA) LTD.
                  TORONTO: 1367 Danforth Avenue, 6

NEW ZEALAND: BUTTERWORTH & CO. (NEW ZEALAND) LTD.
                  WELLINGTON: 49/51 Ballance Street
                  AUCKLAND: 35 High Street

SOUTH AFRICA: BUTTERWORTH & CO. (SOUTH AFRICA) LTD.
                  DURBAN: 33/35 Beach Grove

U.S.A.:   BUTTERWORTH INC.
                  WASHINGTON D.C.: 7235 Wisconsin Avenue, 14

ANIMALS AND PLANTS
OF THE
CENOZOIC ERA

SOME ASPECTS OF
THE FAUNAL AND FLORAL HISTORY
OF THE LAST SIXTY MILLION YEARS

RONALD PEARSON

M.A., Ph.D., F.R.E.S., F.Z.S.

*Lecturer in Zoology in the University of Liverpool; and
sometime member of the Sub-department of Quaternary
Research, Botany School, Cambridge*

LONDON
BUTTERWORTHS
1964

141366

Suggested U.D.C. number : 56(117)

©
Butterworth & Co. (Publishers) Limited
1964

Made and printed in Great Britain by
Spottiswoode, Ballantyne & Co. Ltd., London and Colchester

CONTENTS

CONTENTS

PREFACE

It is now over fifty years since Osborn's *Age of Mammals* was published. In this period many papers have appeared which report work carried out by botanists, geochemists, geophysicists, geologists and paleontologists. These have added considerably to our knowledge of the climatic, faunal and floral events of the last sixty million years. However, much of this work has been published in books and periodicals which are usually read by only a limited section of those people who might be interested in the results. It therefore seemed to me that there was a need for a volume which would go some way towards introducing these potential readers to those aspects of the Cenozoic Era which lay outside their own special interest.

This seemed especially true of students of the mammals, on the one hand, and of the Anthophyta on the other. The first-named student will obtain some idea of the environment in which the mammals evolved, and the last-named obtain a picture of a group which has undergone a considerable amount of evolution whilst his groups have remained bradytelic. Whilst it is clear that such a book will be greeted by many criticisms, if it stimulates some readers to appreciate the potentialities of other aspects of Cenozoic biology I will feel that my intentions have been achieved.

Many writers will find that I have presented their work with only a slight periphrasis in order to avoid possible misinterpretations. If I have quoted without acknowledging my source I hereby acknowledge this indebtedness. I would especially like to acknowledge the debt which I, and all other zoologists, owe to the works of Romer and Simpson together with the *Traité de Paléontologie* and the *Traité de Zoologie*.

I wish to express my personal appreciation to Professor H. Godwin, F.R.S., who, in his capacity of Director of the University sub-department of Quaternary Research, Botany School, Cambridge, gave me unlimited good advice and never failed to encourage and stimulate his students; also to Professor R. J. Pumphrey, F.R.S., for his encouragement and patience in tolerating a somewhat unusual mammal course in this University; to Dr. D. Walker, of the Department of Pacific Studies, University of Canberra; Dr. R. G. West of the Botany School, Dr. E. H. Willis of the Radio-Carbon Dating Laboratory and Dr. John Smart of the Zoological Laboratory, Cambridge, for many stimulating discussions. Needless to say they are in no way responsible for any inadequacies in this book. I would also like to acknowledge a far older debt to D. G. Mackean and J. Gray.

Ronald Pearson

Brownlow Hill,
Liverpool.
January, 1964

1

INTRODUCTION

GENERAL INTRODUCTION

The Cenozoic Era or 'Age of Mammals' is clearly divided into two unequal periods, the long Tertiary and the shorter Quaternary or 'Glacial Period'. The Tertiary is further subdivided, a division originally made on the basis of the changing values for the percentage representation of modern species of marine molluscs. In recent years the entire span of the Cenozoic Era has been the subject of renewed interest which has been largely focused on the pollen, macroscopic plant remains, foraminifera, molluscs and insects. These studies have now provided an extensive and detailed picture of the environmental changes which took place during the period. Since it was, as the name 'Age of Mammals' suggests, the period during which the mammalian faunas of the world were evolving and in which the living species were achieving their present distribution, it is obviously of considerable importance that zoologists should obtain as detailed and clear an understanding as possible of these complex climatic and vegetational changes.

At the beginning of the period the various genera of placental mammals were still very similar in their morphology to their presumed insectivorous ancestors of the foregoing Cretaceous Period. These had, in fact, only comprised a relatively minor component of the total Mesozoic mammalian faunas which have been reviewed by Piveteau (1955), Romer (1945) and Simpson (1935b). The gradual appearance of modern vegetation together with the characteristic faunal components of the various periods is summarized in *Table 1*. From reptilian ancestors, represented in the Triassic by the ictidosaurs, there was an early Jurassic proliferation which produced the plagiaulacid multituberculates, the triconodonts, symmetrodonts and pantotheres. During the Cretaceous this faunal assemblage was replaced by one which included advanced ptilodontid multituberculates together with early placentals and marsupials.

With the widespread reduction in the numbers of the reptiles which had taken place by the end of the Cretaceous the marsupials and placentals began to increase in importance as components of the world vertebrate fauna. In fact, many dinosaur groups flourished as late as the Upper Cretaceous and in classical terms their extinction at the Mesozoic/Cenozoic transition is, as Romer (1945) pointed out, one of the most dramatic events of vertebrate history. Although the events leading to this extinction have been widely argued, it is thought that the Laramide revolution with the elevation of the Rockies and other mountain chains, together with the climatic deterioration of the Upper Cretaceous times (see Chapter 5), were probably the principal factors. These environmental changes would have greatly affected the vegetation available to herbivorous forms as well as placing a premium on

1

Table 1. The geological periods of the northern hemisphere together with their principal vegetation types and their characteristic fossil groups

Era	Period	Age (millions of years)	Type of vegetation	Characteristic fossil groups
Cenozoic	Quaternary	1–2	Modern	Mammals
	Tertiary	60–70	Modern	Mammals
Mesozoic	Cretaceous	ca. 127	Gymnosperms dominant in Lower Cretaceous. (Conifers and Bennettitales)	Ammonites; Diapsid reptiles; Plagiaulacid and ptilodontid multi-tuberculates; Insectivora; Marsupialia
	Jurassic	152	Luxuriant forests of gymnosperms and ferns	Ammonites; Diapsid reptiles; Triconodonts; Symmetrodonts; Pantotheres
	Triassic	190	Sparse desert flora giving way to luxuriant forests of gymnosperms and ferns during the Upper Triassic	Ammonites; Diapsid reptiles; Tritylodonts; Ictidosaurs
Paleozoic	Permian	200	Tall swamp forests with early gymnosperms, tree lycopods, Calamites and ferns giving way to desert flora of conifers Bennettitales	Goniatites; Cotylosaurs; Pelycosaurs; Therapsida
	Carboniferous	250	Early gymnosperms, tree lycopods and ferns	Goniatites; Trilobites; Cotylosaurs; Labyrinthodonts
	Devonian	313	Herbaceous marsh plants (*Psilophyta* and *Zosterophyllum*). *Rhynia* vegetation in Middle Devonian. Early gymnosperms and lycopods in Upper Devonian	Goniatites; Trilobita; Acanthodians; Antiarchs and Ichthyostegalia
	Silurian	350	Marine algae	Graptolites; Trilobites; Agnatha
	Ordovician	425	Marine algae	Graptolites; Trilobites; Agnatha
	Cambrian	500	Marine algae with some evidence of land plants	Graptolites; Trilobites
	Pre-Cambrian	−4,500	Fungi and bacteria reported from 2,000 million B.P.	No fossils of correlative value. Various invertebrate remains

any methods of maintaining a stable body temperature in the face of a declining environmental one.

At about this time the ancestors of all the placentals were probably present in the form of insectivores comparable with the deltatheridioid genera of the Mongolian Djadochta deposits. The skulls of these animals were very generalized and lacked the specializations of recent genera which usually take the form of an elongated snout, weak zygomatic arches and peculiar incisors. In fact the paracone and metacone of many teeth were barely separated at their tips and therefore recall the condition of the amphicone in the early Pantotheres.

During the Cenozoic Era evolution from this basal stock has resulted in an elaborate series of carnivorous, herbivorous and omnivorous genera. Modifications in the limbs and dentition associated with these various habits have produced the ridged teeth and cursorial form of the herbivorous ungulates and the shearing carnassials of the carnivores. Such adaptations have often occurred several times in related and unrelated lines during the approximately sixty-million-year period involved, to produce lines of large gravigrade, long-legged cursorial and arboreal forms. It is hoped that this book will help to give some idea of the inter-relationships between these animals and the environments in which they lived. One may start by a brief review of the main sources of mammalian material and the type of stratigraphical complexity with which one is dealing. Subsequently a review of the vegetational changes in association with the available absolute chronology based upon radioactive isotope assays may be used as an introduction to the evolution of the animals themselves.

CENOZOIC DEPOSITS CONTAINING MAMMALIAN MATERIAL

THE PALEOCENE PERIOD

The earliest of the three divisions into which Lyell divided the Tertiary system was of course the Eocene. An earlier Paleocene period is not well represented in the marine deposits but the composition of continental deposits, particularly those in North America, indicates a definite pre-Eocene phase. In other continents Paleocene mammalian remains are scarce, or, as in the case of Australia and Africa, unknown. The Eurasian mammals of assumed Paleocene age are largely derived from the Thanetian deposits at Cernay in France and the Gashato deposits in Mongolia. Both these series are of Upper Paleocene age but as can be seen from *Table 2* older material occurs in North America.

The Lower Paleocene horizon in this last-named region comprises the Puerco Beds of New Mexico and part of the Polecat Bench series in Wyoming. These are followed within the Middle Paleocene horizon by the Torrejon Beds of New Mexico, an intermediate portion of the Polecat Bench formation in Wyoming, the Crazy Mountain Field in Montana and the Dragon fauna in Utah. Finally the Upper Paleocene horizons in which mammalian remains occur in North America include the Clark Fork, Silver Coulee and the upper Polecat Bench deposits in Wyoming, the Tiffany Beds of New Mexico and the other deposits represented in *Table 2*.

Table 2. Deposits of presumed Paleocene age. For a further discussion of the status of the European localities see text (Modified after Romer, Simpson and others)

	European localities	Asiatic localities	African localities	North American localities	South American localities
UPPER	Cernay, France; Thanet Sands, England	Gashato, Mongolia		Clark Fork, Wyoming; Fort Union (in part), Wyoming; Paskapoo, Alberta; Plateau Valley, Colorado; Polecat Bench (in part), Wyoming; Silver Coulee, Wyoming; Tiffany, New Mexico	Rio Chico, Patagonia; Pernambuco, Brazil
MIDDLE				Crazy Mountain Field, Fort Union, Montana; Dragon fauna, Utah; Polecat Bench (in part), Wyoming; Torrejon, New Mexico	
LOWER				Polecat Bench (in part), Wyoming; Puerco, New Mexico	

4

Within the Polecat Bench formation there is in fact material spanning the interval between the end of the Cretaceous and the Lower Eocene. Unfortunately a comparable sequence does not occur in South America so that the earliest phase of the elaborate Tertiary fauna of that region remains unknown. Nevertheless a relatively early, albeit Upper Paleocene, phase is represented by the Rio Chican Beds of Patagonia.

Although workers in the various regions of the world have not yet finally established the inter-relationships of the early Tertiary stratigraphical horizons, the principal features can in fact be seen in *Table 2* together with the European substages which will be considered further in Chapter 2.

THE EOCENE PERIOD

As noted previously, the Eocene period was defined by Lyell on the basis of the molluscan fauna. During this period the well-known deposits of the London Clay and Bagshot Sands were deposited in the British Isles. In fact two great European regions may be distinguished. The first is the Anglo-Gallic province and includes the area of the British Isles, France and Belgium. Within this area the similarity of the various facies suggests that it was one great tract of sedimentation. The second region, which is generally known as the South European or Alpine, is much more extensive and includes the whole of southern Europe together with related facies in the Sahara, Egypt and eastwards through Java and Sumatra to the Philippines.

Within this last named region there existed a huge sea, of which the Mediterranean is a remnant. The fauna of this sea included the foraminiferal genus *Nummulites* which gave rise to extensive beds of limestone. These contain a wealth of fossils varying from large reef-building corals to molluscs and echinoderms and will be referred to in Chapters 2 and 5.

Since these extensive Eurasian deposits are of marine origin it is in North America that one finds the principal mammalian remains of Eocene age. The deposits of the Eocene are in fact summarized in *Table 3* but one may note the classical Lower Eocene fauna from the Wind River Basin in Wyoming, the Middle Eocene Bridgerian fauna of Wyoming and the Upper Eocene deposits of the Uinta Basin in the north of Utah.

In South America the Casa Mayor Beds contain the important *Notostylops* fauna and the Musters Beds the *Astraponotus* fauna. These provide an early picture of the endemic and highly specialized fauna which evolved in the region during the Tertiary. In a similar way the Qasr-el-Sagha and related beds of the Egyptian region contain remains which are of prime importance for the understanding of the inter-relationships of more recent and relatively specialized genera.

THE OLIGOCENE PERIOD

In fact the Oligocene period includes deposits originally classified by Lyell as Eocene or Miocene. It was only later that Beyrich removed them from these two divisions and established the separate Oligocene. There are a number of deposits of this age in the European region and of these those at Ronzon in France and Mainz in Germany are perhaps the best known.

As far as the classical work on mammalian remains is concerned the bulk of the information concerning the oriental fauna during Oligocene times is

Table 3. Deposits of presumed Eocene age which contain mammalian remains. For a further discussion of the French localities see text (Modified after Romer, Simpson and others)

	European localities	Asiatic localities	African localities	North American localities	South American localities
UPPER	Castres, Calcaire de St. Ouen, Débruge, Gargas, Montmartre gypsum, Quercy phosphorites (in part), Robiac, France; Isle of Wight, England; Mormont, Switzerland	Ardyn Obo, Irdin Manha, Shara Marum, Mongolia; Pondaung, Burma	Qasr-el-Sagha Beds of Fayum, Upper Mokattam Beds, Egypt	Duchesne River, Utah; Sespe (in part), California; Washakie (in part), Wyoming	
MIDDLE	Argenton, Buchsweiler, Issel, France; Bracklesham, England; Mount Bolca, Italy; Egerkingen, Switzerland		Birket-el-Qurûn Beds, Mokattan Beds, Egypt	Bridger Basin, Wyoming; Green River (in part), Wyoming, Colorado, Utah; Huerfano (in part), Colorado	Musters Beds, Patagonia
LOWER	Epernay, Meudon, Argile plastique of Soissons, France; London Clay, England; Erquelines, Orsmael, Belgium			Almagre, New Mexico, Colorado; Big Horn Basin, Wyoming; Huerfano (in part), Colorado; Wind River Basin, Wyoming	Casa Mayor Beds, Patagonia

derived from deposits in Mongolia. Of these the Hsanda Gol and Ulan Gochu are probably the most important. Of particular importance elsewhere are the Lower Oligocene deposits of Fayum in Egypt and the White River localities of the South Dakota area in North America. A continuation of the story of the mammalian evolution in South America is provided by the Deseado Beds of Patagonia, in which *Pyrotherium* occurs, and the Upper Oligocene Colhué Huapi Beds whose fauna shows affinities with that of the Lower Miocene.

THE MIOCENE PERIOD

Romer (1945) considers that this period of the Middle Tertiary was an epoch of considerable length. It was originally defined by Lyell to include some of the present Oligocene beds, on the basis of the intermediate values for the percentage representation of living species.

Within the European arena the principal localities occur in France and Germany and are tabulated in *Table 4*. In the Afrasian region Miocene deposits are not too numerous but the Loh and Tung Gur Beds of Mongolia probably date from the end of the period. In India the early part of the Siwalik formation is of Miocene age and one may look forward to a wealth of further material from this region. In recent years, however, interest has been directed to the primate fossils of Kenya which provide an important link in the story of primate evolution.

Within the region of North America fossiliferous deposits which contain mammalian remains occur especially in the Great Plains area. These, as can be seen from *Table 5*, include localities in South Dakota, Nebraska and Oregon. In South America there are marine deposits which indicate a marine transgression during the early phases of the Miocene. The Santa Cruz formation which was laid down subsequent to this transgression contains remains of the mammalian fauna which followed that of the Oligocene Deseado Beds.

THE PLIOCENE PERIOD

The Pliocene period together with the subsequent Quaternary are periods which have been investigated in great detail by palynologists in the last 40 years. The later part of the Pliocene in fact merges into the Quaternary, from which it is distinguished by certain relatively formal definitions, since this latter short period of ice-ages represents the nadir of the climatic deterioration which occurred in the later phases of the Tertiary.

Deposits of Pliocene age occur widely in the Mediterranean region and in eastern and central Europe. From the classical sites which are located in this region the characteristic Pliocene fauna is incorrectly known as the Pontian facies of the Tertiary series. Outside the European region this series of deposits is continued in the Persian Maragha localities and the middle part of the Indian Siwalik formations together with material in Honan and Shansi in China.

The North American series is comparable to the Miocene deposits of that region in that, as far as mammalian faunas are concerned, it is largely restricted to the Great Plains area. Within that area sites containing Pliocene material include Snake Creek, Nebraska, the Clarendon Beds of Texas, the Santa Fe deposits of New Mexico and the Republican River Beds of Kansas.

Table 4. Deposits of presumed Oligocene age (Modified after Gignoux, Romer, Simpson and others)

	European localities	Asiatic localities	African localities	North American localities	South American localities
UPPER	Beauce limestones, Oyster marls, Agen, France; Mainz Basin, Germany; Cadibona, Italy	Hsanda Gol, Mongolia; Turgai, Turkestan		Protoceras beds of the White River series, North Dakota, South Dakota, Colorado, Nebraska and Wyoming	Colhué Huapi Beds of Patagonia
MIDDLE	Aveyron, Bournoncle St. Pierre, Quercy phosphorites (in part), France; Flonheim, Weinheim, Germany			Oreodon beds of the White River series, Colorado, North Dakota, Nebraska, Wyoming	
LOWER	Brie limestone, Lobsann, Quercy phosphorites (in part), Ronzon, France; Hampstead Beds, England	Ulan Gochu, Mongolia	Upper Beds of Fayum, Egypt	Titanothere beds of the White River series as above	Deseado Beds of Patagonia

Table 5. Deposits of presumed Miocene age (after Gignoux, Romer, Simpson and others)

	European localities	Asiatic localities	African localities	North American localities	South American localities
UPPER	Antwerp, Belgium; Sevastopol; U.S.S.R.	Kamlial, Indian Siwalik formation; Tung Gur, Mongolia	Moghara, Egypt	Barstow, California; Madison Valley, Montana; Mascall, Oregon; Pawnee Valley, Colorado	Chasico Beds of southern Pampas; Rio Frias Beds of Patagonia
MIDDLE	Grive St. Alban, St. Gaudens, Sansan, Simorre, France; Eggenburg, Eibiswald, Austria; Molasse of Central Europe (in part); Oeningen, Steinheim, Germany; Monte Bamboli, Italy	Loh, Mongolia		Calvert, Maryland; Hawthorne, Florida; Marsland and Sheep Creek, Nebraska; Temblor, California	Santa Cruz Beds of Patagonia
LOWER	Faluns of Touraine, Orleans Sands, St. Gerand le Puy, France; Molasse of Central Europe (in part); Mainz Basin, Ulm, Germany	Bugti Beds, Baluchistan	Kenya colony; Namib, South West Africa	Gering, Nebraska; Middle and Upper John Day, Oregon; Lower Harrison and Monroe Creek, Nebraska; Rosebud, South Dakota	

INTRODUCTION

The extensive earlier Tertiary sites in Patagonia have no Pliocene equivalent. What is known about the Ponto-Calabrian fauna of South America is derived from sites elsewhere in Argentina. These include the Araucanian series in the foothills of the Andes, which cover much of the period, and the Monte Hermosa localities of the southern Pampas.

THE QUATERNARY PERIOD

Although this is the shortest of the subdivisions of the Cenozoic and is at most probably 1–2 million years in length, it is probably better represented by deposits than any of the foregoing subdivisions. This is especially the case in temperate latitudes where the successive advances and retreats of the polar ice, together with the advances of glaciers in the Alpine, Appalachian, Andean etc. regions, have resulted in extensive deposits of morainic material, out-wash gravels and river terraces. The complex sequence of events which is indicated by the series of five glaciations Donau, Gunz, Mindel, Riss, Würm, was originally proposed by Penck and Brückner (1909) on the basis of terraces and associated gravels and end-moraines in the Alpine region. Subsequently, and more especially in the last 20 years, extensive work in other regions has revealed a widespread series of comparable deposits. Although the exact stratigraphical relationship of these deposits is still not finally worked out a well authenticated review of the probable affinities is provided by the report of the subcommittee on correlations of the Fourth International Quaternary Conference (INQUA, 1956). Within these deposits vast numbers of Quaternary mammalian remains have been found that have been the basis of numerous articles. A lead to this enormous literature will be obtained from the references in Chapters 4 and 5, together with Charlesworth (1956), Deevey (1949), Flint (1949; 1957), Godwin (1956), and Zeuner (1945).

2

THE TERTIARY SEQUENCE IN THE
PARIS BASIN

THE NUMMULITIC OR PALEOGENE

Those deposits which date from the early part of the Tertiary show certain similarities and as a result are often classed together as a single unit. This, the Nummulitic or Paleogene system, is broadly characterized by the presence of the foraminiferal genus *Nummulites* in the limestone deposits dating from the period. In general terms it comprises the period between the Cretaceous and Upper Oligocene and is equivalent to the Eocene of Lyell. The relative individuality of the system is enhanced by the presence of two periods of marine transgression, the one at the beginning and the other at the end. However, areas in which it is possible to observe a continuous series of marine deposits which encompass the entire period of time from the Cretaceous through the Paleogene to the Neogene are extremely rare.

Actually the stratigraphical succession of the Paleogene was first investigated within the Paris Basin. During that period there were a series of marine transgressions and regressions in the area which have given rise to a series of more or less accurately defined substages. These have been reviewed by Gignoux (1955) and may be taken as a preliminary example of the changes which occurred during the early Tertiary. However, although it was only towards the end of the Paleogene that the sea actually retired from the Parisian area, the effects observed there are naturally only representative of local conditions and it is not surprising that the succession in German and Russian regions was somewhat different. In the last-named areas the transgressions with which the series begins have been assigned to the Oligocene and the name Eocene is restricted to the earlier part of the Paleogene. Nevertheless, although this division may apparently be arbitrary it is of considerable significance in terms of mammalian evolution.

At the time that the first Tertiary marine transgression occurred in the European arena there was a vast continent situated to the north. In the south there was an equally extensive Mediterranean Sea and in the absence of the Alps, which were still to be formed, the principal ridges comprised the Hercynian Massifs of Central Europe. The North Sea to the north and east and this extensive Mediterranean to the south comprised two large faunal reservoirs and were in fact separated by the various components of the Hercynian range namely the Bohemian, Central French and Rhenish Massifs. In spite of this separation some faunal exchanges did however take place.

11

Montian

Wartime investigations into the nature of the deposits exposed within numerous wells have now enabled Soyer to detail some 48 localities scattered over a wide area in which deposits of this early Montian substage occur. In Chapter 1 the period of time representing both this Montian period and the subsequent Thanetian is referred to the Paleocene. In using the term Eocene in this Chapter to embrace the entire span from the Montian to the Ludian the usage of Gignoux (1955) is followed for reasons that will become clear in the following section. In the sea in which deposition took place the fauna included certain gastropods which have clear affinities with those of other Tertiary deposits. As examples one may cite *Turritella montensis* and *Cerithium inopinatum*. In contrast to this, however, the lamellibranchs appear to suggest that the fauna should be associated with that of the Upper Cretaceous. Gignoux (1955) has suggested that these apparent contradictions can be explained if the uppermost layers of the chalk in the Paris Basin are considered to have been cut into by lacunae. Following this dissection by lacunae, deposition of further beds with Cretaceous characteristics occurred and then finally those which represent the true Montian.

The Landenian

Following the early Montian substage of the Parisian series, of which the European mammalian fauna is unknown, two phases occur which are considered to be phases of a single Landenian substage by Gignoux (1955) following Leriche (1929). According to these two authors the earlier of the two phases, the Thanetian, is simply the marine facies and the later, the Sparnacian, the lagoon facies of the Lower and Upper Landenian respectively. The distinction on the basis of these differences is therefore only of extremely local significance.

The Lower Landenian is therefore represented by deposits which portray an extensive marine transgression. This has been preserved over a wide area. In fact it seems probable that the entire northern part of the Paris Basin was involved in an extensive sea. Within this area the Cretaceous chalk deposits are overlain by the sands of Bracheux named after the site of a fossiliferous deposit south of Beauvais. The littoral components of the fauna comprise large shells of *Cucullaea crassatina*, *Venericardia pectuncularis* and *Ostrea bellovacina*. Although some genera of cyprines and astartes appear to resemble modern northern genera the fish, algae and corals suggest tropical affinities. Within these Bracheux sands there do in fact exist a number of faunal zones which are characterized by their molluscan and echinoderm species. These enable one to trace the successive southward penetration of the Franco-Belgian region by the sea during the Thanetian marine transgression. Indications of the non-marine fauna and flora are provided by the presence of the sinistral coiled shells of the mollusc *Physa gigantea* in a lacustrine limestone and by impressions of insects and angiosperms in the deposits of calcareous springs.

The Sparnacian phase of brackish lagoons is represented by the Upper Landenian lignites of Soissons and the more southern plastic clays. These include clays containing beds of lignite. In certain areas they are fossiliferous and there characterized by the presence of the shells of *Cyrena cuneiformis*, *Cerithium variabile* and *Melania inquinata*. Within the series mammalian remains occur in the Mendon conglomerate, which lies at the base of the plastic clay, and in some of the lignites.

The Ypresian

During the period in which the London Clay was being deposited (Chapter 3) a second and more recent marine transgression took place within the Paris Basin. This comprises the subsequent Ypresian substage of the Tertiary during which the northern sea penetrated further to the south depositing the Cuise Sands in what is now the northern outskirts of Paris itself.

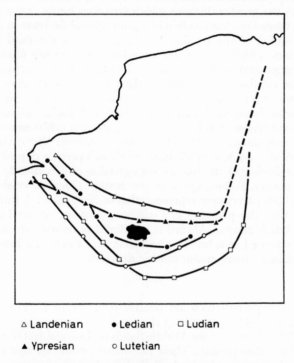

△ Landenian   ● Ledian   □ Ludian

▲ Ypresian   ○ Lutetian

Figure 1. A map showing the limits of the successive marine trans-gressions in the Paris basin during the early Tertiary (from Strati-graphic Geology *by Maurice Gignoux. After M. Leriche; the Lutetian after A. Abrard, San Francisco: W. H. Freeman and Company, 1955)*

The foraminiferal and molluscan faunas of these sands have warm southern affiliations similar to those of the marine Thanetian phase of the Landenian. It is in fact at this time that the genus *Nummulites* reached the Paris Basin, having entered it by way of the incipient English Channel, and is represented there by the *Nummulites planulatus-elegans* group. The affinities of the marine fauna with its contemporary faunas elsewhere are exemplified by the occurrence of such molluscs as *Velates schmiedelianus*. Besides occurring in the European arena this species is also known from deposits of presumed Ypresian age in India and Madagascar (Abrard, 1925).

It is probable that following this extensive marine transgression the sea receded again. Indeed since lacustrine deposits which contain the remains of angiosperms occur above the marine sediments in the stratigraphical succession, it would appear that there was an extensive marine regression prior to the subsequent transgression of the Lutetian period.

The Lutetian

Having retreated at the end of the Ypresian the sea once again penetrated south to the Paris Basin during the following Lutetian phase of the early Paleogene. Once again the transgression exceeded those which had preceded it and this time the sea reached south of Paris to Fontainebleau. This fact, together with the greater distance which separates many of the known sites from the old shore-line, has resulted in a proportional decrease in the percentage representation of the continental components of the fossil fauna. The clays and sands which contain the remains of the earlier faunas are now replaced by organic deposits in which rock-boring molluscs are common and in which the stratigraphy is characterized by the *Nummulites laevigatus—lamarcki* group of foraminifera and by ornate molluscs such as *Venericardia planicosta*, *Corbis lamellosa*, *Cerithium giganteum* and *Lucinia gigantea*. On the basis of the occurrence of the foraminifera and such echinoderms as *Echinolampus calvinomontanus* and *Echinanthus issyavensis* Abrard (1925) has suggested that there are at least five subdivisions of these Ypresian deposits. The first marks the beginning of the marine transgression and is usually in a sandy glaucomitic matrix. Following this in the stratigraphical succession is a zone which has a high percentage representation of *Nummulites*. A third, which is characterized by the presence of *Cerithium giganteum*, occurs in the upper strata. The fourth zone of Abrard is a miliolid limestone which, occurring near Paris, is valued as a building material, and the fifth a brackish water deposit overlain by more recent marine deposits.

The Ledian

The marine deposits which are considered to be of Ledian age mark a change of facies. The limestones of the previous sections give way to sandy material which is known as the Middle Sands to distinguish it from the sandy deposits of the earlier periods. These first-named sands are best known from sites at Beauchamp near Paris. At their lateral edges they are intercalated with limestone deposits of lacustrine origin giving a complex local stratigraphical sequence. This complexity arises of course from variations in the Ledian shore-line and, according to Abrard, it is probable that the whole series is best considered as a single unit in spite of the fact that earlier workers had subdivided it further.

The Ludian

As was the case in the foregoing Ledian substage the base of the last Eocene or Ludian deposits is marked by a change in the character of the sedimentation. As before, the marine transgression extended further to the south than its predecessors had and in fact there are two principal areas of deposition which lie to the north-west and south-east of the line of the Marne from Rheims to Champigny. Within this region the material varies according to its origin. To the north-west lie the marine deposits of the ancient gulf whilst to the south-east there lie the Champigny limestones which were deposited under lacustrine conditions.

Within the marine province to the north-west it seems that there was a progressive reduction in the amount of water as represented, for example, by the reduction in the shells of *Pholadomyia ludensis*. It seems probable that there was in fact a progressive reduction of the water to give an inland sea and that this finally disappeared. During the period in which this disappearance was taking place the evaporation of the water gave rise to extensive deposits of the so-called Montmartre gypsum. This material, which is the classical source of plaster of Paris, contains many vertebrate fossils. The differences between the deposits on either side of the line of the Marne therefore represent lateral variations originating in ecological differences as opposed to differing times of deposition.

THE OLIGOCENE PERIOD

It was noted earlier that deposits of Oligocene age had been recognized in the German and Russian regions. The gypsiferous marls and freshwater limestones of the Ludian underlie stratigraphically marls and limestones which contain new faunal components. Important changes took place in Central Europe at this time and zones of subsidence occurred in the Hercynian Massif. As these subsided they gradually became filled with marine deposits and as they continued to sink became the sites of deep Oligocene deposits. Within the Paris Basin area they are contemporaneous with a series of sands and marls which have therefore given their names to the subdivisions of the period.

The Sannoisian

At Sannois near Argenteuil in the north-west of Paris the supra-gypsiferous marls show what has come to be considered a classical series. First in the succession comes a blue marl which contains only a few rare lagoonal crustacean fossils. It has been suggested (Gignoux, 1955) that it originated as a salt-marsh. Above this level lies a white marl in which are the remains of *Lymnea strigosa*, a fact which suggests that although marine influences still existed the area was losing some of its marine characteristics.

This white marl is itself replaced by marls which appear to have the characteristic usually associated with deposition under brackish-water conditions. They contain a fauna which includes such molluscs as *Cyrena convexa* and *Cerithium plicatum*. Finally these beds are overlain by green marls which contain *Cytherea incrassata* and are clearly of marine origin. Elsewhere, south-east of the Marne for example, the marly facies is replaced by freshwater limestones in a comparable manner to the lateral replacement of the Champigny limestones of Ludian age by gypsum.

The Stampian

During the Stampian substage, which owes its name to certain deposits near Étampes, the Paris Basin was inundated by a marine transgression for the last time. The shores of the sea seem to have been well down to the south and east although they are unfortunately not precisely defined. In general the Stampian deposits of France seem to fall into two categories. The first of these is characterized by a lower oyster marl and the second by an upper series of Fontainebleau or Upper Sands whose average vertical depth appears to be approximately 40 metres. In the oyster marl the two species of oyster *Ostrea cyathula* and *Ostrea longirostris* attained high percentage representations. Besides these two species the general features of the fauna, which includes the molluscs *Cytherea splendida*, *Natica crassatina* and *Pectunculus obovatus*, are quite different from those of the various phases of the Eocene.

The period ended in a marine regression which resulted in large areas of dry sands becoming exposed. These were reworked and subjected to considerable erosion by the wind and as a result became preserved in the form of great parallel sand dunes which appear to have been separated by swamps in the slacks. The deposits of muds and clays laid down in these swamps gave rise to the layers of clay which are found in the Stampian sands. These are probably analogous, as suggested by H. Alimen in Gignoux (1955), to the *bahrs* which are aligned in the zone separating the marshes of Chad and the dunes of the Saharan *ergs*.

The Chattian and Aquitanian

As was noted above, the Paris Basin was invaded by the sea for the last time during the Stampian. This final phase of marine transgression was followed by a period during which the region was occupied by an extensive lake. Within the waters of this lake the freshwater limestones which are today known as the Beauce Limestones were laid down. Unfortunately no mammalian fauna is known from the deposits but in spite of this Gignoux (1955) suggests that they may probably be correlated, at least in part, with the marine facies of Aquitaine (considered to be Miocene by Romer (1945)). This last marks the beginning of a new marine transgression which failed to reach the Paris Basin. The Lower Aquitanian, which is most probably contemporaneous with the Upper Beauce limestones, has a somewhat brackish-water appearance. Between Bordeaux and La Réole it consists of marls containing the so-called 'Oysters of Agen', *Ostrea aginensis*. On the other hand, the Upper Aquitanian comprises brackish and lacustrine deposits in the eastern regions and is totally marine only on the eastern bank of the Garonne. In fact a complicated series of deposits results from the alternation of conglomerates and lacustrine limestones. As the result of the delicate interplay of these various sedimentary facies the Aquitaine Basin has an importance similar to that of the Paris Basin in the study of the European Nummulitic.

THE NEOGENE

It was pointed out previously that the Paleogene was separated from both the earlier Cretaceous deposits and subsequent Neogene deposits by an extensive marine transgression. The early part of the Neogene is therefore marked by a marine transgression of Miocene age. Following a further regression it was succeeded by yet another major transgression of early Pliocene age. A final regression was to lead to the early phases of the Quaternary era with its complex series of climatic oscillations which are outlined in Chapters 4 and 5.

16

As in the case of the marine transgressions of the Nummulitic, the sources of the water for these inundations are the three great reservoirs of the North Sea, Atlantic and Mediterranean. However, during the Neogene the North Sea was never so extensive as during the Paleogene and the Atlantic Ocean only encroached upon limited areas of the north and west of France. The result of this is that it is the Neogene deposits which are associated with the Mediterranean Sea that are of the greatest importance.

Since the Alpine orogenesis had taken place by the beginning of the period the physical appearance of Europe had been changed. As a result of this the western marine transgressions are largely restricted to the peripheral peri-Alpine depression. Also in contrast to the earlier situation the Neogene Mediterranean was transformed in the east into an inland sea with an endemic fauna.

THE MIOCENE SERIES

The beginning of the first Neogene transgression occurred in the last phase of the Aquitanian in the Upper Oligocene. The material deposited during this early phase contains a number of marine shells which do not occur in the Later Miocene deposits. This last-named period therefore begins with the *Burdigalian* phase which is typified by the Bordeaux faluns. During this period the marine transgression resulted in an advance of the sea across the entire peri-Alpine depression. Faunistically it is most easily characterized by the mammals and more especially by the appearance of the proboscideans *Trilophodon angustidens, Zygolophodon turricensis* and *Deinotherium cuvieri* together with *Anchitherium aurelianense* and *Procervulus aurelianense*.

Following this *Burdigalian* occurred the *Vindobonian* phase as defined in the French region. However, the result of extensive investigations in Austria has been that the Austrian workers have decided to modify the earlier concepts. Nevertheless, in general the second phase still remains and has two further subdivisions. The first of these is the *Helvetian* and is characterized by type deposits consisting of marine molasse in Switzerland. The second division, which is probably only a facies, is based on blue marls with a deep-water facies which contain pleurotomid gastropods. It is generally referred to as the Tortonian.

In deposits of this last-named age there occur faunal remains which, besides representing some forms common to the earlier Burdigalian, also include the proboscidean *Deinotherium bavaricum* and the early Muntjac *Dicrocerus elegans*.

The Miocene sedimentary cycle in Europe is finally completed with a period of land emergence. This phase, which is known as the *Pontian*, has no marine facies. During the period the evolution of the equid hippomorphs (Chapter 10) resulted in the appearance within the European fauna of *Hipparion* and that of the proboscideans resulted in the appearance of the last species of *Deinotherium*, viz. *Deinotherium giganteum*.

THE PLIOCENE SERIES

This last of the principal subdivisions of the Tertiary period is represented in the western European arena by two marine faunas. The first of these

17

differs from the earlier Miocene faunas in the appearance and disappearance of numerous species. By this time the majority of the Mediterranean species are to be found in the deposits of neighbouring regions. Alongside these there are many which are either found today on the west coast of Africa or are extinct.

The early Pliocene comprises two facies with their respective faunas. A clay facies from Plaisance in northern Italy is of relatively deep-water origin. It is rather similar to the *Tortonian* facies of the Miocene and like it has a high percentage representation of large pleurotomid gastropods. In contrast, a sandy facies known from Asti in Piedmont, and hence called *Astian*, is more littoral in character. It contains the shells of large lamellibranchs and is probably of a more recent date than is the *Plaisancian*.

Both these early Pliocene series antedate the *Calabrian* marine phase. This is the marine equivalent of the continental *Villafranchian* fauna which marks the Pliocene/Pleistocene or Tertiary/Quaternary transition. The marine faunas from this late Pliocene time show considerable similarities with those of the present mediterranean region. It is especially well represented in Italy but in general terms the Upper Pliocene period is best known from the continental deposits. The type deposit is at Villafranca d'Asti, also in Piedmont.

In the Pliocene faunas of western Europe associations such as *Trilophodon arvernensis*, *Zygolophodon borsoni*, *Rhinoceros leptorhinos* and large antelopes occur. In the more recent *Villafranchian*, the elephant *Archidiskodon meridionalis*, and the horse *Equus stenonis* occur alongside the last European *Mastodon*. Within these faunas the limits of the Quaternary fauna of the Upper Villafranchian were set by the International Geological Congress (1950). A more recent definition of the general Pliocene/Pleistocene boundary in marine deposits is provided by Ericson, Ewing and Wollin (1963).

3

TERTIARY VEGETATION

INTRODUCTION

More or less extensive plant lists are now available from Tertiary deposits scattered throughout the world (e.g. Bogolepov, 1955; Chaney, 1947; Hammen, 1957). In order to give some idea of the changes which took place, a few selected floras are considered below. These have been selected with the intention of providing information on the gross overall changes and also the local ecological variations as far as they are known. In certain cases the deposits also contain zoological material, or, alternatively, are in relatively close association with fossiliferous strata. In these cases it is of considerable interest to compare the ecological and bioclimatological data from the several sources. However, it is only when the entire picture of mammalian and vegetational history of the Cenozoic is considered that the fully integrated picture emerges. For this reason the zoological data are kept to a minimum in this chapter.

PLANT REMAINS OF EOCENE AGE

THE LONDON CLAY FLORA

The classical work of Prestwich (1854) on the actual limits of the Eocene flora of the London Clay laid the foundations for the immense later studies of Reid and Chandler (1933; Chandler, 1961). If one allows for the variations that are due to oxidation, the mass of the London Clay deposits comprise a brown clay lying on a sandy basement bed. In thickness the deposits vary from a few feet in Wiltshire to 50 or 60 feet in Berkshire, and 500 feet in the south of Essex. In fact the bulk of the plant remains, consisting of fruits and seeds, have been recovered from the foreshore at Sheppey. Remains of logs and small fragments of *Teredo* bored wood occur in the cliffs. The animal remains, with the exception of the Mollusca, are regarded as showing tropical affinities. Since the Mollusca show both tropical and temperate characteristics it has been suggested that this is the result of the communication between the warm southern waters of the Tethys or the Nummulitic Sea and the colder northern ocean.

It has also been suggested that the combination of the Mollusca with the terrestrial vegetation is the result of the deposit having been laid down beyond the mouth of a great river, which swept both silt and rafts of vegetation out to sea. The Sheppey detritus does in fact compare very closely with that washed out by tropical rivers, for example the Ambernoh River in New Guinea. The reports on this detritus in the account of the Challenger expedition record that the sea was blocked with driftwood at a great distance

19

from its mouth. The material was disposed at right angles to the direction of the river mouth, and in the water amongst the logs were large quantities of both fruits and seeds, comparable to those occurring in the Eocene deposits at Sheppey.

Amongst the families represented by the fruits and seeds, 5 are exclusively tropical—the Nipaceae, Burseraceae, Icacinaceae, Bixaceae and Sapotaceae—and equal 11 per cent of the total remains. A further 14 families representing 32 per cent of the total are almost entirely tropical, but do have species which occur outside the tropics:

Palmae	Meliaceae	Elaeocarpaceae
Oleaceae	Anacardiaceae	Sterculiaceae
Menispermaceae	Sapindaceae	Dilleniaceae
Anonaceae	Sabiaceae	Myrsinaceae
Lauraceae		Apocynaceae

From this it would therefore appear that 43 per cent of the list of families recorded from this British Eocene deposit are either entirely, or are largely, restricted to the tropical regions of the world at the present time. A further 21 of the families present are today equally represented in both the tropical and extra-tropical regions. Only 5—the Taxaceae, Trochodendraceae, Saxifragaceae, Halorrhagaceae, and Onagraceae—are largely temperate. The comparison between the London Clay flora and the modern tropical floras is contained in *Table 6*, which shows that there is a marked similarity in the percentage representation of mainly tropical families.

Table 6. Comparison between the London Clay flora and modern tropical floras
(Reid and Chandler, 1933)

	Exclusively tropical %	Mainly tropical %	Equally tropical and non-tropical %	Mainly extra-tropical %
Living tropical families	15	32·5	32·5	20
London Clay families	11	32	46	11

A more precise comparison between the plant remains and modern forms was also undertaken by Reid and Chandler. The results of this analysis showed that of the 70 genera indentified from the Sheppey material, 33, or 47 per cent, are most closely related to modern genera which exist in tropical lowlands. A further 29 genera, representing 41·5 per cent of the total, occur both in lowland tropical areas and also either in montane areas in the tropics or are extra-tropical in latitudinal distribution. Finally 8 genera, or 11·5 per cent, are exclusively montane in tropical regions. Of the genera, *Nipa*, which is exclusively tropical, grows only at sea level and requires brackish water. *Oncosperma* is also a strand genus in the Malayan regions, and *Allophylus* and *Ehretia* have species which contribute to the tropical strand flora. The evidence of both families and genera therefore indicates that the London Clay was laid down at a time when the region had a tropical climate. In fact in the London Clay flora the predominant component is that existing today in the jungles of the Indo-Malayan region. The whole association comprises elements found today from the Himalayas through southern China, Burma and the Malay peninsular to Australia on the one hand, and to Africa on the other. The most marked relationship is with the vegetation of the Malayan islands. Similarities with the modern vegetation of the whole of Europe and Western Asia are virtually absent. By considering the composition of more recent floras, Reid and Chandler also concluded that, during the interim period between the Eocene and the far more recent Cromerian interglacial, there was a progressive increase in the non-woody floral elements in the European flora.

Saporta considered that the climate of the early Paleocene (Gelinden) was of a warm temperate type and may have approximated to that of southern Japan. The later deposits at Sezanne showed more tropical characteristics. Similar views have also been expressed about the flora of the older Woolwich and Reading Beds and the new Oldhaven Beds. Seward and Holttum (1924), when considering the flora of Mull, which is thought to be of Paleocene age, concluded that it indicated temperate conditions. After comparing this evidence with their own, Reid and Chandler suggest that a climatic change took place in the Paleocene which had its culmination in the London Clay–Bracklesham period. They further conclude that this period in the Lower and Middle Eocene is an important turning point in the floral and climatic history of western Europe. The result of such a postulated climatic change would be a migration northwards of any stenothermal cold elements of the Paleocene. That this was the case is suggested by the fact that, of the London Clay genera characteristic of the tropical regions and those characteristic of both the tropical and extra-tropical regions, it is the latter class which occur in the floras older than the London Clay, for example *Araucarites, Sabal, Symplocos* and *Magnolia*.

THE GOSHEN FLORA

Chaney and Sanborn (1933) reported a flora from four localities in the vicinity of Goshen, Lane County, Oregon. In this region the marine Eugene formation outcrops over a wide area, dipping to the north-east, and contains an Oligocene invertebrate fauna. To the south and underlying the Eugene deposits is a widely outcropping series of terrestrial deposits consisting of sandstone, ash, conglomerates and rhyolitic flows. This, the Fisher formation, has a known thickness of 1,500 feet. The numerous leaf impressions occur in lenses of limited thickness and horizontal extent, and the principal Goshen material in fact comes from a single site where a dacite vitric tuff up to 5 feet in thickness is embedded in a yellowish brown tuffaceous sandstone, itself crossbedded with finely laminated carbonaceous films and grit, all well down in the Fisher formation.

From the fact that the floral remains are tropical in character and comprise families and genera common in the Cretaceous and Eocene in North America, Chaney and Sanborn conclude that the deposit was laid down at an early Tertiary time. The stratigraphical position suggests an Upper Eocene or Lower Oligocene date, and the similarity between the flora and that of Eocene floras in both Europe and North America indicates an Eocene age for the flora.

21

The actual species recorded from the Goshen flora are tabulated in *Table 7*. Within this list there occur species which indicate a variety of climatic situations. The two species of *Quercus* represent a genus whose principal distribution at the present time is in temperate latitudes. On the contrary, of

Table 7. The representation of individuals of the generically determined species in the Goshen flora
(calculation after Chaney and Sanborn)

Species	No. of individual plants	% of total
Meliosma goshenensis	133	17·8
Nectandra presanguinea	88	11·8
Ficus quisumbingi	83	11·1
Tetracera oregona	58	7·8
Aristolochia mexiana	35	4·7
Aristophyllus wilsoni	31	4·1
Ilex oregona	22	2·9
Anona prereticulata	20	2·7
Magnolia reticulata	20	2·7
Quercus howei	20	2·7
Siparuna ovalis	19	2·5
Chrysobalanus ellipticus	18	2·4
Lucuma standleyi	18	2·4
Diospyros oregona	15	2
Laurophyllum merrilli	15	2
Siparuna standleyi	12	1·6
Ocotea eocernua	11	1·5
Symplocos oregona	11	1·5
Calyptranthes arbutifolia	10	1·3
Hydrangea russelli	9	1·2
Meliosma rostrata	9	1·2
Smilax goshenensis	8	1·1
Cordia oregona	7	0·9
Drimys americana	6	0·8
Ficus goshenensis	6	0·8
Ocotea ovoidea	6	0·8
Viburnum palmatum	6	0·8
Viburnum eocenicum	5	0·7
Cupania packardi	4	0·5
Ficus plinerva	4	0·5
Inga oregona	4	0·5
Meliosma aesculifolia	4	0·5
Platanus aceroides	4	0·5
Psychotria oregona	4	0·5
Sapium standleyi	4	0·5
Callichlamys zeteki	3	0·4
Viburnum thomae	3	0·4
Cordia rotunda	2	0·3
Cupania oregona	2	0·3
Lindera oregona	2	0·3
Lucuma sp.	2	0·3
Magnolia hilgardiana	2	0·3
Astronium oregonum	1	0·1
Dillenites sp.	1	0·1
Quercus lanensis	1	0·1

the three species of *Ficus*, two appear to have their nearest living relatives in the paleotropics, whilst the third resembles a Mexican species. In a similar way to *Ficus*, the remains of *Aristolochia* seem to indicate a close relationship with *Aristolochia mexiae*, although species from both the Philippines and Malay peninsular also have a similar form. This was the first fossil record of this genus from the region of the Pacific coast, but there are a number of other fossil records from deposits of Eocene, Oligocene and Miocene age which have been ascribed to the originally Cretaceous genus *Aristolochiaephyllum*.

The Ranales is the most extensively developed order, and all of the four ranalian families recorded from the Goshen flora are predominantly tropical today. Both the Rosales and Sapindales are also represented by four families, and the overall character of many of the genera represented is tropical.

The genus *Drimys* of the Magnoliaceae occurs in the southern hemisphere from New Zealand and Australia to Borneo, and from Mexico to Cape Horn. The 90 modern species of *Siparuna*, which are shrubs in the neotropical region, vary considerably in leaf form. Both linear and ovate forms exist whilst the leaf margins also show a gradation from entire to serrate. The Goshen species are broadleafed. The one with the entire margin is considered by Chaney and Sanborn to resemble *Siparuna guianensis* of Guiana and the serrate margined one to have a marked similarity to *Siparuna griseo-flavescens* of Costa Rica.

The family with the highest numerical representation in the Goshen flora, 4 genera and 5 species being present, is the thick-leaved Lauraceae. The genus *Nectandra* is exclusively neotropical. Of the other three, *Ocotea*, *Lindera* and *Laurophyllum*, the sub-genus *Oreodaphne* to which *Ocotea eocernua* belongs, also occurs in the New World. *Lindera* is represented in both hemispheres with numerous species ranging from Java to Japan in the Old World, and has only two species occurring in temperate regions of America. The leaves of the Goshen *Lindera oregona* resemble these latter American species rather than the paleotropical ones. Chaney and Sanborn suggest that the fourth lauraceous genus *Laurophyllum* is perhaps an ancestral form of the modern south east Asian genus *Machilus*.

The rosaceous genus *Chrysobalanus* is essentially a plant of low latitudes. The modern species are typically strand plants and very widely distributed. *Chrysobalanus icaco* occurs in the West Indies and Brazil, and what is thought to be the same species occurs on the west coast of Africa. The similarity between *Chrysobalanus ellipticus* of the Goshen flora and *Chrysobalanus inequalis* of the Wilcox flora in Mississippi and Tennessee suggests that a similar wide-spread occurrence of identical or closely allied species of *Chrysobalanus* may also have occurred during the Tertiary.

Although the *Leguminosae* is well represented in the Wilcox and other Eocene floras, and occurs in large numbers in the forests of lower latitudes, there is only one species of the genus *Inga* in the Goshen flora. The sub-family Mimosoidea to which this genus belongs is largely tropical in its distribution, and the genus is restricted to the New World.

The Sapindales is represented by 5 genera and 8 species. In spite of the fact that the genus has temperate species, the *Ilex* remains are probably most closely related to a South American and Mexican species. The genus *Cupania* (Sapindaceae) is confined to the lower latitudes of America where it occurs

23

as a shrub with simple or compound leaves. The Goshen species *Cupania oregona* and *Cupania packardi* are represented by leaflets of pinnate compound leaves. Chaney and Sanborn suggest that both these two species are related to South American forms, notably *Cupania vernalis* and *Cupania hirsuta*. Similarly the two species of the genus *Cordia* (Polemoniales) resemble neotropical forms, and *Psychotria oregona* of the Rubiales is closely related to the Central American and West Indian species *Psychotria undata*.

The foregoing account shows that the principal affinities of the Goshen plant remains are with the flora of neotropical regions. Chaney and Sanborn analysed this relationship in more detail by considering the leaf characters of the Goshen species in relation to modern low latitude trees in the neotropical region. To accomplish this they used various parameters measured on collections of leaves sampled from the forest floor at four points along the Snyder Molino trail on Banro Colorado Island.

Table 8. The analysis of the leaf characters of the modern Panama flora and Eocene Goshen flora (Chaney and Sanborn, 1933)

	Length		Organization		Nervation		Margin		Dripping point		Texture	
	over 10 cm	under 10 cm	simple	com-pound	pinnate	palmate	entire	not entire	present	absent	thick	thin
Panama No. of species	23	18	35	6	34	7	36	5	31	10	40	1
% of flora	56	44	85	15	83	17	88	12	76	24	98	2
Goshen No. of species	26	23	43	6	40	9	30	19	23	26	48	1
% of flora	53	47	88	12	82	18	61	39	47	53	98	2

In the first place counts were made of the number of species represented by leaves in the ground litter of one square foot. Records were also made of the length, organization (simple or compound), nervation, margin, shape at apex and texture of the leaves sampled. 41 species were represented in the total of 316 specimens. The results are summarized in *Table 8*.

Chaney and Sanborn admit, in all fairness, that 41 species from the modern forests of Panama cannot be relied upon to give an accurate picture of the character of tropical forests very widely distributed in time and space. The forest on Banro Colorado Island does not, therefore, represent the exact equivalent of an Eocene forest in the Goshen region. It is apparent from *Table 8* however that there are distinct and close similarities between this modern flora and the Eocene one. In both the majority of the species have leaves more than 10 cm in length and there is a close correspondence in the percentage representation of simple leaves with a pinnate nervation and thick texture. A notable difference is the smaller number of Goshen species which have entire margins and a less conspicuous dripping point. The determination of the biserial η for these data, by statistical methods, gave a value of 0·17 indicating, suggest Chaney and Sanborn, a high degree of relationship, which is even more significant when compared with the values computed for data on temperate floras.

Sinnott and Bailey (1915; 1916) had earlier discussed the significance of characters of this type from the standpoint of climatic investigations. Amongst the modern floras of the world the simple pinnate condition constitutes 60–70 per cent of the species. A difference is apparent, however, between the relative numbers of compound leaves in warm and in temperate regions, and these authors conclude that compound leaves are more abundant in warm regions. In a third paper, Sinnott and Bailey state that leaves are of a comparatively large size in moist tropical regions, and that these leaves are commonly semi-xerophilous in structure. They reached the following general conclusions:

1. A marked correlation exists between the form of the leaf margins and the environment in the world distribution of the Dicotyledons.

2. Leaves and leaflets with entire margins are overwhelmingly predominant in lowland tropical regions. Those with non-entire margins occur, on the contrary, in mesophytic cold temperate regions.

3. In the tropical zones non-entire margins are favoured by moist uplands, equable environments and protected, comparatively cool habitats. In the cold temperate regions entire margins are favoured by arid environments and physiologically dry habitats.

Table 9. The percentage representation of entire and non-entire dicotyledon leaves in the Goshen flora compared with the Wilcox flora and various modern plant associations (Chaney and Sanborn, 1933)

	% of entire leaved dicotyledons	% of non-entire leaved dicotyledons
Goshen flora	61	39
Panama forest	88	12
Simla forest	58	42
Upper Gangetic Plain forest	71	29
Upper Hawaiian Forest	56	44
Lowland Hawaiian Forest	76	24
Wilcox flora	83	17

Table 9 shows the percentage of entire and non-entire dicotyledon leaves in the Goshen flora, and in the Panama forest according to Chaney and Sanborn (1933). Also included are similar values for upland and lowland forests in India and Hawaii (Sinnott and Bailey 1916) and for the Eocene Wilcox flora (Berry 1916).

It can be seen that the ratio of entire to non-entire leaves in the Goshen flora corresponds to that in the upland forests of Simla and Hawaii. There is in fact a larger number of non-entire leafed species when compared with the

3   25

lowland forests of Panama, the Gangetic Plain or Hawaii. Chaney and Sanborn suggest that this may be interpreted as indicating a relatively moist habitat which was somewhat colder than that of the modern lowland forests of the tropics.

They also noted a relatively close resemblance in leaf form between the temperate rain forest element of the Goshen flora and the modern vegetation at 5,000 feet at La Estrella in Costa Rica and at the same altitude in the Andes near Merida, Venezuela. From the data considered above and the fact that the Goshen flora is similar in type to both these American floras, Chaney and Sanborn conclude that it was intermediate in type between modern tropical rain forest and modern temperate forest.

THE COMSTOCK FLORA

A flora with tropical characteristics was reported by Sanborn (1935) from a series of deposits in Oregon. The flora is of particular interest as it is associated with a marine fauna of known Eocene age. The beds containing the floral

Table 10. The species of the Comstock flora whose modern analogues occur in the Old World (Sanborn, 1935)

Fossil species	Modern Old World Species	Occurrence
Aporosa pattersoni	Aporosa banahaensis	Philippines
Cinnamomum dilleri	Cinnamomum pedunculatum	Japan, S. China
Cryptocarya praesamarensis	Cryptocarya samarensis	Philippines
Diospyros orientalis	Diospyros hypoleuca	Philippines
Laurus princeps	Litsea elongata	South China
Mallotus comstocki	Mallotus albus	South China
Mallotus oregonensis	Mallotus philippinensis	South China
Polyalthia chaneyi	Polyalthia lani	South China
Pterospermum preobliquum	Pterospermum obliquum	Philippines
Trochodendroides zaddachi	Tetracentron sinensis	South China

remains comprised a series of sandstones, tuffs and shaly silts intercalated in three groups of beds. These give an estimated total thickness of 10,000 feet (Turner, 1934) and comprise:

1. The Fisher formation, consisting of massive tuffs and conglomerates of upper Eocene age.

2. The Comstock formation of sandstone tuffs and silts.

3. Umpqua Tyee sandstones interbedded with shales, 8,800 feet in thickness. The Upper Eocene molluscan fauna is at the top of the section.

The total number of specimens in the flora is 739, and of this number 23 per cent are *Cinnamomum dilleri* and 10 per cent are *Magnolia californica*. The leaves of these two species represent 33 per cent of the total remains. The leaflets of *Aralia* and *Astronium* represent another 20 per cent, so that 53 per cent of the flora is composed of these four species, which were presumably a dominant feature of the local vegetation at the time of deposition. The total list of species with known associations is contained in *Tables 10* and *11* and shows relationships with both New and Old Worlds. Amongst these species

26

in *Table 10*, *Aporosa*, *Cinnamomum*, *Mallotus*, *Polyalthia* and *Trochodendroides* do not occur in the New World today. On the other hand the genera *Cryptocaria*, *Diospyros* and *Litsea* occur in both hemispheres and the two latter genera have species in America which are closely similar to the fossil species and hence they compare in this respect with the species of *Table 11*.

Lonchocarpus, another genus whose modern analogues are distributed in the New World, occurs widely in the low latitudes of America. It is pan-tropical and has species in Africa and Australia.

The inclusion of *Allophylus wilsoni* in this list follows Sanborn's suggestion that the fossils show a greater resemblance to *Allophylus punctatus* than to the Malayan *Allophylus glaber*. Amongst the similar New World species 1 occurs

Table 11. Fossil species whose modern analogues occur in the New World
(Sanborn, 1935)

Fossil species	Modern New World species	Occurrence
Allophylus wilsoni	Allophylus punctatus	Bolivia
Anona coloradensis	Anona muricata	Yucatan
Aralia taurinensis	Aralia californica	California
Astronium oregonum	Astronium graveolens	Panama
Celastrus ferrugineus	Celastrus scandens	Eastern and Southern U.S.A.
Cordia rotunda	Cordia sebastana	Mexico, Central America
Ficus goshenensis	Ficus bonplandiana	Mexico
Lonchocarpus oregonensis	Lonchocarpus rugosus	Yucatan
Lonchocarpus standleyi	Lonchocarpus monospermus	Honduras
Magnolia californica	Magnolia acuminata	Southern U.S.A.,
Persea prelinque	Persea linque	Chile
Persea pseudo-carolinensis	Persea carolinensis	Southern U.S.A.
Platanus aceroides	Platanus occidentalis	Eastern U.S.A.
Rhamnus marginatus	Rhamnus sp.	Mexico

today in the region of California, 1 in the eastern U.S.A., 3 in the southern U.S.A., 7 in Mexico, Central America and Panama and 2 in South America. Sanborn concludes that the Comstock flora is therefore equivalent to species widely distributed in both hemispheres and New and Old Worlds. The majority are however restricted to low latitudes. 13 species are probably comparable with trees at the present time, 10 species are probably to be considered as having occurred as shrubs, and 1, *Celastrus ferrugineus*, was probably a vine.

At the family level, *Ficus goshenensis* is a member of the Moraceae, and this family occurs in the warmer areas of both hemispheres. In contrast, the species whose modern equivalents occur in the temperate regions are members of the Araliaceae, Celastraceae, Magnoliaceae and Platanaceae, and belong to genera which are either tropical, or range into the tropics.

As the result of all these considerations of species, genera and families the association may therefore be taken as indicating warm temperate to tropical conditions in Oregon during the Middle Eocene.

Table 12. A comparison of the analysis of the leaf characteristics of the modern Panama flora and the Eocene Comstock flora (after Sanborn, 1935)

	Length		Organization		Nervation		Margin		Dripping point		Texture	
	over 10 cm	under 10 cm	simple	com-pound	pinnate	palmate	entire	not entire	present	absent	thick	thin
Comstock No. of species	14	11	20	5	22	3	19	6	15	10	23	2
% of flora	56	44	80	20	88	12	76	24	60	40	92	8
Panama No. of species	23	18	35	6	34	7	36	5	31	10	40	1
% of flora	56	44	85	15	83	17	88	12	76	24	98	2

A comparison of the leaf characters with those in tropical regions at the present day, comparable with that undertaken by Chaney and Sanborn for the Goshen flora, is contained in *Table 12* and suggests a warm moist climate. Deducing that the presence of several species with a temperate range may indicate an adjacent upland habitat, Sanborn concludes that the Comstock climate was somewhat less tropical than that usually associated with the late Eocene and early Oligocene periods.

PLANT REMAINS OF OLIGOCENE AGE

THE LA PORTE FLORA

In 1935 Potbury reported a fossil flora from the western flank of the Sierra Nevada. During the late Jurassic period mountains were formed in the Sierra Nevada and it is probable that the local gold originated during crustal movements which occurred at that time, together with the associated volcanic activity. A later period of erosion, stretching into the Eocene, cut out deep channels on this base. The contorted form of the leaves and the absence of bedding planes in the fossiliferous deposit indicate that they were laid down hurriedly by the rapidly moving streams, which also deposited the gold. In contrast, the underlying carbonaceous shales appear to have been deposited in the quieter waters of a lake or slowly flowing stream. Since the flora overlays unconformably Middle Eocene beach gravels, Potbury suggested that it was not older than Upper Eocene. A detailed comparison with other floras showed that its greatest similarity was to the Chalk Bluffs flora, and it had more general similarities with the Eocene and lowest Oligocene floras of the Pacific coast.

The systematic list of the species represented amongst the plant remains of the La Porte flora is contained in *Table 13*. As in the case of other Tertiary floras, a comparison with the present distribution and appearance of related living species enabled a division into the probable life forms. Potbury concluded that 46 per cent of the remains represent tree species, 41 per cent small trees or shrubs and 13 per cent represent vines.

Considering the species list the author points out that the occurrence of Cycad remains is of interest since, although they are widespread in Mesozoic deposits, they are otherwise rare in the Tertiary. The remains of Taxaceae are restricted to the modern oriental genus *Cephalotaxus* and the monocotyledons are restricted to the two families, Palmae and Liliaceae. In fact the Palms, which are today a characteristic element of sub-tropical and tropical vegetation, were an important component of the warm Tertiary vegetation of America.

Although the Ranales is only represented by two families, it is the most extensive order in the assemblage, and the Menispermaceae include climbing shrubs which are also common in tropical and warm temperate forests. Similarly *Hyperbaena diforma* resembles *Hyperbaena smilacina* from Central America, whilst the genus *Cissampelos* exists in the neotropical regions and in the Asiatic, Malayan and African regions. As in the Eocene Goshen flora the thick-leaved Lauraceae actually predominates in terms of the number of species.

29

The Rosales constitutes the second largest order and includes the Leguminosae and the Hamamelidaceae. The genus *Liquidambar* of this last family has been discussed by Laurent (1919) who considers that all the forms belong to a single species. According to Laurent the actual differences arise from climatic effects on a polymorphic species and the plant remains presumably indicate a climate comparable to the present areas in which it occurs.

Table 13. The systematic list of plant remains in the La Porte flora of Plumas County, California (Potbury, 1935)

Polypodiaceae	Leguminosae
Polypodites	*Leguminosites falcatum*
Cycadaceae	*Lonchocarpus coriaceus*
Zamia mississippiensis var.	*Mimosites acutifolius*
macrophylla	*Sophora repandifolia*
Taxaceae	Euphorbiaceae
Cephalotaxus californica	*Acalypha serrulata*
Palmae	*Aleurites americana*
Sabalites rhapifolius	*Euphorbiophyllum multiformum*
Liliaceae	*Microdesmus occidentalis*
Smilax goshenensis	Aquifoliaceae
Fagaceae	*Ilex oregona*
Quercus nevadensis	Sabiaceae
Quercus suborbicularia	*Meliosma goshenensis*
Ulmaceae	Rhamnaceae
Ulmus pseudo-fulva	*Rhamnidium chaneyi*
Moraceae	Tiliaceae
Ficus goshenensis	*Columbia occidentalis*
Menispermaceae	Sterculiaceae
Cissampelos rotundifolia	*Sterculia ovata*
Hyperbaena diforma	Dilleniaceae
Lauraceae	*Davilla intermedia*
Cinnamomum acrodromum	Cornaceae
Cinnamomum dilleri	*Cornus kelloggii*
Laurophyllum intermedium	Styracaceae
Laurophyllum raminervum	*Styrax curvatus*
Ocotea eocernua	Sapotaceae
Persea prelinque	*Chrysophyllum conforme*
Persea pseudo-carolinensis	Apocynaceae
Hamamelidaceae	*Tabernaemontana intermedia*
Liquidambar californicum	Verbenaceae
	Petraea rotunda

The family Euphorbiaceae of the Geraniales is represented by four genera and the modern species of one of these genera, *Acalypha*, are common in warm climates. For example, *Acalypha schlectendahliana*, which most closely resembles *Acalypha serrulata*, is found in Mexico and Central America. The living species of *Aleurites* are confined to warm Asiatic regions. A similar comparison is also suggested by the similarity between *Microdesmus occidentalis* and the living *Microdesmus cesearifolia*. This is corroborated by the resemblance of the remains of the oak *Quercus nevadensis* to the Chinese *Quercus hainanensis*. In contrast the leaves of *Euphorbiophyllum* resemble those of the species *Drypetes alba* and *Mabea indorum* of the West Indian and South American region.

In general the climatic conditions indicated by the La Porte flora can be seen to be similar to those suggested by the foregoing floras of tropical character and the principal comparison is with the tropical regions of both new and old worlds. The more detailed list of species shows 28 which have their modern relatives in the American region and 9 whose relatives are Asiatic and are found in south-eastern China and the Philippines. A comparable analysis of leaf form to that in earlier sections showed that the La Porte leaf forms resemble the Goshen flora in organization, margin and dripping point, and resemble the Bridge Creek flora in length and nervation. Potbury therefore suggests that this is indicative of an intermediate climate, the vegetation being neither strictly sub-tropical nor temperate, but more tropical than temperate.

THE FLORISSANT FLORA

The plant remains from the Tertiary deposits at Florissant were recorded by MacGinitie (1953). The deposits in this region are largely of volcanic origin and were deposited on the uplifted and eroded surface of the granite of Pikes Peak, whose summit is 5,000 feet higher than the undulating surface of the Rocky Mountain Peneplain. These deposits consist of lava flows, massive pumiceous tuffs, river gravels, agglomerates and finely laminated fossiliferous paper shales of lacustrine origin. The lake-bed shales from the most prominent outcrops constitute only a minor part of the total thickness. MacGinitie emphasized that the beds did not comprise a single unit, but rather a complex and varied series of sediments and volcanics which are easily separated into five members. This series spans the Lower and Middle Oligocene periods. The plant-bearing layers comprise less than one-third of the total thickness and are the only components of lacustrine origin. Impressions of leaves, seeds and insects occur in these layers, and wood of *Sequoia* is found in the overlying tuffs. The systematic list of species is contained in *Table 14*.

The 97 angiosperms comprise 84 genera and 39 families. The best represented families are the Leguminosae (eight genera), Rosaceae (seven), Sapindaceae (six), Anacardiaceae (four) and Pinaceae, Ulmaceae, Rhamnaceae, Lauraceae and Saxifragaceae (three genera in each). MacGinitie points out that large groups of the Lauraceae and Leguminosae are now expected in the older Tertiary floras, whilst the Fagaceae and Pinaceae occur in younger Tertiary floras. The combination of both groups in the Florissant flora gives it a rather peculiar aspect, and MacGinitie suggests that the composition is correlated with the sub-humid characters of the climate and flora. Many of the living analogues of the fossils are adapted to xeric conditions and are drought resistant. The only other Tertiary flora of North America with a similar composition is in fact the Green River flora.

The genus *Picea* appears to be adapted to cooler climates than *Abies*, which has been reported from many localities in the Oligocene and Miocene periods of the western states. The identifiable fossil remains of *Sequoia* are similar to the Californian Redwood *Sequoia sempervirens* End. The abundant silicified stumps of this genus have their roots in place and testify to the former presence of groves of Redwood in the moist ground around the ponded areas. At least three distinct layers of fossil trees can be seen below the leaf bearing

Table 14. List of species from the Oligocene beds at Florissant, Colorado
(MacGinitie, 1953)

Bryophyta Musci. Grimmiaceae
  Plagiopodopsis scudderi Britton and Hollick
  Plagiopodopsis cockerelliae Steere
Pteridophyta Equisetaceae
  Equisetum florissantense Cockerell
Polypodiaceae
  Dryopteris guyottii (Lesquereux)
Gymnospermae
  Taxaceae
    Torreya geometrorum Cockerell
  Pinaceae
    Abies longirostris Knowlton
    Picea lahontense MacGinitie
    Picea magna MacGinitie
    Pinus florissanti Lesquereux
    Pinus hambachi Kirchner
    Pinus wheeleri Cockerell
  Taxodiaceae
    Sequoia affinis Lesquereux
  Cupressaceae
    Chamecyparis linquaefolia
  Gnetaceae
    Ephedra miocenica
Angiospermae
  Typhaceae
    Typha lesquereuxi Cockerell
  Gramineae
    Stipa florissanti Knowlton
  Cyperaceae
    Cyperacites lacustris MacGinitie
  Liliaceae
    Smilax labidurommae Cockerell
  Salicaceae
    Populus crassa Cockerell
    Salix coloradica MacGinitie
    Salix libbeyi MacGinitie
    Salix ramaleyi Cockerell
    Salix taxifolioides MacGinitie
  Juglandaceae
    Carya libbeyi Lesquereux
  Betulaceae
    Carpinus fraterna Lesquereux
    Fagopsis longifolia Hollick
  Fagaceae
    Castanea dolichophylla Cockerell
    Quercus dumosoides MacGinitie
    Quercus knowltoniana Cockerell
    Quercus lyratiformis Cockerell
    Quercus mohavensis Axelrod
    Quercus orbata MacGinitie
    Quercus peritula Cockerell
    Quercus predayana MacGinitie
    Quercus scottii MacGinitie
    Quercus scudderi Knowlton

Ulmaceae
  Celtis mccoshi Lesquereux
  Ulmus tenuinervis Lesquereux
  Zelkova drymeja Brown
Moraceae
  Morus symmetrica Cockerell
Proteaceae
  Lomatia lineata MacGinitie
Aristolochiaceae
  Aristolochia mortua Cockerell
Berberidaceae
  Mahonia marginata Arnold
  Mahonia obliqua MacGinitie
  Mahonia subdenticulata MacGinitie
Lauraceae
  Lindera coloradica MacGinitie
  Persea florissantia MacGinitie
  Sassafras hesperia Berry
Saxifragaceae
  Hydrangea fraxinifolia Brown
  Philadelphus minutus MacGinitie
  Ribes errans MacGinitie
Rosaceae
  Amelanchier scudderi Cockerell
  Cercocarpus myricaefolius MacGinitie
  Crataegus copeana MacGinitie
  Crataegus hendersoni Cockerell
  Crataegus nupta MacGinitie
  Malus florissantensis MacGinitie
  Malus pseudocredneria MacGinitie
  Prunus gracilis MacGinitie
  Rosa hilliae Lesquereux
  Vauquelinia coloradensis MacGinitie
  Vauquelinia liniara MacGinitie
Leguminosae
  Caesalpinites acuminatus MacGinitie
  Caesalpinites coloradicus MacGinitie
  Cercis parvifolia Lesquereux
  Conzattia coriacea MacGinitie
  Leguminosites lespedezoides MacGinitie
  Phaca wilmattae Cockerell
  Prosopis linearifolia MacGinitie
  Robinia lesquereuxi MacGinitie
  Vicia sp Knowlton
Platanaceae
  Platanus florissanti MacGinitie
Rutaceae
  Ptelea cassiodes MacGinitie
Simarubaceae
  Ailanthus americana Cockerell
Burseraceae
  Bursera serrulata MacGinitie
Meliaceae
  Cedrela lancifolia Brown
  Trichilia florissanti MacGinitie

Table 14—*continued*

Angiospermae—*continued*	Rhamnaceae
Euphorbiaceae	*Colubrina spireaefolia* MacGinitie
Euphorbia minuta MacGinitie	*Rhamnites pseudo-stenophyllus* MacGinitie
Anacardiaceae	*Zizyphus florissanti* MacGinitie
Astronium truncatum Cockerell	Vitaceae
Cotinus fraterna Cockerell	*Parthenocissus osbornii* MacGinitie
Rhus lesquereuxi Knowlton and Cockerell	*Vitis florissantella*
Rhus stellariaefolia MacGinitie	Tiliaceae
Schmaltzia vexans Cockerell	*Tilia populifolia* Lesquereux
Celastraceae	Thymelaceae
Celastrus typica MacGinitie	*Daphne septentrionalis*
Staphyleaceae	Myrtaceae
Staphylea acuminata Lesquereuxi	*Eugenia arenaceaeformis* MacGinitie
Aceraceae	Araliaceae
Acer coloradense MacGinitie	*Oreopanax dissecta* MacGinitie
Acer florissanti Kirchner	Styracaceae
Acer heterodentatum MacGinitie	*Halesia reticulata* MacGinitie
Acer oregonianum Knowlton	Oleaceae
Dipteronia insignis Brown	*Osmanthus praemissa* Cockerell
Sapindaceae	Convolvulaceae
Athyana haydeni MacGinitie	*Convolvulites orichitis* MacGinitie
Cardiospermum terminalis MacGinitie	Verbenaceae
Dodonaea umbrina MacGinitie	*Holmskioldia speirii* MacGinitie
Koelreuteria alleni Edwards	*Petraea perplexans* MacGinitie
Sapindus coloradensis Cockerell	Caprifoliaceae
Thouinia straciata MacGinitie	*Sambucus newtoni* Cockerell

shales, each one separated from the other by deposits of volcanic mud and ash. Some of the annual rings exceed an inch in width and indicate that the trees were fast growing. They did in fact reach diameters of over ten feet in 500 to 700 years. Fragments of branches with foliage and pistillate cones are common, and foliage with staminate cones occurs more rarely. These leaves are more slender and the cones smaller than in the living Redwoods. MacGinitie suggests that they may in fact have been living nearer to the edge of their zone of tolerance. Indeed, by a consideration of their associated species, he concluded that they had tended to become specialized towards endurance of hot sun and low humidity. In areas out of reach of the summer fogs, the coast Redwood of California is restricted to ravines and river bottoms, and moist sites on north-facing slopes. Near the coast, where the ground is kept moist by fog drip during the nearly rainless late summer, it expands to hills. The sierra Redwood, *Sequoiadendron giganteum* Birch, is found on moist flats between divides, where the roots can reach down for water. In relation to this it is interesting that the fossil companions of the Redwood show that it has always been primarily an inhabitant of moist soil in riverside or lakeside habitats from the Paleocene to the Pliocene (Chaney, 1951).

The most abundant conifer in the Florissant flora is *Chamaecyparis linquaefolia*. The *Chamaecyparis* of the Oregon coast grows from sea level to moderate heights in the immediate vicinity of the fog belt. Inland it inhabits moist north-facing slopes of the Coast Range at altitudes up to 5,500 feet. It is only rarely found in association with the Redwood at the present time, and in the

Redwood forests of North Carolina its place is taken by *Thuja*. The presence of these two genera alongside species whose modern analogues are xeric species, suggests that both the cedar and *Sequoia* lived in close proximity to the site of sedimentation, and had adapted themselves to moist sites in a sub-humid climate.

Amongst the Gramineae the fruits of the genus *Stipa* are similar to the wild oats of northern Mexico. *Smilax*, which is also recorded from more recent deposits, is a eurytopic genus which occurs in both the temperate and tropical regions. Quite clearly the combination between the leathery foliage and its frequent occurrence in streamside habitats increase the chances of its being preserved.

The genus *Populus* is typically north temperate in distribution at the present time. In the Florissant deposits it is represented by specimens of both leaves and associated fruits. MacGinitie in fact suggests that the abundance of *Populus* may explain the absence of *Salix* on the grounds of inter-generic competition.

In his consideration of the Betulaceae, MacGinitie draws attention to the fact that the majority of the species of *Carpinus* occur in eastern Asia today. Pollen is recorded from the Green River shales, but no other species of the genus had then been recorded from the early Tertiary of the U.S.A., although it is present in the Eocene floras of British Columbia and Alaska. Of the Fagaceae, the oaks, with the exception of *Quercus scudderi*, are nowhere common in the Florissant shales. In view of the rather large number of species together with the small number of remains of each, they probably comprised a high ground flora which existed some distance away, a flora which was perhaps dominated by evergreen oaks comparable to those of the oak forests of northern Mexico.

The remains of *Morus symmetrica* include leaves which are closely similar to *Morus microphylla*, a xerophytic shrub or small tree growing on rocky hillsides and ravines in central and west Texas, New Mexico, Arizona and Mexico. Similar relationships with comparable living xerophytic species in the same regions are suggested by the form of one of the *Mahonia* species, and that of the *Ribes*, *Crataegus*, *Vauquelinia* and *Ptelea* remains.

In contrast to these conclusions the remaining species of *Mahonia* resemble modern Asiatic forms. The genus *Ailanthus* is also now confined to China, southern Asia and Australia and a similar phytogeographical relationship is suggested by the Florissant leaf remains of *Cedrela*. Unlike the modern American species these leaves have crenate margins and resemble the temperate Chinese species. The presence of *Staphylea* is ambivalent as the genus is known from the more recent deposits of the Dutch Pleistocene and is widespread in both Asia and parts of America today. It is in fact said to be a component of the widespread Arcto-Cretaceo-Tertiary flora.

MacGinitie suggests that the most obvious conclusion to be drawn from the list of analogous modern species is that the flora as a whole has an overwhelmingly warm temperate facies, and is in no sense tropical or even sub-tropical. There are, however, some genera, for example *Holmskioldia* and the group of plants from southern Mexico, which occur in sub-tropical environments. Such a group of plants occurs in many of the Tertiary floras of the western states and particularly those of the Middle and Lower Miocene.

MacGinitie suggests that if not relics they may represent ecotypes of living tropical species that are adapted to more temperate conditions. As corroboration of this suggestion he instances the present-day occurrence of the species of *Persea* and *Diospyros* in eastern North Carolina, whilst the rest of the species are tropical.

A detailed study shows that 57 per cent of the similar living forms of the Florissant flora occur within a 400 mile radius of south western Coahuila, Mexico, an area in which the microphylls and xerophytes *Bursera*, *Cercis* and *Vauquelinia* occur. A further 29·7 per cent of the living analogues inhabit southern and central China. In fact where there are living analogues in both American and Asiatic regions the Asiatic species usually have the greatest similarity to the fossils.

Considering the possible increased temperature of the temperate regions of the U.S.A. during pre-Pliocene time, MacGinitie suggests that it may have been due to a higher minimum temperature, which may result from a warmer oceanic circulation (cf. Chapter 6). Such an effect of temperature minima is instanced by the tropical vegetation of coastal California from Monterey to Fort Bragg. This region has an average annual temperature of 55°F and an annual minimum of 17–21°F. In contrast to this one may instance the vegetation of north-eastern Kansas and north-central Missouri. Although the two areas have a similar annual average temperature this latter region has an annual minimum of −26°F.

Amongst American, Tertiary, fossil floras the Florissant plant list resembles those from Green River and Bridge Creek. However, the presence of more extinct genera and more warm species, together with less megasporic coniferous fossils, suggests that the Green River flora is older. The Bridge Creek, dating from the Uppermost Oligocene or Lower Miocene period, is an evergreen oak–birch–*Metasequoia* association. It differs from the Florissant in its lack of the characteristic xeric components of both the latter and the Madro-Tertiary flora generally (Axelrod, 1949), and in the high percentage representation of the warm temperate element.

From these facts MacGinitie concludes that the Florissant plant remains were laid down during the Lower Oligocene, although probably not the earliest part. He suggests that the Florissant flora is derived from the Green River flora. On the one hand there had been selection for plants tolerating the cooling and drying consequent upon the moderate uplift of the Rocky Mountain Axis. On the other hand, there was supplementation with temperate species from the earlier northern Arcto-Cretaceo-Tertiary flora.

THE WEAVERVILLE FLORA

The Weaverville flora occurs at five localities in which the strata are typical of the flood-plain and channel deposits of a large stream. Three-fourths of the material is gravel and derived from local formations including schists and intrusive bodies. MacGinitie (1937), when reporting the flora, recorded plant remains from all the five localities known as Redding Creek, Hayfork (two localities), Hyampo and Big Bar, but the most extensive collections were from Hayfork and Redding Creek.

At the Hayfork localities it is not possible to reconstruct the stratigraphy in its entirety owing to the presence of small folds and faults together with the overlying Quaternary gravels. MacGinitie suggests, however, that the total thickness of the Tertiary deposits is of the order of 2,000 feet. The stratigraphy is in fact characterized by the thickness of the five beds, the abundant lignite and the presence of leaf impressions resulting from a carbonized swamp vegetation. The presence of seeds of the aquatic plant genera *Trapa* and *Nyssa*, together with the genera of freshwater molluscs represented, suggest that the beds were deposited in a flood-plain environment.

The list of the species recorded in the flora is too provincial in character to be accurately assigned to a particular period. The most significant correlation noted by MacGinitie is with the Goshen flora of *Table 7*, although many of the sub-tropical forms of the latter are lacking. The Middle Eocene flora of Chalk Bluffs also has four species in common with the list from the Redding Creek locality of the Weaverville Beds. The *Taxodium-Nyssa-Salix* association does not give any particularly precise information about the age, because these plants occur in numerous early Tertiary floras. The similarity with Miocene floras largely involves genera whose eurythermal character would permit them to exist under widely varying climatic conditions, and there is almost no similarity with the Lower Miocene flora of Bridge Creek.

From these considerations, MacGinitie concludes that the plant remains in the Weaverville Beds represent a flora whose age lies between the Upper Eocene Goshen and the Lower Miocene Bridge Creek floras. In view of the general characteristics of the Weaverville flora he suggests that in broad terms it is Oligocene, and that the beds were probably laid down during the earlier or middle parts of that period.

The order with the largest representation is the Rosales which has seven species. The Ranales and Sapindales are each represented by four species, whilst the Salicales and Parietales have three species and the Urticales and Myrtales two. All the other orders have only one species each in the flora.

The presence of lichen remains in these Weaverville beds is of interest because, in spite of their texture, lichens only occur rarely in the plant lists from the Tertiary period. A lichen similar to that in the Weaverville flora occurs today in the humid regions of north-west California. In this area it grows on tree trunks in association with *Polypodium*, fossil remains of which also occur in the small outcrop from which the lichen was recorded. Mac-Ginitie suggests that the scarcity of lichens in the fossil record is due to their epiphytic habit. The family Stictaceae, to which the lichen remains are ascribed, contains two genera *Sticta* and *Lobaria*. Both of these genera are represented by species in both hemispheres although the genus *Sticta* is more common in the southern hemisphere.

One of the most widespread and characteristic members of the flora at the five localities is the single conifer *Taxodium dubium*. It is represented by wood, cone scales, staminate aments and leafy twigs, all of which are identical with those of the living *Taxodium distichum*.

The appearance of the remains of the willow *Salix inquirenda* from the uppermost tuffs at Redding Creek and Hayfork, suggests that this species was related to the living forms which occur in the Californian flora. The other species, *Salix longiacuminata*, resembles no living form but seems to be related to a species in the Green River flora.

In contrast to those plants which are probably closely related to species which occur in America today, there are also, as in the foregoing floras, species which seem most closely related to those in the modern Asiatic floras. Amongst these latter fossils is *Ulmus eolaciniata* which bears a striking resemblance to the Asiatic *Ulmus laciniata*.

The living species of *Hydrangea* occur in both the Asiatic and American regions and extend from the Himalayas through China to North and South America. They appear to have the central node of their modern distribution in China. In association with this *Hydrangea reticulata* corresponds in leaf form to the modern *Hydrangea paniculata* Sieb. of central China. MacGinitie came to a similar conclusion for the relationships of holly leaves to those of *Ilex aquifolium* var. *chinense* and *Ilex dipyrena* from central China. Similarly the *Tilia, Rhamnus* and *Berchemia* remains also resemble Asiatic species rather than the modern American species of the genera, and the genus *Idesia*, whose remains are numerous at the Hayfork exposures, is monotypic and occurs in south Japan and central and western China.

The analysis of the fossil leaf characters shows that the Weaverville flora resembles the Goshen leaf forms in terms of length and dripping point, but there is a great difference in the proportion of palmate and comparatively thin textured leaves. An outstanding characteristic of the Weaverville remains is the large size of the leaves when compared with those at Bridge Creek, Mascall, Latah and Florissant. MacGinitie suggests that on the basis of the leaf characters it is reasonable to conclude that the flora was intermediate between strictly cool temperate forest and the tropical forest of Panama.

The analysis of the living analogues suggested that within the vegetation 12 of the species, or 33 per cent of the total list, were trees, 14 species, or 39 per cent, were shrubs or small trees, and 16 per cent were scandent shrubs or vines. With the exception of *Ficus* and *Quercus* all the modern analogues require a wet sub-stratum and inhabit river bottoms or swamps. *Taxodium* and *Nyssa* are usually associated in such habitats and occur alongside *Salix, Persea, Platanus, Berchemia, Rhamnus, Smilax* and *Rhus*. However, in marked contrast, the Tupelo gum/swamp cypress association of the Weaverville beds actually shows more striking differences than similarities when compared with suitable modern associations. *Tetracera* and *Juglans* are constant and abundant dominants whilst the presence of exotic legumes, *Idesia* and *Calyptranthes*, is quite out of character. The differences are heightened by the absence from the Weaverville plant lists of *Liquidambar styraciflua, Magnolia glauca, Acer rubrum, Celtis occidentalis* and *Fraxinus* sp., all of which regularly occur in the comparable modern floras.

The overall conclusions would therefore suggest that there was not only a warmer climate but also a more abundant summer rainfall than occurs along the Pacific coast south of 40°N today. Indeed a summer rainfall in this region is rare under the atmospheric conditions at present prevailing in the north-east Pacific.

PLANT REMAINS OF MIOCENE AGE

THE MASCALL FLORA

The physical conditions in the Pacific north west of the U.S.A. during the Miocene were apparently highly favourable for the preservation of plants.

Along the flanks of the volcanoes of the Cascade Range, thick fans of coarse volcanic sediments were laid down and within these deposits there were contained lenses of fine textured sands and tuffaceous clays. It is in these that the vegetational record was preserved. In valleys which had become dammed by volcanic obstructions, lakes and swamps were formed. In these, logs, leaves, fruits and seeds which had been washed down from the apparently extensive deciduous forests of the region, became embedded. In areas which now have a sparse *Salix* and *Betula* plant cover, the diverse components of the Arcto-Cretaceo-Tertiary geoflora formed an extensive forest during the Miocene. This forest filled the Columbian Plateau and extended into the uplands. Previous work on the fossil plant remains of this region were reviewed by Chaney and Axelrod (1959) who described the Mascall flora in the strict sense from six sites at which the Mascall formation is exposed on the east fork of the John Day River at Picture Gorge. The formation is largely composed of the products of explosive eruptions which took place during the late Miocene. The series of rhyolitic tuffs and sand is of a considerable size and at its maximum depth appears to reach 2,000 feet. The floral remains from this series of deposits are summarized in *Table 15*.

The assumed growth habits of the plants analysed by Chaney and Axelrod suggest that 52 were probably trees, 20 were shrubs or small trees, and 2 were vines. The pollen of the Caryophyllaceae and Chenopodiaceae, together with the spores of the perhaps epiphytic *Polypodium*, indicates the presence of herbaceous plants in the vicinity. The actual composition of the plant associations was analysed by comparison with the known distribution of leaves in forest litter, in relation to the distance away of the trees concerned. The figures that they cite were actually obtained in the Californian Redwood forest but are typical of a large number of investigations undertaken throughout the world. The leaves of four species occurring at an average of 5·25 feet from the site of deposition compose 91 per cent of the litter. On the other hand the leaves of four species which occur at 25·25 feet from the site compose 8 per cent, whilst four species at 220 feet from the site compose only 0·02 per cent of the litter. Although the living analogues of the species in *Table 15* include several genera now found living in low latitudes, none are wholly confined to the tropical or sub-tropical forests. The leaves of the oaks preserved in the Mascall formation are largely lobed and deciduous in contrast to the entire or serrate margined leaves of the tropical species of *Quercus*. Although the genera *Liquidambar*, *Ostrya* and *Zelkova* range a long way south they are restricted to higher altitudes. Similar distributions characterize *Taxodium* in the New World and *Metasequoia* in the Old World. Both these conifers were ascribed by Axelrod to the Arcto-Cretaceo-Tertiary geoflora rather than the neotropical Tertiary geoflora. The genera *Keteleeria* and *Cephalotaxus* both occur up to the edge of the tropics in central China where they extend up to four thousand feet. In a similar way the genera *Albizzia*, *Cedrela*, *Diospyros*, *Lindera*, *Persea* and *Phoebe* are members of tropical families which regularly extend into temperate latitudes and altitudes. The genus *Taxodium* was of course widely distributed in the northern hemisphere during the Tertiary. The most southerly occurrence known for it during this period has long been in the Miocene in southern California (Condit, 1938). Its progressive restriction to the summer wet region of south-eastern U.S.A. has

Table 15. Systematic list of the floras of the Mascall formation (Chaney and Axelrod, 1959)

Ginkgoaceae
  Ginkgo adiantoides Heer
Taxaceae
  Cephalotaxus californica Perry
Pinaceae
  * *Abies chaneyi* Mason
  Abies klamathensis Axelrod
  * *Keteleeria heterophylloides* Brown
  * *Picea magna* MacGinitie
  Picea sonomensis Axelrod
  * *Pinus harneyana* Chaney and Axelrod
* Taxodiaceae
  Metasequoia occidentalis Chaney
  Taxodium dubium Chaney
* Cupressaceae
  Libocedrus masoni Chaney and Axelrod
  Thuja dimorpha Chaney and Axelrod
* Typhaceae
  Typha lesquereuxi Cockerell
Liliaceae
  Smilax magna Chaney
  Smilax wardii Lesquereux
Salicaceae
  * *Populus lindgreni* Knowlton
  Populus voyana Chaney and Axelrod
  * *Salix boisiensis* Smith
  Salix hesperia Condit
Leitneriaceae
  Leitneria pacifica Chaney and Axelrod
Juglandaceae
  * *Carya bendirei* Chaney and Axelrod
  * *Juglans*
  * *Pterocarya mixta* Brown
Betulaceae
  * *Alnus hollandiana* Jennings
  Alnus relatus Brown
  * *Betula fairei* Knowlton
  Betula thor Knowlton
  * *Ostrya oregoniana* Chaney
Fagaceae
  Fagus washoensis La Motte
  Quercus bretzi Chaney
  Quercus columbiana Chaney
  Quercus dayana Knowlton
  Quercus merriama Knowlton
  Quercus prelobata Condit
  Quercus pseudolyrata Lesquereux
  Quercus smileyana Chaney and Axelrod
Ulmaceae
  Celtis dayana Chaney and Axelrod
  Ulmus paucidentata Smith
  Ulmus speciosa Newberry
  Zelkova oregoniana Brown

Nymphaeaceae
  Nymphaeites nevadensis Brown
Cercidiphyllaceae
  Cercidiphyllum crenatum Brown
Berberidaceae
  Mahonia simplex Arnold
Lauraceae
  Laurophyllum merrilli Chaney and Sanborn
  Lindera oregoniana Chaney and Axelrod
  Persea pseudocarolinensis Lesquereux
  Sassafras columbiana Chaney and Axelrod
Saxifragaceae
  Hydrangea bendirei Knowlton
Hamamelidaceae
  Hamamelis merriami Chaney and Axelrod
  Liquidambar pachyphyllum Knowlton
Platanaceae
  Platanus dissecta Lesquereux
Rosaceae
  Amelanchier couleeana Brown
  Amelanchier covens Chaney and Axelrod
  Crataegus gracilens MacGinitie
Leguminosae
  Albizzia oregoniana Chaney and Axelrod
  Gymnocladus dayana Chaney and Axelrod
Rutaceae
  Ptelea miocenica Berry
Meliaceae
  Cedrela trainii Arnold
Aceraceae
  Acer bendirei Lesquereux
  Acer bolanderi Lesquereux
  Acer columbianum Chaney and Axelrod
  Acer glabroides Brown
  Acer minor Knowlton
  Acer oregonianum Knowlton
  Acer scottiae MacGinitie
Nyssaceae
  Nyssa hesperia Berry
Ebenaceae
  Diospyros oregoniana Chaney and Axelrod
Oleaceae
  Fraxinus coulteri Dorf
  Fraxinus dayana Chaney and Axelrod
* Chenopodiaceae
* Aquifoliaceae
* Caryophyllaceae
* Buxaceae
* Araliaceae
Umbelliferae
* Ericaceae
* Gramineae

* Signifies presence of the pollen of this genus or family

followed a pattern common to several other genera of the Arcto-Cretaceo-Tertiary geoflora which comprise the swamp cypress component of the Miocene forests of the Columbian Plateau.

From the above it can be seen that the dominant elements in the Mascall flora are east American and east Asian. An investigation of the vegetation of Slidel in coastal Louisiana showed that the source of the leaves and fruits which might be deposited in the Lake Pontchartrain region, and therefore give rise to the modern sedimentary record of the Mississippi Delta, came from a series of habitats.

(a) Brackish water swamp bordering the alluvial delta and including *Acer rubrum, Fraxinus pennsylvanica, Nyssa aquatica, Sabal minor, Salix nigra, Taxodium distichum* and *Typha latifolia*.

(b) Alluvial delta near swamps, including *Aralia spinosa, Berchemia scandens, Bignonia capreolata, Celtis mississippiensis, Cephalanthus occidentalis, Diospyros virginiana, Gleditsia aquatica, Liquidambar styraciflua, Magnolia grandiflora, Menispermum canadense, Quercus nigra* and *Vitis*.

(c) Pine uplands with *Liquidambar* and *Nyssa* the dominant species.

(d) *Taxodium distichum* dominant areas.

From the plant lists of this area Chaney suggests that there are 15 species analogous to those which occur in the Mascall flora. These 15 species actually represent 60 per cent of the total fossil specimens.

A similar investigation of the Indiana swamp cypress forests showed that 21 species of the Mascall flora have counterparts in the Wabash valley. Adding to this 9 fossil species only generically related to the Wabash valley flora and 5 fossil species not actually present in the Mascall deposits but known to have occurred in the Columbian Plateau in the Miocene, then 35 fossil Miocene species have specific or generic equivalents in the mixed deciduous forest of the southern part of Indiana. Totalling the fossil specimens belonging to these genera and species which have modern equivalents in the area shows that they represent 81 per cent of the Mascall plant remains. Of these species the fossil *Quercus dayana*, a dominant component of the Mascall flora and several other Miocene forests, and the modern *Quercus virginiana*, a dominant component of the Indiana vegetation, are closely related.

As the result of these investigations Chaney and Axelrod (1959) conclude that the climate in which the Mascall floral remains were deposited was comparable with that which prevails today in the areas of lowland vegetation of the Mississippi basin and Atlantic coastal plain. However, the presence of 5 species which are not referable to the *Taxodium distichum* vegetation suggests that another forest component was present in the Mascall flora. These species and their modern analogues, which are *Alnus hollandiana* (*A. rugosa*), *Amelanchier covens* (*A. spicata*), *Populus voyana* (*P. tremuloides*), *Ptelea miocenica* (*P. trifoliata*), *Thuja dimorpha* (*T. occidentalis*), represent the so-called Appalachian components (Chaney, 1959), and comprise elements of the mixed mesophytic forest of the Cumberland Mountains and elsewhere in the Appalachians. The fact that of the five species four have a low percentage representation (0·02–0·21) suggests that they represent a vegetation growing at a considerable distance from the site of deposition.

In this respect the results of Downs (1956), who investigated the Mascall fauna, are of interest. He considered that the equids *Merychippus severus*, *Parahippus avus* and *Archeohippus ultimus*, together with *Dromomeryx borealis*, comprised large upland forms with high crowned teeth suitable for eating grass, whilst smaller horses and artiodactyls browsed in lowland forest and were preyed upon by tomarctid and amphicyonid dogs.

In detail Chaney and Axelrod conclude that the area consisted of wooded valleys with streams, small lakes and swamps near to uplands with an open vegetation. As a preliminary estimate of the climate they suggest that it might be similar to that of Blytheville, Arkansas. This region has a mean annual temperature of 62°F, an average winter temperature of 42° and an average winter minimum approaching 0° with an absolute minimum of −8°. It is not proven that this low winter temperature occurred during the Miocene as the topography of the times was quite different. Today the Cascade Range is much higher than during the Miocene, and the shore is further west. The difference in August temperature between the coast and the Mascall exposures is 9°F. As the altitude has risen by about 1,500 feet then this is presumably a greater difference than that occurring during the Miocene. In view of this, although the temperature may have gone below 0°C, Chaney and Axelrod suggest that it is improbable that there was prolonged winter cold. They further suggest that the modifying influence of well-distributed precipitation on temperature is seen in many modern forests, and the low winter temperature is modified in regions such as Central Honshu where a large amount of precipitation is distributed throughout the year. In view of these considerations Chaney and Axelrod (1959) conclude that in the absence of a living forest which exactly duplicates the Mascall flora, the swamp cypress forests of the Mississippi valley, and the vegetation of the uplands of eastern North America and eastern Asia, provide a basis for reconstructing the vegetation of the Columbian Plateau in the Miocene period.

THE BLUE MOUNTAINS FLORA

Within the drainage basin of the middle fork of the John Day River, Chaney and Axelrod also recorded another flora contained within belts of volcanic ash. In the fossiliferous region the beds are of limited extent and thickness. On the basis of the similarities between the plant list and that of the Mascall beds, the Blue Mountains flora was at first ascribed generally to the Miocene period. However, it has a lithological similarity to the Stinking Water flora from further south, which is probably Upper Miocene.

The total list of around 50 species includes amongst the trees *Sequoia* and *Thuja*, together with Pinaceae, *Alnus* and *Betula* amongst the Betulaceae, and *Fagus* and *Quercus* in the Fagaceae. In the list of shrubs there is a similarity with the Mascall flora. Evidence from pollen-analytical studies suggests that *Juglans*, *Ilex*, *Liquidambar*, *Pterocarya* and *Cedrus* all grew in the locality. A total of 23 species are in fact common to both the Mascall and Blue Mountains plant lists, but only the oak *Quercus pseudolyrata* and the plane *Platanus dissecta* are abundant in both groups of deposits. In general the dominant components of the Blue Mountains flora are either rare in the Mascall flora, for example *Fagus washoensis*, *Quercus simulata*, *Betula fairii*, or are actually absent, for example *Gordonia idahoensis* (Theaceae). Amongst the coniferous elements there are even more marked differences, since the two floras have no dominant species in common.

By comparison with modern analogues 39 of the species were trees, 13 shrubs or small trees, 2 vines, and 5 probably herbaceous plants. Of the 2,112 specimens recorded 37 per cent are in fact leaves of *Fagus*. This is a much higher percentage representation than the genus has in any other Tertiary flora of the western states. In view of the similar high value of 29 per cent for the representation of *Quercus*, Chaney and Axelrod (1959) draw attention to the apparent absence of fruits of either oak or beech. Various species occur as megafossils (leaves) in either the Mascall or Blue Mountains floras although they are represented only by pollen in the other. An example of this is *Carya bendirei*, which, although limited to pollen in the Blue Mountains list, is represented by megafossils in the Mascall flora. The living analogue of *Carya bendirei* is, according to Chaney and Axelrod, *Carya ovata* a species characteristically found in lowland regions although extending up to 3,000 feet.

All the Blue Mountains species have a north temperate distribution today. A comparison with the lowland vegetation of southern Hokkaido, Japan, shows the combination of Asian with Appalachian components similar to that noted in the Mascall flora. Despite minor inconsistencies, for which Chaney suggests a wide altitudinal range may be the explanation, the numerical representation is generally suggestive of an upland flora comparable to the forests of the Appalachians. The genera, *Aesculus*, *Castanea*, *Cornus* and *Liriodendron* are absent although they occur in neighbouring floras of Miocene age. All the east Asian analogues of the Blue Mountains species occur within the *Castanea-Liquidambar-Quercus glandulosa-Betula* middle altitude climax forest. It is in this forest that *Metasequoia* occurs between 3,000 and 4,000 feet in the Shui-hsa-pa area of Central China. The west American elements in the Blue Mountains plant list also occur at middle altitudes today with a lower percentage representation at sub-alpine levels. In view of this Chaney and Axelrod suggest that the fossil *Gordonia* remains may represent a species more closely related to the east Asian *Gordonia axillaris* that is found at altitudes up to 3,000 feet, rather than the lowland American species *Gordonia lasianthus*, which, if present, would have been expected to occur in the Mascall flora.

As the result of his analysis of the components of the Blue Mountains flora, Chaney suggests that the climate may have been comparable with that which prevails today in Central Japan. However, it had no more than 50–60 inches of well-distributed annual precipitation. If this were the case, the authors point out, it would indicate basic alterations in the ocean circulation and topography of North America to give the stabilizing influence comparable with that in Japan today.

THE STINKING WATER FLORA

The geology and paleontology of the area of south eastern Oregon from which Chaney and Axelrod (1959) reported a flora of probably Upper Miocene age is only incompletely known. The Stinking Water basin is between 7 and 10 miles wide, situated in Harney County and bordered by the Stinking Water mountain range. A broad downfolding of basalt has provided a base upon which there lie volcanic sediments. Within these there occur sandy shales and a fine white ash. Since the various components inter-digitate it is clear that the deposition occurred during a period of active local volcanism.

The plant list from the sedimentary sand components of these deposits has a marked similarity to those reported by MacGinitie (1933) from Trout Creek, by La Motte (1936) from Upper Cedarville, by Kirkham (1931) from Succor Creek and Chaney (1959) from the Mascall formations. These fossil floras either occur beneath the upper flows of the Upper Miocene Columbia River basalt or are associated with mammalian fossils which are known to be Miocene. However, although the list of plant remains from the Stinking Water deposits has much in common with the Mascall and Blue Mountains floras, there are certain outstanding differences. There is a marked absence of *Taxodium dubium* and an equally marked replacement of this species by *Glyptostrobus oregonensis*.

With the exception of the presence of the genera *Cedrela*, *Glyptostrobus* and *Keteleeria* the composition of the Stinking Water plant list suggests that it represents a flora which was essentially north temperate in character when judged by its modern analogues. *Glyptostrobus* occurs in the Canton delta and adjacent areas today. Both *Cedrela* and *Keteleeria* also range into the northern and central regions of China; in Hupeh and Szechuan they occupy the lower altitudinal levels. They also range higher and occur in the middle altitudes where there are also many other American Miocene genera in the temperate forest associations.

Pterocarya and *Ailanthus* are no longer represented in the flora of North America, whilst, on the contrary, *Platanus* is absent from eastern Asia. Further similarities with the Asiatic flora are also suggested by the fact that 18 species are, according to Chaney, closely allied to living analogues which occur in Japan. It is suggested that they may be correlated in particular with the forests of Hokkaido—in northern Japan. Further, although the genus *Glypto-strobus* does not occur in that region at the present time, it did do so during the Tertiary era. Indeed its absence from regions of south China today may be correlated with the presence or absence of suitable swamps in which *Glyptostrobus pensilis* can grow.

Although there are these striking similarities with certain components of the Asiatic flora it should not be forgotten that there are also many modern American analogies. As an example of these one may cite the 20 species whose living analogues suggest them as the so-called Appalachian element in the Stinking Water flora, e.g. *Acer bendirei* and its analogue *Acer saccharinum*. In this respect it is also interesting to note the similarities and contrasts between the composition of this flora from the Stinking Water basin and the Miocene flora from the Mascall formation.

As far as the similarities are concerned one may cite the occurrence of two-thirds of the east American element of the Stinking Water flora in the Mascall flora. The differences between these two plant associations which are closely comparable in both geographical situation and time may therefore probably be ascribed to the ecological conditions under which deposition occurred. Chaney suggests that such an explanation would account for the differential occurrence of *Glyptostrobus* and *Taxodium*. The presence of *Glyptostrobus* not *Taxodium* in the Stinking Water deposits would on these grounds be related to the dominance of river bank habitats as opposed to the swamp habitats which contributed to the vegetation of the Mascall deposits. This suggestion, which is based on the present-day ecological preferences of the two genera, is supported by independent evidence. In the Mascall formations the diatom species *Melosira granulata* is abundant whereas no diatoms occur in the Stinking Water deposits. The characteristic swamp-living Tupelo-gum was a co-dominant in the Mascall, and the river-bank *Alnus harneyana* and *Alnus rhombifolia* occurred in the Stinking Water flora.

Table 16. The slope associations of the Stinking Water flora (Chaney and Axelrod, 1959)

Abies chaneyi	*Liquidambar* pollen
Acer bendirei	*Mahonia reticulata*
Acer bolanderi	*Mahonia simplex*
Acer columbianum	*Nyssa* pollen
Acer minor	Onagraceae pollen
Acer oregonianum	*Picea lahontense*
Acer scottiae	*Picea sonomensis*
Ailanthus indiana	*Pinus harneyana*
Alnus harneyana	*Platanus dissecta*
Alnus hollandiana	*Ptelea miocenica*
Betula pollen	*Pterocarya mixta*
Carya pollen and wood	*Quercus hannibali*
Caryophyllaceae pollen	*Quercus prelobata*
Compositae pollen	*Quercus simulata*
Chenopodiaceae pollen	*Rhamnus columbiana*
Corylus pollen	*Rosa harneyana*
Fagus pollen	*Salix hesperia*
Fraxinus pollen and wood	*Salix succorensis*
Gramineae pollen	*Smilax magna*
Gymnocladus dayana	*Spiraea harneyana*
Hydrangea bendirei	*Tsuga* pollen
Juglans pollen	*Ulmus speciosa*
Keteleeria heterophylloides	*Vaccinium sophoroides*

A consideration of the possible altitudinal relationships enables one to draw up three principal lists of species of the plant remains from this late Tertiary deposit. There are however several species, as for example *Acer bendirei* mentioned above, with widespread altitudinal tolerance. Nevertheless some 11 species are suggested by their modern analogues as a montane element and another twelve as a lowland element viz.

Alnus harneyana	*Quercus dayana*
Alnus relatus	*Quercus hannibali*
Glyptostrobus oregonensis	*Quercus prelobata*
Picea magna	*Quercus pseudolyrata*
Platanus dissecta	*Quercus simulata*
Populus lindgreni	*Ulmus speciosa*

However, the largest single altitudinal element is the slope component. This list also includes 12 genera which are represented by pollen and were therefore somewhat further away from the site of deposition. Naturally, as in

44

the case of *Acer bendirei*, there is some variation. As an example one may quote the hickory wood. *Carya pecan*, the living hickory, is a lowland species in the southern region of the U.S.A. and in this region it grows in lowland valleys. However, in the more southern regions of its range this is not the case and in Mexico it is sufficiently different to be considered a montane component of the Mexican flora. The altitudinal variation or lack of precision of some of the living analogues therefore result in certain species being listed in both the slope and lowland associations, *Table 16*.

The number of herbaceous pollen grains suggestive of an open vegetation, notably the Caryophyllaceae, Chenopodiaceae Compositae and Gramineae, is twice that in the Mascall flora. Indeed the total vegetation when compared with that suggested by the John Day site of the Mascall formation indicates a climate including drier summers and approximately 10 inches less annual rainfall. In the valleys *Quercus pseudolyrata* was dominant and occurred alongside alders, water-pine, sycamore, cottonwood and elm. The restriction of forests to the valleys with woodland and open vegetation on the progressively higher slopes is suggested by Chaney to represent the early stages in the climatic and vegetational changes leading to the present semi-arid climate and extremes of temperature on the Columbian Plateau.

PLANT REMAINS OF PLIOCENE AGE

THE MOUNT EDEN FLORA

In 1935–36 Axelrod worked on the plant remains contained within the Mount Eden Beds of southern California. These are well-exposed at the western end of the San Gorgonio Pass (Axelrod, 1937). The beds had previously been shown to include two series of deposits:

1. The Mount Eden shales and sandstones which contain vertebrate and plant remains.
2. The lower Red Bed which consists of conglomerates which grade into gritty sandstones at the top and have no fossils.

It is probable that the mountains of the area were thrown up by orogenic movements which occurred in the early Quaternary. The upper fossiliferous strata were in fact originally assigned to a Lower Pliocene age. Simpson (1933) amended this and suggested instead that they were in fact of Middle Pliocene age and more recent opinions would modify this to late Middle Pliocene. It has been suggested that whatever the correct or actual date of these deposits they were laid down during a period in which the area had an arid climate.

Of the total list of species in the flora, *Table 17*, it seems probable that 7 were large trees, that 3 were normally small trees and 12 normally shrubs. 9 of the species are in fact known from other deposits of Pliocene age. Some of the genera in *Table 17* are in fact only infrequently represented and indeed *Arbutus*, *Lepidospartum* and *Rhus prelaurina* are only single impressions. The approximate order of abundance is *Platanus paucidentata* (leaves), *Pseudotsuga premacrocarpa* (cones), *Pinus pieperi* (cones, seeds and scales), *Pinus hazeni*

45

(cones, seeds and scales), *Juglans beaumontii* (fruits and leaflets), *Salix coalingensis* (leaves), *Populus pliotremuloides* (leaves) and *Pinus pretuberculata* (cones). The complete flora as analysed by Axelrod includes a xeric element which is probably a desert border unit, a coniferous element related to the endemic Californian conifers, and a riparian element together with species of savanna and woodland.

Table 17. List of species from the Mount Eden Beds (Axelrod, 1937)

Equisetum sp.	Platanaceae
Pinaceae	*Platanus paucidentata*
Pinus hazeni	Rosaceae
Pinus pieperi	*Cercocarpus cuneatus*
Pinus pretuberculata	*Prunus preandersoni*
Pseudotsuga premacrocarpa	*Prunus prefremontii*
Cupressaceae	Leguminosae
Cupressus preforbesii	*Prosopis pliocenica*
Gnetaceae	Anacardiaceae
Ephedra sp.	*Rhus prelaurina*
Typhaceae	Sapindaceae
Typha lesquereuxi	*Sapindus lamottei*
Salicaceae	Rhamnaceae
Populus pliotremuloides	*Ceanothus edensis*
Salix coalingensis	*Ceanothus* sp.
Salix sp.	Ericaceae
Juglandaceae	*Arbutus* sp.
Juglans beaumontii	*Arctostaphylos preglauca*
Fagaceae	*Arctostaphylos prepungens*
Quercus hannibali	Oleaceae
Quercus lakevillensis	*Fraxinus edensis*
Quercus orindensis	Compositae
Quercus pliopalmeri	*Lepidospartum* sp.

Within the xeric element Axelrod includes *Ephedra*, *Prosopis pliocenica* and *Sapindus lamottei* together with the oak *Quercus pliopalmeri* and the two *Prunus* species. All these are species whose modern analogues are characteristic of arid regions. Under typical conditions they are to be found growing on desert slopes, along drainage gulleys or by the mouths of streams; *Prunus fremontii* actually growing on the slopes adjoining the Colorado desert with the Yucca's and desert shrubs. 12 other analogues of the Mount Eden flora also grow within a few miles of this area. *Sapindus* is designated a desert or xeric component by Axelrod on the grounds that it grows well out along stream courses in the desert scrub of the south-west in association with *Ephedra*, *Juglans*, *Prosopis* etc. Axelrod suggests that the whole of this desert element was growing on the dry exposed slopes provided by the steep granitic hills of the Mount Eden area.

The riparian element of Axelrod includes the species of *Fraxinus*, *Juglans*, *Platanus* and *Lepidospartum*. Various species within the list occur on banks of streams. *Juglans* reaches its optimum development under the influence of the coastal breezes and fogs on the western slopes of the Santa Ana mountains and the Puente Hills. Indeed in the more arid regions of its realm it is characteristically a species of stream courses. According to Axelrod it is probable that both *Juglans* and *Sapindus* no longer occur in the Californian region because of a shift from a climate with summer rain and a winter maximum to a climate with dry summers and rain limited to the winter.

The savanna and woodland element is according to Axelrod the group of species *Pinus pieperi*, *Quercus hannibali*, *Quercus lakevillensis* and *Quercus orindensis* together with *Juglans* and *Arbutus*. It is suggested that this latter genus is an upland component of the Mount Eden flora. Indeed the 10 analogous described species of *Arbutus* are probably only variants of *Arbutus xalapensis*. The northern forms which occur in a semi-arid habitat have leaves that are smaller than the Mount Eden specimens and are more entire margined. The leaves of the fossils are in fact more comparable with the more mesic variants of *Arbutus* growing at higher elevations, with more rainfall and less extremes of temperature, on the Mexican plateau. From this Axelrod concludes that the Mount Eden *Arbutus* is indicative of a cool moist habitat.

Discussing these facts, Axelrod reviews the climate and topography of the region at the time the sediments were laid down. The lithology of numerous deposits suggests that there were shallow lakes in the region of the Mohave and Colorado deserts at the period of the Pliocene and early Pleistocene. The coast of southern California was submerged in the Pliocene and this immersion persisted into the Pleistocene. However, the number of xeric species leads Axelrod to suggest that this could not have had a very marked moderating effect. At that time the San Bernadino and San Jacinto mountains were considerably lower so that the area was not so discrete a biogeographical unit. With the retreat of the sea and the orogenesis to the east and west the conditions of high temperature and low humidity of this interior area today were made possible.

In view of these conclusions it is interesting that Frick (1921), discussing the vertebrate fauna of the Mount Eden Beds, concluded that there was a low-lying basin with an adjacent plains/savanna habitat and adjoining forested uplands. Within this environment there lived the rodent *Hypolagus*, the carnivores *Procyon*, *Hyaenarctos* and *Hyaenognathus*, horses of the genus *Pliohippus*, two camels and a proboscidean. The presence of a plains grazing fauna in the Pleistocene Bautista Beds a few miles away suggests that similar conditions persisted or re-occurred in the region during the Pleistocene.

THE FLORA AT KROŚCIENKO, POLAND, AND EUROPEAN FLORAL HISTORY IN THE LATE TERTIARY

Following the initial finds of lignified wood at the National Park in Pienony, Poland, in 1938, Szafer undertook an extensive investigation of plant remains extracted from a clay pit at Krościenko on the river Dunajec. This work is reported in Szafer (1946). Pollen-analytical investigations were carried out on material from 39 feet of Pliocene deposits and from a more loamy deposit at the village of Grywałd some 1½ km away. In view of the conditions under which Szafer was carrying out these researches and the situation in occupied Poland, his 1946 work is an incredible testimony to his patience and endurance. One can but quote from the terse sentence of his introduction 'Finally I cannot but confess that it was the uncertainty of my personal fate that led me to finish my manuscript so hastily'.

In his exposition he analysed the plant remains into geographical divisions comparable with those of Reid (1920). These included 1. A cosmopolitan element, 2. Holarctic element, 3. Eurasian element, 4. Amphiatlantic, 5. Amphipacific, 6. West Asiatic, 7. Central European, 8. South European, 9. Balkan-colchican (including the Balkans, Caucasus and Transcaucasia), 10. East Asiatic, 11. Eastern North America, 12. Western North America, 13. Mediterranean, 14. Macaronesian (chiefly Canarian), 15. South-eastern Asiatic, Malaysian or Paleotropical, 16. Neotropical. As in the case of the foregoing Tertiary plant lists these groupings were based upon the present day distribution of the actual or closely allied species.

The plant species from Krościenko which represent the phytogeographical divisions 1, 2, 3, 7, 8, 9, 10, 11 are contained in the following lists and suggest the climatic characteristics shown in *Figure 2*. Asterisks denote extinct species.

1. *Cosmopolitan or almost cosmopolitan species*
    Alisma plantago
    Ceratophyllum demersum
    Polygonum aviculare

2. *Holarctic (Circumpolar) species*
    Carex cf. *panicea*
    Carex pseudocyperus
    Cicuta virosa
    * *Circaea lutetianoides*
    Polygonum convolvulus
    Rubus cf. *idaeus*
    Sparganium ramosum (also in Northern Africa)

3. *Eur-Asiatic species*
    Caldesia cf. *parnassifolia*
    Physalis cf. *alkekengi*
    Rubus cf. *caesius*
    Sagittaria sagittifolia
    Sambucus cf. *racemosa*
    Solanum dulcamara
    Thalictrum cf. *minus*
    Valeriana officinalis

7. *European species (mostly central European) sometimes passing to the western part of Asia*
    Abies cf. *alba*
    Acer campestre
    Acer cf. *platanoides*
    Ajuga reptans (also in Tunisia)
    Alnus glutinosa
    Alnus incana
    Carpinus betulus
    Corylus avellana
    Crataegus monogyna (also in northern Africa)
    Fagus cf. *silvatica*
    Oenanthe cf. *aquatica*
    Ostericum cf. *palustre*
    * *Peucedanum moebii*
    Picea abies
    Pyrus communis
    Pyrus malus

48

Prunus spinosa (also in northern Africa)
Ranunculus polyanthemos
Sambucus cf. *ebulus* (also in northern Africa)
Viola cf. *uliginosa*

8. *South European species, sometimes passing to south-western Asia*
   * *Ranunculus reidi*
   * *Trapa natans* var. *tuberculata*
   * *Staphylea pliocaenica*
   Vitis silvestris

9. *Balkan-Caucasian-and Transcaucasian species*
   Aesculus hippocastanum
   Corylus cf. *maxima*
   * *Picea omoricoides*
   Pinus peuce
   Ostrea carpinifolia
   Prunus domestica
   Pterocarya fraxinifolia
   Staphylea colchica

10. *East Asiatic species*
    Acanthopanax sp.
    Acer japonicum
    Acer palmatum
    Acer cf. *pictum*
    Acer sp. (aff. *Tschonoskii*)
    * *Actinidia faveolata*
    Actinidia polygama
    Alangium kichhelmeri
    Aralia sp.
    Bucklandia cf. *populnea*
    * *Carex flagellata*
    Carex sp. (sect. Frigidae)
    Carpinus laxiflora
    * *Carpinus minuta*
    Carpinus cf. *Tschonoskii*
    Chamaecyparis pisifera
    Coriaria cf. *japonica*
    Cornus controversa
    * *Corylopsis urselensis*
    (*Corylus* cf. *rostrata*)
    * *Euryale carpatica*
    * *Fothergilla europaea*
    Hibiscus aff. *siriacus*
    Keteleeria sp.
    * *Larix ligulata*
    * *Magnolia cor*
    * *Meliosma europaea*
    * *Olea Zablockii*
    Phellodendron amurense
    Phellodendron japonicum
    Picea cf. *glehnii*
    Picea polita
    Pieris sp.
    Pinus sp. (aff. *Massoniana*)

    Pinus cf. *tabulaeformis*
* *Stewartia europaea*
* *Styrax obovatum*
* *Sinomoenium dielsi*
    Thuja orientalis
* *Trichosanthes fragilis*
* *Vitis Ludwigi*
    Vitis sp. (aff. *Thunbergi*)
    Zelkova serrata

11. *East American species*
    Acer sp. (aff. *floridanum*)
    Betula cf. *populifolia*
    Carya sp.
    Ceanothus americanus
    Corylus cf. *rostrata*
    Crataegus cf. *pentagyna*
* *Dulichium vespiforme*
    Fagus ferruginea
    Juglans cinerea
* *Liquidambar europaea*
    Liriodendron tulipifera
    Nyssa silvatica
    Picea rubra
* *Proserpinaca reticulata*
    Rubus occidentalis
* *Scirpus pliocaenicus*
    Staphylea cf. *trifolia*
    Tsuga caroliniana
    Tsuga europaea
    Viburnum cf. *prunifolium*
    Vitis sp. (aff. *cordifolia*)

As the result of this analysis of the plant remains Szafer suggested that the climate in the region of Krościenko during the period of deposition of this Pliocene flora differed from that at the present time as shown in *Figure 2*. He also proposed an extensive scheme showing the temporal relationships of the changes which occurred in the central European flora during the Pliocene.

In order to do this and to compare these results with those of other neighbouring regions Szafer further analysed the plant records from a number of Pliocene deposits in the European area. He then compared these analyses with comparable analyses for Miocene and Quaternary deposits. In general he considered that the European region comprised three phytogeographical units in late Tertiary times which he designated the 'Outer', 'Inner' and 'Southern' zones. The Outer zone consisted of the area to the north of the Pyrenees/Alpine/Sudetenland/Carpathian line. The Inner zone lay to the south-east of this line and separated the outer zone from the Southern zone which was situated within reach of the modern Mediterranean.

There are distinct differences between the floristic lists from these three zones. In the most northern or north western, namely the Outer zone, the groups 7 (above all) and 3 occupy the principal place in the list of native elements and groups 1, 2, 4, 5 became progressively more important as the Pliocene proceeded. In the group of exotic elements, and here one must emphasize that Szafer considers as exotic any plants not native to his Outer zone at the present time, group 10, the East Asiatic element, had a high percentage representation throughout the Pliocene. Turning to his Inner zone, groups 7 and 8 are the predominant native elements and the North American (11 and 12) together with the Mediterranean element, as represented in the modern Roumanian flora, had the form of Tertiary relics. Finally in the Southern zone the Mediterranean (13) and the south-eastern phyto-geographical elements 6, 8 and 9 prevail among the native groups

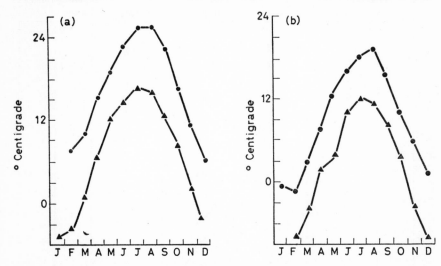

Figure 2. (a) The monthly mean temperatures at Krościenko today (triangles) and the suggested values for the same region during the Middle Pliocene (circles) (from Szafer, 1946); (b) The approximate monthly mean temperatures in the coniferous woods at an altitude of 1,200 metres in the Krościenko region today (triangles) and the probable temperatures at this level in the Middle Pliocene (circles) (from Szafer, 1946)

whilst, although there is no one outstandingly predominant exotic element, there is a characteristic high value for the percentage representation of the Macaronesian (14) and sub-tropical (15 and 16) groupings.

These differences in the phytogeographical composition of Szafer's three zones are explained by him on two grounds. There is first of all the obviously different geographical location of the individual zones involving as it will the variation in the local meteorological characteristics. Secondly, there is a progressive increase in the percentage representation of Miocene species as one proceeds further to the south.

The changes which took place in the Outer zone are summarized in *Figure 3* which is taken from Szafer and shows that there appeared in the early Pliocene a strong wave of the east Asiatic element. The North American element, which had comprised a large percentage of the European Miocene flora, underwent a contemporaneous decrease. Szafer emphasizes that this corroborates the suggestion made by Krischtofowicz and Mädler that the principal invasion of the European flora at the Miocene/Pliocene transition came from the north-east. It was therefore an extension of the Arcto-Tertiary geoflora of Podpera (1925).

In contrast the Inner zone had a vegetation during the Pliocene in which the predominant element was the North American. In this region there was, then, no cataclysmic decrease in the percentage representation of this element at the Miocene/Pliocene transition. Szafer explains this by concluding that the east Asian element failed to penetrate the Carpathian/Sudetenland/ Alpine barrier. The relatively small number of Asiatic species in the flora of

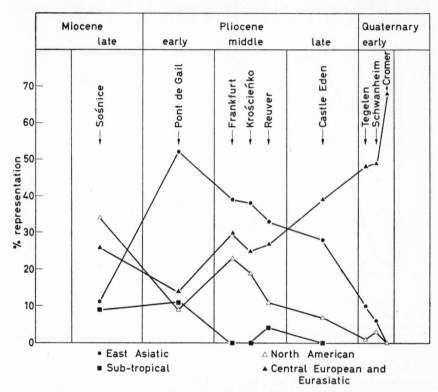

Figure 3. An analysis of the principal floras of Szafer's 'Outer European Zone' showing the progressive change in the percentage representation of the various phytogeographic components during the late Tertiary and early Quaternary period (Szafer, 1946)

the Inner zone during the Pliocene he ascribes to an older origin and suggests that they are derived from the Boreo-Tertiary geoflora of Podpera (1925).

A further variation occurs in the Southern zone although Szafer does not deal with this region in detail. The east Asian element is again absent but the high values for the percentage representation of the North American element which occurred in the Miocene are succeeded by an increase in the values for the Mediterranean and Macaronesian or Canary element. In fact the Miocene/Pliocene transition is rather indistinct in the Inner and Southern zones and does not anywhere have the cataclysmic exchange which occurs in the percentage representation of the North American and east Asian elements within the Outer zone. Following the early Pleistocene glaciations (see Chapter 4) this east Asian element became extinct in those areas where it could not penetrate the mountain barrier.

4

THE QUATERNARY VEGETATION

THE DUTCH SUCCESSION

In the absence of definite widespread surface phenomena of glacial origin, the workers in Holland have shown the existence of a series of glacial and interglacial deposits. This work, which resulted from an analysis of samples from bore-holes, and from the organic material found stratified into clay and gravel pits, has been summarized by Pannekoek *et al.* (1956) and Van der Vlerk and Florschütz (1950). The clays and gravels containing the lenses or beds of organic material often showed evidence of cryoturbation. As mentioned in Chapter 1, it is difficult in the present stage of our knowledge to draw precise comparisons between the glacial and interglacial periods suggested by work done in different regions. The periods of the Dutch series will therefore be referred to by the nomenclature of Van der Vlerk and Florschütz, although the possible homologies will be indicated where recent work has given them a reasonably firm foundation.

THE PRE-TIGLIAN PERIOD

The data of Reid (1915; 1920) on the plant remains obtained from the clay at Tegelen were initially thought to relate to a flora which existed during Late Pliocene times. The difference in the percentage representation of the Indo-Malayan element in the flora by comparison with that from the Reuverian clay was taken as indicating the progressive decrease in this phytogeographical component during the climatic deterioration which foreshadowed the Quaternary. As the result of numerous investigations (e.g. Pilgrim, 1944) the International Geological Congress of 1949 defined the Pliocene/Pleistocene boundary at the base of the Upper Villafranchian phase of the Mediterranean series. The result of this decision was to remove from the Pliocene many deposits previously ascribed to the Tertiary, and ascribe to them an early Quaternary origin. Deposits which comprised material previously thought to have been laid down under relatively stable climatic conditions, were now seen to be involved in the complicated series of climatic changes which occurred at the beginning of the Quaternary complex. In fact, widespread work had suggested that this was the case, and the so-called Pliocene deposits from Tegelen must, in spite of their warm exotic components, have been involved in this Quaternary complex. It was especially of interest to Dutch workers to know whether the Tegelen deposits represented material which had been laid down after an early glacial period.

Actually the investigations of a number of workers on Pre-Tiglian deposits provide evidence that the Tegelen flora is that of an early interglacial, not of a Pre-glacial, period. During the final phases of the Pliocene and the early Pleistocene, the area of the Netherlands was partly submerged beneath the early vestiges of the North Sea (Tesch, 1942), as shown in *Figure 4*. Dam and

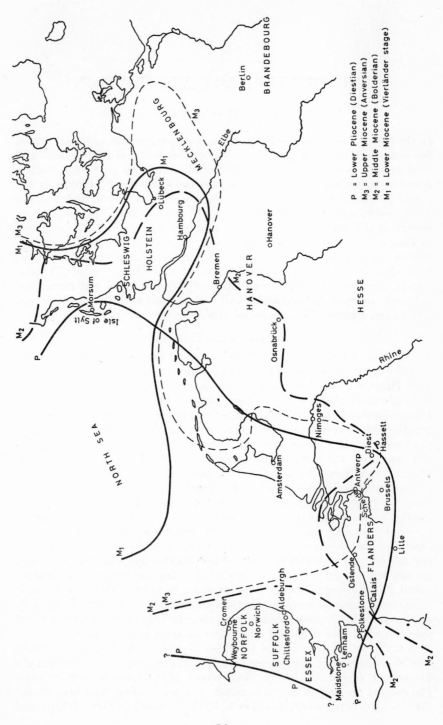

P = Lower Pliocene (Diestian)
M₃ = Upper Miocene (Anversian)
M₂ = Middle Miocene (Bolderian)
M₁ = Lower Miocene (Vierländer stage)

54

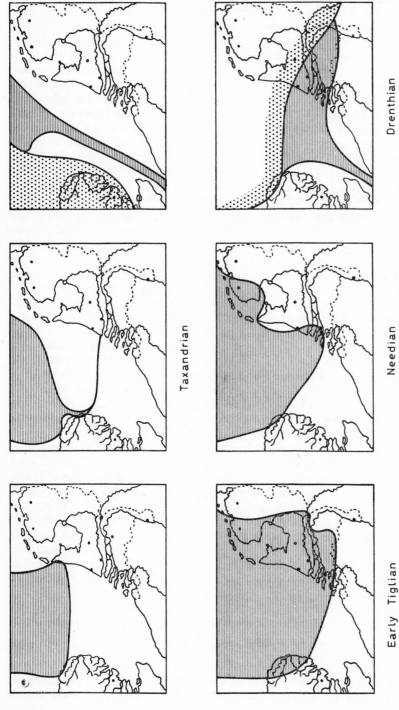

Taxandrian

Needian

Early Tiglian

Drenthian

Figure 4. Diagrams showing the relative distributions of land and sea in the region of the North Sea during the late Tertiary and at various times during the Quaternary. The dots represent the local ice-front (from Vlerk and Florschütz, 1950 and Stratigraphic Geology by Maurice Gignoux. In part after Grip, von Linstow and Tesch, 1942. San Francisco: W. H. Freeman and Company, 1955)

Reinhold (1941) investigated the foraminiferal remains obtained from the cores of bore-holes. From the marine deposits in the bore-holes the foraminiferal associations showed varying zoögeographical characteristics. The percentage representation of arctic and thermophilous stenotherms changed according to the depth from which the sample had been obtained. Below the level of Tiglian deposits, and at a depth of more than 242 metres, the thermophilous species *Cibicides lobatulus* Walk. comprised between 15 and 35 per cent of the total population. The percentage representation of the arctic and boreal species *Elphidiella arctica* Park. at this level was only 10 per cent. Above the depth of 242 metres the relative proportions of the two species were reversed. The number of shells of *Elphidiella arctica* increased until the species comprised approximately 50 per cent of the total number of foraminifera, whilst the number of shells of *Cibicides lobatulus* decreased to only 10 per cent. These results suggested that the marine deposits from which the foraminifera came had been laid down in a period during which the climate of the region had deteriorated from warm temperate conditions to those of the high boreal regions at the present time. This climatic change had been sufficiently intense and widespread to increase the boreal components of the fauna by a factor of five. In association with the enormous amount of information which is available relating to subsequent, and more especially, the last glaciation (see Chapter 5), these striking results of Dam and Reinhold alone may be taken as indicating a glacial period at this early Pre-Tiglian time. They are, however, supported by complementary information obtained from the study of other faunal remains contained in the deposits.

Unfortunately the mammalian remains accurately ascribable to the period are equivocal. Van der Vlerk and Florschütz (1950) record the presence of the pinnepeds *Odobaenus huxleyi* Lank., and *Alachtherium* sp., the cetacean *Choneziphius planirostris* Cuv., the proboscideans *Anancus arvernensis* Nesti., and *Archidiskodon planifrons* Falc., the cervid *Cervus falconieri* Dawk., and the zebrine equid *Equus stenonis* Cocchi. In the absence of any detailed information on the ecological requirements of these species no precise conclusions can be drawn.

On the other hand investigations of the gastropoda contained in samples from similar depths to the foraminiferal samples provide information which is in complete accord with the conclusions noted above. Beets (1946) recorded the shells of the thermophilous *Natica millepunctata multipunctata* Wood, *Vermetes intortus* Lam., and *Neptunea contraria* L. from the lower samples. In samples from the upper material, comparable with that containing the high values for the percentage representation of the boreal foraminiferan *Elphidiella arctica*, Beets records the gastropods *Natica clausa* Brod. and *Lora turricula*, which also live in northern waters at the present time. Similar corroboration has also been obtained by sedimentary petrologists, and all these studies indicate that, prior to the period during which the vegetational remains recovered from the clay at Tegelen were deposited, the Netherlands region, and the Palearctic generally, had undergone at least one glaciation.

THE TIGLIAN PERIOD

This period has been named after the deposits at Tegelen from which the plant remains investigated by Reid, and noted above, were obtained. It has been homologized with the Chillesfordian and Norwichian of the British

Isles (Van der Vlerk and Florschütz, 1950) but the absence of glacial phenomena in these latter beds of the Icenian Crag series, which were laid down in shallow open sea conditions during the early phases of the Pleistocene submergence of the North Sea basin, made correlation difficult (West, 1958) until recently.

The floral assemblage recorded by Reid from this early period in the Quaternary is of considerable importance in the study of the complex series of climatic oscillations which have occurred during the Quaternary, and has contributed greatly to our understanding of the changes which took place in the phytogeographical components of the vegetation during the successive interglacials. The list of species from the clay at Tegelen is summarized in *Table 18*.

Table 18. The list of plant remains recovered from Tiglian deposits (Reid, 1915 : 1920: Van der Vlerk and Florschütz, 1950)

Selaginellaceae
  Selaginella selaginoides Link.
Equisetaceae
  Equisetum ramosissimum Desf.
Salviniaceae
  Salvinia cf. *natans* All.
Azollaceae
  Azolla tegeliensis Florsch.
Pinaceae
  Abies sp.
  Picea sp.
  Pinus sp.
  Pinus pollen type *haploxylon* Rud.
  Tsuga sp.
Cupressaceae
  Juniperus sp.
Sparganiaceae
  Sparganium ramosum Huds.
Potamogetonaceae
  Potamogeton acutifolius Link.
  Potamogeton coloratus Horn.
  Potamogeton crispus L.
  Potamogeton pectinatus L.
Najadaceae
  Najas marina L.
  Najas minor All.
Alismataceae
  Alisma plantago-aquatica L.
  Sagittaria sagittifolia L.
Hydrocharitaceae
  Stratiotes aloides L.
Cyperaceae
  Carex echinata Murr.
  Carex hirta L.
  Carex riparia Curt.
  Cyperus sp.
  Dulichium vespiforme Reid.

  Heleocharis sp.
  Scirpus lacustris L.
  Scirpus tabernaemontani Gmel.
Juglandaceae
  Carya sp.
  Pterocarya limburgensis Reid.
  Pterocarya sp.
Betulaceae
  Alnus cf. *viridis* D.C.
  Alnus sp.
  Betula sp.
  Carpinus betulus L.
  Corylus sp.
Fagaceae
  Quercus sp.
Urticaceae
  Urtica dioica L.
  Urtica urens L.
Ulmaceae
  Ulmus sp.
Eucommiaceae
  Eucommia europaea Madl.
Chenopodiaceae
  Atriplex patulum L.
  Chenopodium rubrum L.
  Chenopodium urbicum L.
Polygonaceae
  Polygonum bellardi All.
  Polygonum convolvulus L.
  Polygonum lapathifolium L.
  Polygonum minus Huds.
  Rumex acetosella L.
  Rumex maritimus L.
  Rumex obtusifolius L.
Caryophyllaceae
  Lychnis flos-cuculi L.
  Stellaria aquatica Scop.
  Stellaria nemorum L.

Ranunculaceae
  Aquilegia vulgaris L.
  Clematis vitalba L.
  Ranunculus aquatilis L.
  Ranunculus nodiflorus L.
  Ranunculus repens L.
  Ranunculus sceleratus L.
  Thalictrum bauhini Crantz.
Menispermaceae
  Menispermum dahuricum D.C.
Magnoliaceae
  Magnolia kobus D.C.
  Magnolia sp.
Nymphaeaceae
  Brasenia purpurea Mchx.
Ceratophyllaceae
  Ceratophyllum demersum L.
Rosaceae
  Mespilus cuneatus Zieb.
  Potentilla argentea L.
  Prunus cf. *lusitanicus* L.
  Prunus maximoviczii Rupr.
  Prunus spinosa L.
  Rubus cf. *spongens* Camb.
Lythraceae
  Decodon globosus Nik.
Oenotheraceae
  Trapa natans L.
Halorrhagaceae
  Myriophyllum verticillatum L.
Violaceae
  Viola arvensis Murr.
Dilleniaceae
  Actinidia faveolata Reid.
Guttiferae
  Hypericum androsaemum L.
  Hypericum perforatum L.
  Hypericum pulchrum L.
Empetraceae
  Corema intermedia
Compositae
  Bidens tripartitus L.

Carduus nutans L.
Cirsium palustre Scop.
Tiliaceae
  Tilia sp.
Rutaceae
  Phellodendron elegans Reid.
Aceraceae
  Acer campestre L.
  Acer limburgense Reid.
  Acer cf. *opulifolium* Vill.
Vitaceae
  Vitis cf. *silvestris* Gmel.
Staphyleaceae
  Staphylea sp.
Araliaceae
  Genus?
Umbelliferae
  Cicuta virosa L.
  Hippomarathrum sp.
  Laserpitium siler Murr.
  Petroselinum segetum Koch.
Valerianaceae
  Valeriana tripteris L.
Solanaceae
  Physalis alkekengi L.
  Solanum dulcamara L.
Scrophulariaceae
  Veronica chamoedrys L.
Verbenaceae
  Verbena officinalis L.
Labiatae
  Calamintha sp.
  Lycopus europaeus L.
  Melissa officinalis L.
  Origanum vulgare L.
  Prunella vulgaris L.
  Stachys longifolia Boiss.
  Stachys sylvatica L.
  Teucrium botrys L.
  Teucrium scordium L.
  Thymus serpyllum L.

A comparison of the plant species listed in *Table 18* with those in the comparable list which comprises the flora of the Pliocene Reuverian clay provides some interesting facts. In the Reuverian clay the species which also occur in the Netherlands region at the present time only comprise 13 per cent of the total flora. In contrast to this, Van der Vlerk and Florschütz point out that 50 per cent of the species from the Tiglian flora are included in the modern Dutch flora. As noted in Chapter 3, this increase in the number of contemporary species is associated with a decrease in the Indo-Malayan element. A list of the species which are present in the Reuverian flora but absent from the Tiglian is contained in *Table 19*. In addition to the species contained in *Table 19* and present in the Reuverian although absent from the

Tiglian deposits, there are also several species of plant which are recorded from the Tiglian although absent from both the Reuverian flora and that of the Netherlands at the present time. These species which were present in the

Table 19. The species of plant recorded from the Reuverian clay (Laurent and Marty, 1923; Reid, 1915) but absent from the Tiglian clay (Reid, 1915; 1920; Vlerk and Florschütz, 1950)

Pinaceae	Corylopsis limburgensis
Pseudolarix kaempferi	Liquidambar orientalis
Taxodiaceae	Liquidambar europaea
Cryptomeria sp.	Magnoliaceae
Glyptostrobus europaeus	Liriodendron aptera
Sciadopitys sp.	Liriodendron tulipifera
Sequoia sp.	Nymphaeaceae
Taxodium sp.	Nelumbium minimum
Araceae	Nuphar canaliculatum
Epipremnum crassum	Sapotaceae
Epipremnum sp.	Mimusops septentrionalis
Juglandaceae	Ebenaceae
Carya angulata	Diospyros lotus
Juglans cinerea	Styracaceae
Pterocarya denticulata	Styrax mucronatum
Fagaceae	Nyssaceae
Castanea vulgaris	Camptotheca crassa
Fagus decurrens	Nyssa sylvatica
Fagus sylvatica	Halorrhagaceae
Ulmaceae	Proserpinaca reticulata
Zelkova sp.	Theaceae
Proteaceae	Stuartia pseudocamellia
Hakea sp.	Hippocastaneaceae
Santalaceae	Aesculus spinossima
Pyrulaca sp.	Sabiaceae
Hamamelidaceae	Meliosoma europaea
Bucklandia striata	

European flora during the Tiglian are the pteridophytes *Azolla tegeliensis* and *Salvinia natans*, and the angiosperms

> Corema intermedia
> Laserpitium siler
> Melissa officinalis
> Menispermum dahuricum
> Physalis alkekengi
> Staphylea sp.

Of this list the extinct species *Corema intermedia* is the member of a genus which is represented at the moment in North America, the Iberian peninsular, Canary Islands and the Azores. The genus *Menispermum* occurs in Asia, principally in Siberia, Mongolia and China (Van der Vlerk and Florschütz, 1950), whilst the umbellifer *Laserpitium siler* and the solanaceous genus *Physalis* do occur in the European region today but in the north and west are only recorded under cultivation. The presence of the remains of *Azolla* in the Tiglian material is of great interest. At the time of its initial discovery it was known only from Tertiary deposits in Europe (Florschütz, 1945) and from the New World. In the Americas the contemporary species *Azolla filiculoides* is widespread and recorded from as far north as Alaska to the region of Guatemala. The species has also been recorded from the later Dutch inter-glacial deposits and from the Cromerian and Hoxnian interglacials in the British Isles (see later). The species *Azolla tegeliensis* recorded from the Tegelen clay differs from both the Tertiary *Azolla teschiana* and the modern species in the size and shape of its mega-sporangia and massulae.

These analyses of the Tiglian flora enable one to reconstruct the changes which occurred in the early Pleistocene flora of north-west Europe. During the interval of time separating the Reuverian deposits from the Tiglian, the Indo-Malayan elements disappeared whilst other exotics were still present at the end of this period. Since the area was exposed to the northern or even periglacial conditions during the one or more Pre-Tiglian glaciations it is necessary to visualize one of the two alternatives:

(*i*) Survival of the residual species during the Pre-Tiglian glacial phase; clearly an untenable hypothesis in view of the southern nature of the species today.

(*ii*) Re-entry of the persisting species after the glaciation.

The modifications which took place in the Pliocene flora of north-west Europe as the result of the early Pre-Tiglian glaciation therefore comprise the eradication of certain tropical and thermophilous elements in proportion to the extent to which they managed to persist during the glaciation in areas from which they could subsequently recolonise Europe if the climatic con-ditions permitted. An ice-advance comparable with that represented by the glacial Tills of East Anglia and the British Isles generally (Chapter 5, West and Suggate, 1959; Farrington, 1947) would almost certainly have resulted in the retreat of the Indo-Malayan species to a considerable distance south of Europe. Unfortunately there is as yet only scanty information on the degree of the climatic variation during these early Quaternary glaciations and the presence of the exotic element in the flora of the Tiglian interglacial period is only open to speculative explanations. It is nevertheless quite clear that during the period of the Tiglian interglacial and the one or more foregoing Pre-Tiglian glaciations, the fauna and flora of north-west Europe were exposed to greater environmental changes than had occurred since the late Cretaceous and early Paleocene times (Chapter 6, MacGinitie, 1958; Frye and Leonard, 1957; Emiliani, 1955; Lowenstam and Epstein, 1954).

THE TAXANDRIAN PERIOD

It was initially considered that the deposits attributed to this period reflected a single climatic oscillation during which there was a single major advance of the polar ice. Further investigations revealed that within this one major cycle there was evidence of at least one, and probably two, minor cycles in which there was considerable climatic amelioration (Van der Vlerk and Florschütz, 1950). As is so often the case with pollen-analytical studies, further work has now shown the presence of thermophilous trees in the Netherlands region during these periods of climatic amelioration, and alongside the remains of *Betula*, there occur *Alnus*, *Quercus* and *Corylus*. West and Godwin (1958) have enunciated a new, non-geomorphological definition of interglacial periods, based on palynological studies. These authors define as an interglacial any period in which the climate, as portrayed by the vegetation, reached the condition of the Post-glacial climatic optimum (see below) for the region in question. It is clear that these Taxandrian inter-stadials may therefore represent the greater climatic changes involved in two interglacials. If this were the case there occurred during the Taxandrian period three major advances of the polar ice. These advances would have been accompanied by the concomitant peri-glacial phenomena elsewhere. Separating these periods of glaciation the climatic amelioration achieved that of the Post-glacial climatic optimum during which *Corylus* even exceeded its present northern limits (Chapter 5).

Van der Vlerk and Florschütz suggest that the Taxandrian period in an earlier single interglacial sense was contemporaneous with the period during which the Cromer Forest Bed (see below) was deposited. That is, that the Taxandrian climatic oscillation coincided with the climatic cycle indicated by the British sequence Weybourne Crag—Cromer Forest Bed—Corton Beds, Lowestoft Till, and Cromer Till. If the suggestions of West (1955) which are discussed below are correct, and the Cromer Forest Bed represents a cycle of climatic amelioration and deterioration which preceded the Elster glaciation in the German series (Woldstedt, 1954), then it is clear from the foregoing paragraphs that there must have been at least three pre-Elster glaciations suggesting a total of at least six glacial periods during the Quaternary (Zagwijn, 1957).

Unfortunately the only mammalian remains ascribed to the Taxandrian by Van der Vlerk and Florschütz are those of the vole *Mimomys intermedius*, and the proboscidean *Parelephas trogontherii* Pohlig.

THE NEEDIAN PERIOD

Plant remains have been recorded from deposits of this age in the Nether-lands by Oostingh and Florschütz (1928), Florschütz (1928) and Florschütz and Jonker (1942). The list of species from the deposits is contained in *Table 20*.

Examination of the list contained in this table will reveal that the pteridophyte family Azollaceae is no longer represented by the species *Azolla tegeliensis* recorded from the Tiglian deposits. Instead the remains of the massulae and mega-sporangia of the modern American species *Azolla filiculoides* are recorded. As stated above, this water fern has been recorded from the Cromerian and Hoxnian interglacials in the British Isles. If the suggested homologies of Van der Vlerk and Florschütz are correct, then the deposits of the Needian are probably contemporaneous with the British Hoxnian (see below), and the species of water fern obviously had a wide area of distribution, at least in the Rhine basin of western Europe, at the time.

Within the list of *Table 20* there are also other species which do not occur in the present Netherlands flora. The genus *Aldrovanda* (Droseraceae) has a widespread distribution in the region limited by eastern and central Europe, southern Asia and Australia today. The genus *Decodon* is monotypic and occurs in aquatic habitats in North America. Of the trees, *Acer, Alnus, Betula, Pinus, Pyrus, Quercus, Salix* and *Tilia* are well represented in the European region today and during recent Post-glacial times. The Needian period

61

appears however to be characterized by the presence of the genera *Picea*, *Abies* and *Carpinus* in surprising quantities, associated with an apparent absence of *Fagus*.

From the data of *Table 20* and the discussion it is clear that during the Needian interglacial, the flora of Holland, and, by implication, that of north west Europe generally, had many of the characteristics of the flora of the

Table 20. The list of plant remains from the Needian
(Florschütz and Jonker, 1942)

Thallophyta	*Menyanthes trifoliata* L.
Chara sp.	*Myriophyllum* sp.
Bryophyta	*Najas minor* All.
Drepanocladus sp.	*Nuphar luteum* Sm.
Homalia trichomanoides Shreb.	*Oenanthe* sp.
Neckera complanata L.	*Picea* sp.
Pteridophyta	*Pinus sylvestris* L.
Azolla filiculoides Lam.	*Pyrus* sp.
Salvinia cf. *natans* All.	*Polygonum lapathifolium* L.
Spermatophyta	*Potamogeton* sp.
Abies sp.	*Prunus spinosa* L.
Acer campestre L.	*Quercus* sp.
Ajuga reptans L.	*Ranunculus flammula* L.
Aldrovanda vesiculosa L.	*Ranunculus lingua* L.
Alisma plantago-aquatica L.	*Ranunculus sceleratus* L.
Alnus sp.	*Rhamnus* cf. *frangula* L.
Batrachium sp.	*Rumex maritimus* L.
Betula sp.	*Salix* sp.
Carex sp.	*Sambucus nigra* L.
Carpinus betulus L.	*Scirpus* sp.
Ceratophyllum demersum L.	*Solanum* cf. *dulcamara*
Chenopodium sp.	*Sonchus* sp.
Cornus sanguinea L.	*Sparganium* sp.
Corylus avellana L.	cf. *Staphylea* sp.
Decodon globosus Nik.	*Stellaria* sp.
Erica sp.	*Stratiotes intermedius* Chand.
Euphorbia palustris L.	*Tilia* sp.
Gramineae	*Trapa* cf. *natans*
Heleocharis sp.	*Ulmus* sp.
Hippuris vulgaris L.	*Urtica* sp.
Hypericum sp.	*Viburnum opulus* L.
Lycopus europaeus L.	*Vitis* cf. *sylvestris* Gmel.

region at the present time. As in the case of the Tiglian interglacial discussed above, the variations in the composition of the vegetation in these later interglacials will have resulted from the multi-factorial variation in the environmental characteristics. In the absence of precise information relating to the extent and duration of the successive climatic cycles one may simply state the possibilities of

(*i*) Each cycle may have been climatically similar to the others at its climatic optimum.

(*ii*) There may have been a progressive deterioration in the climate at the climatic optimum in successive interglacials, and an increase in the extent and severity of the glacials.

(*iii*) The conditions during the successive climatic cycles may have been unrelated to their position in the series.

These various possibilities would result in considerable differences in pockets of peri-glacial and temperate refugia available during the glaciations from which plants could later re-colonize glaciated areas, and also in the species which could undertake this re-colonization. Whatever may have been the exact nature of these variations in the climate and species distributions it is evident that there is a progressive reduction in the foreign, and more especially, the warm exotic elements during the successive interglacial periods. This reduction was associated with the variations in the percentage representation of the thermophilous trees which occur in the European region today.

THE DRENTHIAN PERIOD

The analysis of the mineralogical components of this post-Needian period suggested that it comprised two glacial phases separated by a period during which there was a relatively warm climate. Palynological and other botanical investigations (Steenhuis, 1937; Buresch, Florschütz and Van der Vlerk, 1938) demonstrated that during the interstadial, thermophilous plants occurred in the Dutch vegetation. The list of the genera from the Drenthian material includes the genera

Alisma	*Hippuris*	*Ranunculus*
Alnus	*Limnanthemum*	*Rubus*
Batrachium	*Lycopus*	*Salvinia*
Carex	*Menyanthes*	*Scirpus*
Ceratophyllum	*Myriophyllum*	*Sparganium*
Chara	*Nuphar*	*Stellaria*
Comarum	*Potamogeton*	*Viburnum*
Euphorbia		*Zannichellia*

In the list there are the representatives of several phytogeographical elements. *Alisma* is represented in the north temperate regions and in Australia at the present time. The species *Alisma plantago-aquatica*, of which there are interglacial, Full-glacial and Post-glacial records in the British Isles (Godwin, 1956), is a member of Hultén's (1950) boreal circumpolar group. Of the genus *Ceratophyllum* the species *Ceratophyllum demersum* is recorded from both the Tiglian and Needian interglacials in the lists of *Tables 18* and *20*. It is also known from the Cromerian and Ipswichian interglacials in the British Isles (Godwin, 1956). At the present time, although present in Scandinavia, it only penetrated into Finland during the Post-glacial climatic optimum. The rather fragile remains of *Zannichellia*, present in the Full-glacial, are also recorded from the Cromerian and Hoxnian interglacial periods of the East Anglian sequence. The rather widespread distributions of these plants only give equivocal indications of the climate during the Drenthian climatic amelioration. However the presence of *Corylus* and *Carpinus* together with *Picea*, *Alnus*, *Abies* and *Pinus* suggests similarities with the vegetation in the continental regions of the modern Palearctic (Buresch, Florschütz and Van der Vlerk, 1938).

Above this interstadial flora, and situated in a stratigraphical position between the Drenthian and the Eemian interglacial, Dutch workers have recorded the remains of a subarctic tundra vegetation. The presence of mega- and microspores of *Selaginella selaginoides*, the leaves of the dwarf birch *Betula nana*, the seeds of *Arctostaphylos uva-ursi*, together with pollen of *Pinus*, *Betula* and *Salix*, suggests a comparison between this late Drenthian vegetation with that in peri-glacial regions at the present time. Vegetation of this kind occurs in the arctic regions, on mountains in the more southern regions, and is recorded from deposits of Full-glacial age in the United Kingdom (Godwin, 1956). These results show that prior to the late-glacial phase of the Eemian interglacial, a tundra vegetation occurred in Holland.

THE EEMIAN PERIOD

The classical work on deposits of the last, or Eemian, interglacial in the region of north-west Europe are those of Jessen and Milthers (1928). These Danish workers investigated Eemian deposits in the region of Denmark and the neighbouring areas of Germany. Plant remains from deposits of similar age were recorded in Holland by Florschütz (1930b). The last-named author recorded *Aldrovanda vesiculosa*, *Ceratophyllum demersum* and *Salvinia natans* from organic material embedded between fluvio-glacial sands and deposits containing a tundra vegetation dating from the last glaciation. In view of the detailed information provided by the work of Jessen and Milthers, which has formed the basis for all subsequent work, the results of these authors will be considered here.

As the result of numerous pollen-analytical and stratigraphical investigations, Jessen was able to give a detailed description of the changes which took place in the vegetation in association with the climatic amelioration and deterioration of the Eemian interglacial. In the early part of the interglacial the vegetation comprised herbaceous species which are characteristically found at the moment in the open vegetation of tundra or steppe. This open vegetation, which later included the dwarf birches and willows *Betula nana* and *Salix phylicifolia*, comprised zones *a* and *b* of Jessen's scheme outlined in *Table 21*.

Throughout the periods *c*, *d*, *e* and *f* there was a progressive afforestation in which the thermophilous species of trees gradually became more abundant. This encroachment of the Late-glacial open vegetation by trees culminated in the Quercetum mixtum of Jessen's zone *f*, and his *Carpinus* zone *g*. This climatic amelioration as represented by the changing vegetation is closely comparable with that of the Post-glacial period which has been so amply documented by Godwin (1956). Following the Quercetum mixtum, taken as the climatic optimum of the interglacial, the pollen-analytical investigations indicate that the vegetation underwent a reversion. As the result of the initial stages of the climatic deterioration *Pinus* and *Betula pubescens* became the dominant trees. This deterioration continued and in Jessen's zone *k* a subarctic flora once again occurred in the region of north-west Europe. However, investigations of deposits more recent than those containing this boreal or sub-arctic vegetation reveal that this did not complete the climatic variations of the Eemian. This temporary period of climatic deterioration may represent the time of deposition of the characteristics of the Warthe in the German sequence. Subsequently the climate improved once again to give rise to a temperate phase in the vegetation. The components of the flora during this short cycle suggest that at its optimum there may have been once again a July isotherm as great as 18°C before the climate entered a second phase of climatic deterioration within the last, Würm or Tubantian, period of glaciation.

Table 21. The changes of the vegetation of north-west Europe during the last, Eemian, Interglacial (after Jessen from Vlerk and Florschütz 1950)

Vegetation	Dominant components	Temperature
Sub-arctic flora	n. Betula nana, Betula pubescens	
Upper temperate zones	m. Betula pubescens, Pinus, Picea, Betula nana	July isotherm of 12°C
	l. Deciduous phase	July isotherm of 18°C
Sub-arctic flora	k. Betula nana, Betula pubescens, Pinus, Picea, Juniperus	July isotherm of 12°C
	i. Pinus zone; Picea, Betula pubescens, Populus, Betula nana	
	h. Spruce zone; Pinus, Betula pubescens,	
	g. Hornbeam zone; Picea, Quercetum mixtum	
Lower temperate zones	f. Quercetum mixtum zone; Alnus, Corylus, Carpinus, Picea, Pinus, Betula pubescens	July isotherm of 18°C
	e. Pinus, Ulmus, and Betula pubescens	
	d. Pinus and Betula pubescens	
	c. Betula pubescens and Pinus	
Sub-arctic flora	b. Betula nana, Salix phylicifolia	July isotherm of 12°C
Arctic periglacial flora	a. Dryas octopetala, Salix herbacea and Salix reticulata	

In material which, by its stratigraphical position, would appear to be more recent than the coniferous phase but to antedate the main glaciation, there occurred once again a sub-arctic tundra. Dwarf birches and willows occurred in a vegetation which was dominated by members of the Gramineae and Cyperaceae and in which there occurred species of the Caryophyllaceae, Compositae and Helianthemum.

ORGANIC INTERGLACIAL DEPOSITS IN THE BRITISH ISLES

Recent work on the organic deposits laid down in the region of East Anglia and elsewhere in the British Isles during the period prior to the last glaciation has produced results which are comparable with those obtained by the continental workers (Duigan, 1957; West, 1955, 1956, 1957, 1958, 1961; West and Godwin, 1958; West and Sparks, 1960). These palynological and lithological investigations have enabled West to tentatively suggest the homologies between the East Anglian and German sequences, and also to give impressive details of the vegetational and climatic changes represented in the British interglacial deposits.

THE LUDHAM DEPOSITS

The results of a pollen-analytical investigation of the borehole through 135 feet of the early Pleistocene Crag deposits at Ludham, Norfolk, have shown a succession of alternating temperate and glacial conditions. Five

Table 22. The succession within the East Anglian Crag series together with the percentage representation of northern and southern species of mollusc (After Harmer)

	Deposit	Type fossil of zone	Mollusca	
			% northern	% southern
	Cromer Forest Bed			
ICENIAN CRAG	Weybourn Crag	Tellina balthica	33	
	Chillesford Beds	Leda myalis		
	Norwich Crag	(a) Astarte borealis (b) Spisula sub- truncata	32	7
RED CRAG	(a) Butleyan horizon	(a) Serripes groenlandicus	23	13
	(b) Newbournian horizon	(b) Spisula constricta	11	16
	(c) Oakleyan horizon	(c) Spisula obtruncata	5	20
	(d) Walton-on-Naze horizon	(d) Neptunea contraria	5	20
	Tertiary/Quaternary transition			
	Coralline Crag	Mactra triangula	1	26

principal stages are distinguished (West, 1961) and given names derived from the locality of the site and nearby rivers. From the base upwards they are the Ludhamian, Thurnian, Antian, Baventian and another. The Ludhamian contains the remains of a temperate mixed coniferous/deciduous forest in which both *Tsuga* and *Pterocarya* occur. *Pinus* is the dominant arboreal species and there are also present *Alnus, Betula, Carpinus, Quercus, Picea* and *Ulmus*. The non-arboreal pollen has a much lower frequency than that of the trees. Of this non-arboreal pollen that of the Gramineae and Ericales occurs at low frequencies whilst that of the Chenopodiaceae is frequent throughout. The whole temperate zone is divisible into upper and lower regions due to changes in the frequency of *Tsuga* pollen. This pollen is ascribed by West to the two species *Tsuga diversifolia* and *Tsuga canadensis*, the latter is very similar to that from the Pliocene deposits at Krościenko (Szafer, 1946) whilst *Tsuga diversifolia* seems to be closely related to the modern *Tsuga caroliniana*.

The second lowest major vegetational phase, the Thurnian, is a glacial period which has an oceanic heath type of vegetation. In contrast to the forest suggested by the pollen frequencies of the Ludhamian, the non-tree pollen is dominant in the Thurnian and suggests an open vegetation. Of the trees, *Pinus* is again dominant and occurs together with *Alnus, Betula, Picea* and low frequencies of *Tsuga*. In the open vegetation the percentage representation of Gramineae and Ericales is high, and this ericaceous pollen seems to resemble the tetrads of *Empetrum nigrum* although some grains of *Calluna* and other genera occur.

Following this open-vegetational phase indicative of a climatic deterioration, the percentage representation of the tree pollen again rises in the subsequent, Antian, temperate forest phase. In this the forest comprised *Alnus, Betula, Carpinus, Picea, Pinus, Pterocarya, Quercus, Tsuga* and *Ulmus*. The non-tree pollen, which is now of diminished importance, consists of large quantities of Chenopodiaceae and lower frequency representation of the Ericaceae. Gradually this phase gives way to a second in which the representation of the grasses and Ericales again increases.

This next climatic deterioration is complex and easily divisible into two phases. In the lower of these *Betula, Pinus* and *Alnus* are of equal importance, whilst in the upper *Pinus* is the dominant tree and in the open-vegetational components the percentage representation of the Gramineae and Ericales has fallen.

Following this fourth and double phase, which West suggests is indicative of a second climatic deterioration comparable with the Menapian period of Zagwijn (1960), there occurs the upper temperate phase in which the tree pollen is again the dominant component of the pollen diagram. *Tsuga* pollen only occurs in small quantities and this, together with the absence of *Pterocarya*, contrasts with the earlier temperate phases.

Similar climatic indications also result from the studies of Funnell (1960) on the Protozoa from another nearby borehole. As the result of all the work, West concludes that the series represents two early glacial phases. The earliest temperate forest he suggests is the British equivalent of the Tiglian of Van der Vlerk and Florschütz (1950). By a comparison with the protistan evidence advanced by Funnell, he further concludes that the Ludhamian corresponds to the Newbournian/Butleyan Red Crag and also the *Scrobicularia* crag of the classical marine series. From similar considerations he suggests that the Thurnian, Antian and Baventian correspond to the Icenian Crag series and that, in this marine series, the Weybourne Crag is equivalent to the upper Baventian. The rest of the Baventian, together with the Antian and Thurnian, therefore correspond to the Norwich Crag of the classical East Anglian marine series (*Table 22*).

THE CROMERIAN INTERGLACIAL PERIOD

Boswell (1952) has reviewed the evidence suggesting that the Pliocene/ Pleistocene transition in the British Isles lies at the Coralline Crag/Red Crag transition. In view of the absence of definite evidence of glaciations prior to the Cromer Forest Bed it had several times been suggested that it should still be referred to by the older term of Pre-glacial. Nevertheless, as West and Godwin (1958) pointed out before the work at Ludham was undertaken, the presence of a changing vegetation, indicative of a cycle of climatic ameliora-tion and subsequent deterioration, which is indicated by palynological investigations, conforms to the modern botanical, and non-geomorphological definition of an interglacial period.

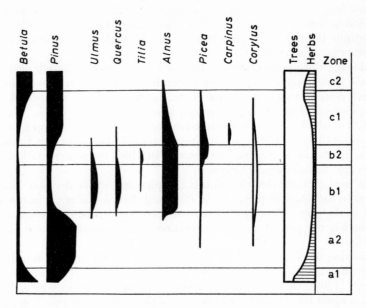

Figure 5. Pollen diagram from the Cromerian interglacial deposits. The pollen is represented as a percentage of the total tree pollen per sample (from West, 1961)

The type deposits of the Cromerian interglacial consist of the Cromer Forest Bed, an organic deposit which is exposed at various places on the coast of East Anglia, but especially at West Runton. The organic material is overlain by sands and itself overlies the Weybourn Crag, which is exposed on the foreshore. The vegetational remains in the deposit were investigated by Duigan (1957) and Thomson in Godwin (1956). These investigations pro-vide evidence of a vegetational sequence comparable to that of other known interglacial deposits. The bulk of the Cromer Forest Bed in fact contains remains of thermophilous plants, and notably the genera *Tilia* and *Corylus*. However, at certain localities fresh-water deposits occur above and below the organic detritus mud, and from these the remains of a sub-arctic tundra vegetation have been recovered. The sequence in the detritus mud itself may be summarized as follows:

(i) An early phase during which *Pinus* and *Betula* are the dominant genera of trees, and occur in association with *Picea, Quercus, Ulmus, Tilia, Alnus* and *Corylus*.

(*ii*) A phase characterized by the decline in the values for the percentage representations of *Pinus* and *Betula* together with a concomitant increase in those of *Tilia*, *Ulmus*, *Quercus* and *Corylus*.

(*iii*) A final, most recent phase, in which the rising values for the percentage representation of *Pinus* occur in association with an increase in those for *Tilia* and *Picea*, and a decrease in those for *Quercus* and *Ulmus*.

West (1961) draws attention to the interesting fact that in the Cromer Forest Bed the values for the percentage representation of the pollen of *Corylus* are lower than in the deposits originating from the Hoxnian and Ipswichian interglacials discussed later.

In the list of plant species which are represented in the deposits either by pollen or the remains of fruits, seeds and leaves, there are the following thermophilous species (Godwin, 1956):

Azolla filiculoides	*Najas minor*
Hypecoum procumbens	*Trapa natans*

together with the extinct member of the Empetraceae, *Corema intermedia*, which was noted in the floral lists from the Tiglian interglacial in Holland. Both *Trapa natans* and *Najas minor* were also noted in the Tiglian and Needian deposits. The former species has a markedly continental distribution at the present time and occurred far north of its present limits in Scandinavia during the period of the Post-glacial climatic optimum. *Najas minor* is discussed further in relation to deposits dating from the Ipswichian interglacial below. *Hypecoum procumbens* does not occur in the British Isles today but occurs in the south of France. It is clear from the presence of these plants in the Cromerian deposits that the climate at the climatic optimum was considerably warmer than that at the present time, and that the flora showed similarities to both the Tiglian and Needian floras.

Van der Vlerk and Florschütz (1950) suggest that the Cromerian interglacial is synonymous with the Taxandrian period. As was indicated previously, this period in the Dutch series was rather more complex than it had initially been thought, exhibiting the characteristics of two interglacial periods. West (1955, 1958), in his synopsis of the East Anglian succession, suggests that the Cromerian interglacial represents an interglacial prior to the Elster glaciation. This fact would not be inconsistent with a Taxandrian age.

THE HOXNIAN INTERGLACIAL PERIOD

The deposits at Hoxne, Suffolk, were given great attention during the last fifty years because of the flint artefacts which were found in the organic material. The artefacts were of the Late Acheulian core industry which West (1956) has ascribed to a definite stratigraphical level in the vegetational sequence. The plant remains from Hoxne were initially investigated by Reid (1896) who, as the result, concluded that a series of vegetational changes were represented. The immense work of West has now produced a detailed description of these changes which may be summarized as follows:

(*i*) An early phase of open vegetation comparable with that of the Late-glacial and dominated by *Hippophaë rhamnoides*, the sea Buckthorn;

69

(*ii*) An early temperate period during which there was the progressive development of a Quercetum mixtum.

(*iii*) A late temperate period during which there is an appreciable percentage representation of the pollen of *Carpinus*, *Picea* and *Abies*.

Within the Quercetum mixtum phase of this sequence there occurred the Late Acheulian core industry. This was at a stratigraphical level identical with that in which there were considerable changes in the percentage representation of the pollen of the trees. The representation of the trees

Table 23. The relationships of the interglacial sequence in the British Isles and Germany on the basis of pollen-analytical and lithological investigations (West, 1955)

Correlation with Woldsted (1954)	East Anglian succession	General names of the East Anglian sequence
	Solifluction Deposits	
Eemian interglacial	Cambridge and Ipswich interglacial deposits	Ipswichian interglacial
Saale glaciation	Gipping Till	Gipping glaciation
Holstein interglacial	Hoxne and Clacton interglacial deposits	Hoxnian interglacial
Elster glaciation	Lowestoft Till Corton Beds Cromer Till	Lowestoft glaciation
Cromerian interglacial	Cromer Forest Bed	Cromerian interglacial

decreased and then subsequently increased. The sequence of changes was in fact identical with those occurring in the Post-glacial deforestation during the Neolithic and Chalcolithic periods, and also in Iversen's experimental investigations into forest clearance. The pollen of the herbaceous plants increases in numerical representation and ruderals, e.g. *Plantago* and the Chenopodiaceae, are present. West takes this as an indication of the extent of the forest clearance achieved by Paleolithic man.

A detailed study of the vegetational changes led West to homologize the Hoxnian interglacial period with the Holstein interglacial of the German series.

According to West (1955) the deposits at Clacton from which the artefacts of the Paleolithic Clactonian flake industry were obtained, are also ascribable to the Hoxnian interglacial. Reid and Chandler (1923) recorded the vegetational remains from these deposits and Pike and Godwin (1953) supplemented their results by studying the plant remains obtained from the core of a borehole. The pollen-analytical results indicated that the organic material dated from the later part of an interglacial climatic sequence. The climatic optimum is suggested by the presence of the thermophilous oceanic species of *Hedera*, *Ilex* and *Taxus*, together with *Viburnum lantana*, *Najas minor*, *Najas marina*, *Petroselinum segetum*, *Valerianella carinata* and *Euphorbia hyberna*. These species

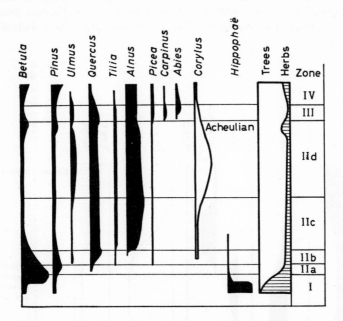

Figure 6. Pollen diagram from the Hoxnian interglacial deposits (from West, 1961)

have a markedly southern distribution at the present time. Iversen (1944) has shown that *Hedera*, although not requiring high summer temperatures, is incapable of withstanding winter frosts and does not occur in areas experiencing a temperature below $-1.5°C$ in this period.

THE IPSWICHIAN INTERGLACIAL PERIOD

The exposure of organic deposits of interglacial age at Histon Road, Cambridge, has enabled investigations to be made into the flora of this interglacial period several times during the last twenty years (West and Sparks, 1960). The vegetational sequence which has been pieced together exhibits an interglacial cycle of climatic amelioration and deterioration. At the period just after the climatic optimum there occurred a phase during which the dominant species within a mixed oak wood was *Carpinus betulus*, as in the case of zone *g* in the scheme of the Eemian interglacial produced by Jessen (*Table 21*).

At the climatic optimum there were the usual thermophilous elements in the vegetation. In particular there occurred the three species of the Najadaceae *Najas flexilis*, *Najas marina* and *Najas minor*. Both *Najas marina* and *Najas minor* have been noted in the Tiglian flora, whilst *Najas minor* also occurred in the Needian period of the Dutch sequence and in the Cromer Forest Bed. *Najas flexilis* has a post-glacial history comparable with that of *Najas marina*, both having occurred north of the present species limits at the time of the climatic optimum. Fruits of *Verbena officinalis* which occurs in southern Europe and as far north as Denmark, and of the species *Cornus sanguinea*, which is a calcicolous species distributed from southern Scandinavia to the Iberian peninsular (Clapham, Tutin and Warburg, 1952), occur alongside the pollen of *Hedera* and *Buxus*.

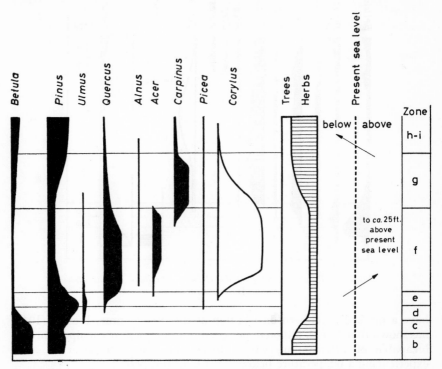

Figure 7. Pollen diagram from the Ipswichian interglacial deposits (from West, 1961)

Evidence of the vegetational sequence prior to the climatic optimum of the Ipswichian is provided by the work of West and Sparks (1960). These workers record the pollen-analytical investigations undertaken into the vegetation at the time an organic detritus mud at Selsey Bill was laid down. A specimen of the rhinoceros *Coelodonta antiquitatis* Blum. had previously been extracted from the deposit, which is in fact sealed in by marine material deposited at the climatic optimum of the Ipswichian interglacial. The organic detritus mud is exposed below the high-water mark on the foreshore and is available at the spring and autumn tides. At the base of the series of palynogical samples there proved to be an open vegetation dating from the late-glacial of the interglacial. The Gramineae and Cyperaceae dominated this vegetation and *Artemisia* occurred with other representatives of the Compositae, Cruciferae, Ranunculaceae and Umbelliferae. Subsequently the progressive afforestation during the climatic amelioration leading to the climatic optimum already noted in Jessen's Eemian scheme, and the Hoxne deposit, culminated in a Quercetum mixtum, and diminished values for the percentage representation of the Gramineae. In the upper region of the deposit, immediately below the marine mud of the marine transgression, the pollen of the thermophilous continental *Stratiotes* occurred together with that of *Corylus* and appreciable quantities of *Hedera*. The genus *Stratiotes* was already noted in the plant lists from the Tiglian and Needian in the Dutch sequence and its fossil history summarized by Chandler (1923). The Tiglian records are designated *Stratiotes aloides*, the only modern species, which occurs today in the continental, east European region. At the present time only the female plants occur in the British Isles, the male plants occurring in the southernmost areas of its distribution. The presence of pollen in the Selsey deposit therefore suggests a climate considerably more warm and continental than that of the British Isles today. This is in agreement with the thermophilous carabid beetle *Chlaenius tristis* Sch. (Pearson, 1961) which was also found at this level.

Information relating to the final phase of the interglacial, perhaps at the period of Jessen's zones *h* and *i* has been obtained from lenses of organic material lying below gravel of the last glaciation at Sidgwick Avenue, Cambridge. From these lenses numerous fruits and seeds (but no pollen), Coleoptera and Gastropoda were obtained. The faunal and floral assemblages include large numbers of the fruits of *Carex*, and remains of heliophilous species, e.g. *Helianthemum canum*. The presence of species not occurring quite so far south at the present, e.g. *Notaris aethiops* and *Grypidius equiseti* suggest a period in which the climate was rather cooler than that at this latitude today. In association with this cool open vegetation there occurred the skull of *Bison priscus*, which is of interest in view of the occurrence of the larger herbivores during the Late-glacial period of open vegetation (Lambert, Pearson and Sparks, 1963).

5

THE FULL-, LATE- AND POST-GLACIAL
PERIODS

As the result of extensive investigations into the sub-fossil remains contained within organic deposits laid down since the beginning of the last glaciation, workers in both the New and Old Worlds have gone a long way towards elucidating the complex climatic and vegetational changes which have occurred during this period. The work in the European region is summarized by Firbas (1949) and the immense work of Godwin (1956). Generally speaking, it is in the lakes and peat mires that one finds the particularly sensitive records of these climatic changes and the outstanding tool which has been used in their elucidation is the technique of pollen-analysis. Indeed it is largely due to the stimulus provided by work of this kind that the extensive investigation of the characteristics of pollen grains has been undertaken (Faegri and Iversen, 1950; Erdtmann, 1952).

THE FULL-GLACIAL PERIOD

Organic deposits dating from the various stadial and interstadial periods of the last (Würm) glaciation have been investigated by numerous authors throughout the world. For convenience, the present account will be restricted to deposits of Full-glacial age in north-west Europe. These comprise material which occurs in an intermediate stratigraphical position to that of Eemian interglacial deposits and Late-glacial deposits. Carbon-14 analysis of the material suggests that the period concerned lasted from *ca.* 75,000 to *ca.* 12,000 years ago. There was a time when many of the deposits of this period were referred to as of late-glacial age. However, in recent years this term has acquired a restricted and well-defined meaning. In order to differentiate between this more recent use of the term and the earlier usage the term is therefore written today with a capital letter.

During the Full-glacial Period the polar ice advanced and retreated at least three times. Between these stadial periods of widespread arctic conditions there occurred intervening periods of climatic amelioration, the interstadial periods. Peri-glacial conditions seem to have occurred over the southern half of the British Isles for most of the time and over the whole region during the periods of ice-retreat. Godwin (1956) has pointed out that at the period during which the material at the Barnwell Station and Lea Valley beds was being deposited (see below) the ice-front cannot have been nearer than the margin of the New Drift, a boundary which has been accurately demarcated in recent years by Suggate and West (1959). In fact the ice could have been considerably north of this line.

The records of Full-glacial vegetation are based almost entirely upon the macroscopic remains of leaves, fruits and seeds, which, by comparison with the pollen present in the deposit, have enabled extremely accurate specific identifications to be made. In general these results indicate that during the period in which the polar ice was extending south to the region of the British Isles the vegetation had a considerable similarity with that of the more recent Allerød climatic oscillation although there were more arctic species present.

A comparable analysis of Coleoptera from Full-glacial deposits (Coope, 1959; Coope, Shotton and Strachan, 1961; Pearson, 1961a, 1962a) shows a similar picture with arctic stenotherms occurring alongside widespread eurytherms and also rather southern species.

THE FULL-GLACIAL DEPOSITS AT BARNWELL, CAMBRIDGE

The arctic plant remains from the glacial gravels at Barnwell were reported in great detail by Chandler (1921). The list of species includes some 90 identifications of leaves, fruits and shoots. Chandler suggested that the list

Table 24. The arctic-alpine plant species in the Barnwell
deposits (Chandler, 1921)

Thalictrum alpinum L.	*Salix arbuscula* Fries.
Ranunculus acontifolius L.	*Salix lapponum* L.
Papaver alpinum L.	*Salix herbacea* L.
Draba incana L.	*Salix polaris* Wahl.
Cochlearia officinalis L.	*Salix reticulata* L.
Arenaria biflora L.	*Betula nana* L.
Potentilla fruticosa L.	*Potamogeton filiformis* Nol.
Potentilla alpestris L.	*Eriophorum polystachion* L.
Dryas octopetala L.	*Carex capitata* L.
Saxifraga oppositifolia L.	*Carex lagopina* Wahl.
Vaccinium uliginosum L.	*Carex capillaris* L.
Primula scotica Hook	*Selaginella selaginoides* L.
Armeria arctica Wallr.	*Isoetes lacustris* L.
Polygonum viviparum L.	

could be analysed further into five principal groups according to their present day distributions. Of these groups the most outstanding is the arctic-alpine group.

There are many fossils whose modern representatives occur in both the arctic and temperate regions. However, when found in the temperate regions they only occur on upland moors and on mountain slopes. When growing within the Arctic Circle they are no longer restricted in this way and may occur at sea level. In the Barnwell flora these species, with a disjunct temperate and continuous arctic distribution, comprise 42 per cent of the total list and are tabulated in *Table 24*.

In addition to these markedly arctic or alpine species other members of the Barnwell flora were species which have a wider geographical range today. These more eurythermic species occur in lowland habitats within the temperate regions of the Palearctic but also flourish on high ground. The species included in this eurythermic group now characterize such varied habitats as water, marsh, meadow and heaths. They are tabulated in *Table 25*.

Although some of these records are no longer considered valid (Godwin, 1956) the rest form an interesting comparison with the Coleoptera considered to represent the eurythermal element of the Colney fauna by Pearson (1962) and noted below.

Chandler also identified nine species with a predominantly southern distribution at the present time. In view of the presence of remains of these species in the deposits which date from the Eemian interglacial, one may, perhaps, follow the suggestions made by Godwin (1956) for *Carpinus* remains and look for their origin in the reworking of older interglacial material.

Table 25. The plant species noted by Chandler (1921) in the deposits at Barnwell, Cambridge, which have a widespread distribution

Ranunculus flammula L.	*Salix repens* L.
Ranunculus repens L.	*Sparganium simplex* Hudson
Ranunculus bulbosus L.	*Sparganium minimum* Fries.
Viola palustris L.	*Potamogeton heterophyllus* Schreber
Potentilla anserina L.	*Potamogeton zizii* Roth.
Potentilla tormentilla Meck.	*Eleocharis palustris* R. and S.
Myriophyllum spicatum L.	*Scirpus lacustris* L. (?)
Hippuris vulgaris L.	*Carex arenaria* L. (?)
Gentiana cruciata L.	*Carex goodenovi* Gay
Menyanthes trifoliata L.	*Carex flava* L.
	Carex rostrata Stokes

Finally, there occurs in the lists of Chandler (1921) a group of species forming her estuarine component. These are *Rumex maritimus* L., *Zannichellia pedunculata* Reich., *Carex arenaria* L. and *Carex divisa* Hud. Although she states that with the exception of the *Zannichellia* remains no single member of this group gives incontrovertible evidence of tidal influences, they again form an interesting comparison with those Coleoptera of Full-glacial deposits which are halophilous today (Pearson, 1963).

A similar explanation to that noted below and suggested by Pearson (1962a) for Colney Heath Coleoptera may be applicable; a marine influence in the Cambridgeshire region is not unreasonable in view of the history of the fenland although at this Full-glacial period the sea level would have been at least 70 metres below the modern ordnance zero datum.

THE LEA VALLEY DEPOSITS

The numerous plant remains from various gravel pits in the Lea Valley were summarized by Reid (1949). Further contributions were made by Allison, Godwin and Warren (1952) and Pearson (1962a). Reid included a list of 122 definitive specific identifications and, as Chandler had done for the Barnwell flora, she analysed these according to their modern geographical characteristics. A comparison of these 122 species with the flora of West Greenland led her to conclude that high arctic species occurred in at least seven of the sub-fossil localities from which her material came. However, in

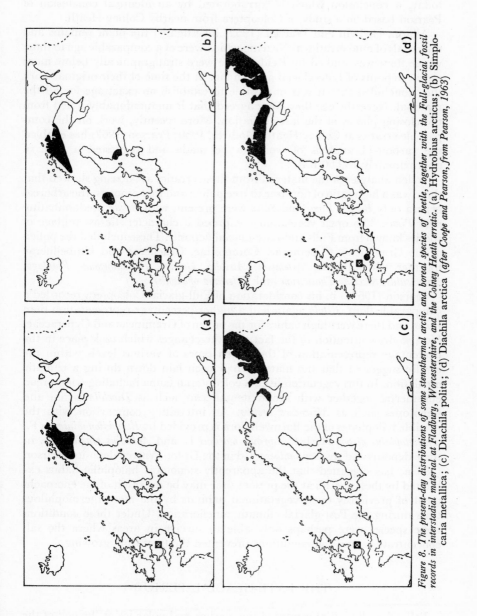

Figure 8. The present-day distributions of some stenothermal arctic and boreal species of beetle, together with the Full-glacial fossil records in interstadial material at Fladbury, Worcestershire, and the Colney Heath erratic. (a) Hydrobius arcticus; (b) Simplocaria metallica; (c) Diachila polita; (d) Diachila arctica (after Coope and Pearson, from Pearson, 1963)

spite of this, the greater number of the species, although having a widespread distribution, have their principal distribution further south. Reid took this to indicate that the conditions were less rigorous than those of the high arctic today, a conclusion which is corroborated by an identical conclusion of Pearson based on a study of Coleoptera from nearby Colney Heath.

Allison, Godwin and Warren (1952) investigated the plant remains and mammals of mud erratics at Nazeing which were of a comparable age to those whose flora was studied by Reid. These were stratigraphically below more recent deposits of Late-glacial age. In fact at the time of their original work they concluded that it was impossible to establish an exact age for all the material. Nevertheless, they were agreed that it unquestionably dated from the closing phases of the last glaciation. More recently, work on the comparable erratics at Colney Heath (Godwin, 1960; Pearson, 1962) has enabled the carbon-14 analysis of wood to be made and suggested a date of approximately 13,600 B.P.

Pollen analyses of the material from these erratics at Nazeing showed that there was a high ratio of non-tree to tree pollen and that amongst the arboreal genera only *Betula*, *Pinus* and *Salix* were present, with *Betula* predominating over *Pinus*. The open vegetation comprised a characteristic assemblage of species known from Full- and Late-glacial deposits. These included the pollen of the Gramineae, Cyperaceae, Compositae, Cruciferae and Umbelliferae together with *Armeria*, *Artemisia*, *Atriplex*, *Galium*, *Helianthemum*, *Plantago*, *Ranunculus*, *Succisa*, *Thalictrum* and *Valeriana officinalis*.

Pearson (1962a) in his consideration of Full-glacial Coleoptera recorded a comparable flora. *Betula* again had a higher percentage representation than *Pinus*, and there were high values for the pollen of Gramineae and Cyperaceae. He also drew attention to the fact that the changes which took place in the percentage representation of the pollen types at various levels within the erratic suggested that the material had been lain down during a climatic oscillation. In this vegetation lived a coleopteran fauna including widespread eurytherms together with arctic stenotherms such as *Diachila arctica* and stenotopes such as *Miscodera arctica*. An interesting comparison with the possible halophytes of the Barnwell flora is provided by *Bembidion minimum* F., *Thanatophilus dispar* Herbst., *Gyrinus marinus* L. and *Aphodius plagiatus* L. in these deposits and *Agonum sahlbergi* Cd in the Upton Warren deposits. Pearson (1962a) has suggested that the apparently stenotopic halophilic habits exhibited by these species at the present time may be the result of the encroachment of previously open vegetational habitats by the more thermophilous trees during the Post-glacial climatic amelioration. Under these conditions these species were perhaps only able to survive in areas where the salt concentrations and soil conditions prevented the trees from growing.

THE LATE-GLACIAL PERIOD

Following the initial retreat of the glaciers and polar ice at the end of the last glaciation there were several minor climatic oscillations during which the ice underwent a temporary re-advance. The first to occur was the so-called Bølling oscillation and the second the more extensive Allerød oscillation.

This latter was named after the site in Denmark where the type deposits were first described (Hartz and Milthers, 1901).

These Allerød deposits typically comprise two layers of relatively inorganic material with a layer of more organic material contained between them. Within the upper and lower inorganic strata remains of *Dryas octopetala* occur and the periods during which they were deposited were hence considered to represent two periods of relatively cold conditions, the early and late *Dryas* times. Similar deposits of this Late-glacial or Allerød type are now known from widespread localities in Europe and America (Davis, 1961; Deevey, 1951; Godwin, 1949; Pennington, 1947; Środon, 1952; Walker, 1955a, 1955b, 1956).

As the result of investigations in the Fennoscandian region there is a considerable amount of evidence that the Allerød period itself corresponds to the Gotiglacial stage of ice-retreat from southern Scandinavia. The older *Dryas* period (zone I of the general British scheme of Godwin, 1956), is broadly comparable with the Daniglacial retreat phase together with the early part of the Gotiglacial. Zone III, the Upper Dryas time, is therefore approximately synonymous with the period of deposition of the Norwegian Raa, the Central Swedish and the Finnish Salpausselka moraines. This period of time between the Daniglacial and the laying down of the Raa moraines, or from zone I to the zone III/IV boundary in the British scheme was originally considered to have lasted from about 13,000 to 8,000 B.C. on the basis of the varve chronology of De Geer. Recent dating methods using carbon-14 analyses have given added precision to this and will be considered below.

Godwin (1956 etc.) has pointed out that this classical stratigraphical sequence of Late-glacial deposits, with upper and lower inorganic layers and an intervening organic layer, may be represented by other facies in different regions. In the British Isles there were, during the Late-glacial period, only highland valley glaciers and corrie glaciers (Donner, 1957; Seddon, 1957). In fact in the shallow lakes and gently rolling landscape of East Anglia the stratigraphical evidence may be absent.

The favourable climatic conditions of the Allerød period are best exemplified by the points quoted by Schutrumpf (1943) and derived from a consideration of investigations in Holstein. These points include:

1. The colonization of the lake together with sedge peat formation.
2. The recession of the non-tree pollen.
3. The attainment of high values for the percentage representation of *Pinus* pollen.
4. The decrease and ultimate disappearance of *Selaginella* spores together with the pollen of *Empetrum* and also Ericaceae. All presumably shaded out by trees.
5. The absence of the macroscopic remains of *Betula nana* and other dwarf species. These are abundant in the levels above and below.

Contrariwise evidence for a further subsequent deterioration of the climate is provided by:

1. The rise in the non-tree pollen together with the recurrence of the remains of *Betula nana*.

2. Rise in the percentage representation of the pollen of *Betula* at the expense of that of *Pinus*.

3. Rise in the percentage representation of the pollen of *Salix*.

4. A return of the spores of *Selaginella* and the pollen of *Empetrum* and also members of the Ericaceae.

5. A return of the pollen of *Hippophaë*, the sea Buckthorn.

Figure 9. The modern Fennoscandian distribution of Tomocarabus convexus, *together with its approximate western limits and the Late-glacial record at St. Bees*

In fact from the results obtained in numerous investigations by various authors (summarized in Godwin, 1956) it is now clear that a grass/sedge tundra with scattered stands of birch was widespread over southern Sweden, Norway and most of Denmark. The tundra vegetation preceding and following the mild phase included the Gramineae, Cyperaceae, dwarf species of *Betula* and *Salix* together with the arctic species *Dryas*, *Oxyria*, *Armeria*, *Empetrum* and *Selaginella*. In addition there were the genera *Artemisia*, *Rumex*, *Thalictrum*, *Hippophaë* and *Helianthemum*. The presence of these plants led Iversen (1947) to suggest a comparison with the central European alpine, rather than northern arctic, conditions. This last-named author proposed the term 'Park-tundra' for this vegetation. It was apparently widespread and, as such, provided an ideal habitat for the large ungulates which have been shown to have occurred at this time and probably ranged in large herds

(Blackburn, 1952; Degerbøl and Iversen, 1945; Isberg, 1949; Mitchell and Parkes, 1949). Amplification and further corroboration of these results is provided by the presence of heliophilous Coleoptera in the Late-glacial deposit at St. Bees, west Cumberland, together with *Tomocarabus convexus*, a carabid with a markedly continental distribution at the present time (Pearson, 1962b).

THE POST-GLACIAL PERIOD

THE PRE-BOREAL PERIOD

This stage of the Post-glacial climatic amelioration and concomitant afforestation of modern temperate latitudes and altitudes corresponds to zone IV of the general British scheme of Godwin (1940a, 1940b, 1956, 1960).

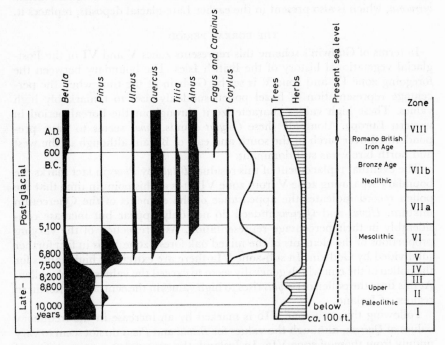

Figure 10. Simplified diagram of the pollen frequencies observed in deposits of Late- and Post-glacial age in the British Isles (after Godwin, 1956, from West, 1961)

The name Pre-boreal derives from the scheme of Post-glacial climatic change which was proposed by Blytt and Sernander. In the last section above the open vegetation of the Late-glacial period was stated to have had at least some tree cover especially during zone II. However, the high values for the percentage representation of non-tree pollen in the upper part of the Late-glacial finally fell at the beginning of the Post-glacial *sensu stricto* in the face of a rapid increase in the birch pollen values. This change marks the boundary between zones III and IV in the general British scheme of Godwin. In fact the changing value of the pollen, representing as it does a change in the

81

dominant land plants, indicates the replacement of the 'Park-tundra' with its open vegetation by a closed but, according to Godwin (1956) not dense, woodland. In certain areas the change is less marked and in north west Ireland the percentage representation of the pollen of *Empetrum* falls more slowly in zone IV than it does in other areas of the British Isles.

The fact that the pollen of *Salix* occurs more frequently in this period than in the previous or subsequent ones suggests that there was a local temporary growth of willow thickets in marshy areas. *Pinus* pollen occurs in material of this age and the increasing frequencies to the south suggest that it became progressively more dominant in the southern regions and indeed appears to have entirely dominated the woods of central Europe. In the British Isles the forests at this time appear to have been largely birch although the species differs in different areas and *Pinus* occurred in the south and east. In Ireland *Betula pubescens* seems to have been dominant, whilst in England *Betula verrucosa*, which is also present in the earlier Late-glacial deposits, replaces it.

THE BOREAL PERIOD

In terms of Godwin's scheme this represents zones V and VI of the Post-glacial vegetational history of the British Isles. The boundary between the foregoing zone IV and zone V is set by Godwin at the time when the percentage representation of hazel pollen suddenly rises to remarkably high values. These high values characterize it throughout the Boreal period in western Europe. Alongside these *Corylus* stands, *Pinus* seems to have pre-ponderated over birch in the south and east of Britain although in the west and north birch was still dominant.

The eventual replacement of this residual *Betula* by *Pinus* in fact marks the boundary separating zone V from zone VI. It is at this point in time that the pollen record indicates the appearance of the elements of the Quercetum mixtum. *Ulmus* and *Quercus* indeed do not only appear but increase considerably in their percentage representation. As a reflection of the varying proportions of the elements of the mixed oak forest, zone VI is in fact further subdivided by Godwin. In sub-zone VIa there are extremely high values for the pollen of the elm which generally seem to exceed the values for oak pollen. At this time the pollen of *Corylus* rises to high values in the central and northern regions of Ireland.

Following this, sub-zone VIb is marked by an increase in the frequency values of *Quercus*, although the values for *Betula* and *Pinus* do not seem to vary unduly from those of zone VIa. In Ireland, the percentage representation of *Corylus* is diminished relative to the values of VIa but the frequency values actually remain high. In contrast they fall in zone VIc when the pine pollen frequencies reach their highest Post-glacial values in Ireland, though there is a contemporaneous fall in the representation of this genus in England and Wales. The values for oak and elm are more or less maintained in this last region and they are supplemented by the appearance of *Tilia* and *Alnus* whilst *Betula* continues to decline.

ATLANTIC AND SUB-BOREAL PERIODS (ZONE VII)

A forest consisting of a Quercetum mixtum together with *Alnus* persisted for a long time. Throughout most of England and Wales, *Alnus* suddenly rises from low values to about 40–50 per cent of the total tree pollen count. In the west and the north this rise is relatively slow by comparison with the increase in the south and east. This *Alnus* expansion appears to have taken place at the expense of *Betula* and *Pinus*, and in sub-zone VIIa *Pinus* pollen is reduced to low values in England and Wales.

The differentiation of sub-zones VIIa and VIIb is based principally on the so-called 'elm decline'. However, a concomitant fall in the percentage representation of both *Pinus* and *Tilia* also occurred, whilst *Corylus* increases to reach a maximum at the end of the sub-zone *b*. In general terms Godwin defines VIIa as corresponding to the Atlantic period and VIIb to the Sub-boreal period in the scheme of Blytt and Sernander.

THE CLIMATIC OPTIMUM

Following the early phase of climatic amelioration which took place in pollen zones IV and V, there appears to have been a phase optimum in climatic conditions. During this time the forest belts of Europe moved north

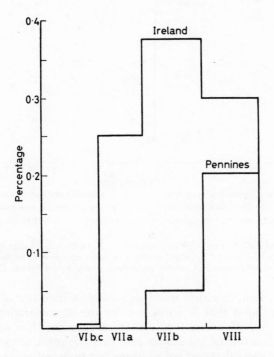

Figure 11. Histograms showing the average frequency of holly (Ilex aquifolium L.) pollen expressed as a percentage of the total tree pollen for the zones of the Post-glacial period in the British Isles (from Godwin, 1956)

to occupy higher latitudes than they do at the present time. They similarly occurred at more elevated altitudes. Proof of this is provided by the occurrence of macro-fossils such as fruits of *Corylus*, remains of *Trapa natans*,

Cladium mariscus, and *Emys orbicularis* (Godwin, 1956), at positions north of their present species limits.

Conway (1942) considers that *Cladium mariscus* is a basicolous heliophyte of temperate to sub-tropical climates. Von Post showed that it occurred in Sweden at the same time as *Corylus* and became and remained abundant in all calcareous areas until the end of the Atlantic Period. Indeed Godwin,

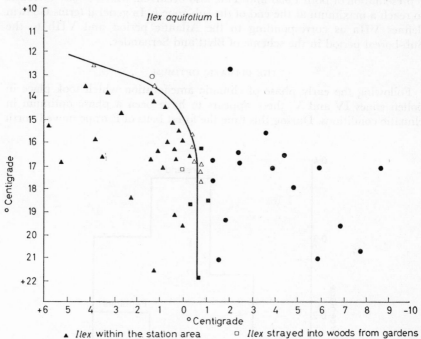

Figure 12. Thermal correlation curve for Ilex aquifolium *L. Ordinate is the mean temperature for the warmest month; abscissa, that for the coldest month. The species appears to be intolerant of winter cold but does not demand high summer temperatures (redrawn from Iversen, 1944)*

following Von Post, considers that it is a climatic indicator of considerable importance, a point that is borne out by the demonstration of its high sensitivity to frost (Conway, 1942). This indicates that it is not capable of withstanding continental conditions and that the onset of such conditions during the Sub-boreal period led to its decline in Scandinavia.

Even more delicate measurements of the climatic conditions at this period of Post-glacial time are provided by Iversen's (1944) work on *Ilex, Hedera* and *Viscum*. The tricolpate pollen grains of the holly are readily recognized by their exine pattern as the ectexine is composed of separate clavate elements which are distinctly variable in size and not united by their swollen heads. Macro-fossils of the ivy *Hedera helix* are known from four deposits. The tricolpate pollen grains have rather short, acutely tapering furrows crossed equatorially by the elongated pore. Godwin (1956) points out that there is some possibility of confusion with *Lysimachia vulgaris* which has, however, a smaller polar area with a finer reticulation. Pollen grains of the mistletoe are also readily identifiable and as such have been found in Boreal, Atlantic and Sub-boreal deposits in Denmark. Fossil ivy pollen is not known from Sweden in Post-glacial time but appears in western Norway in the Boreal and reaches

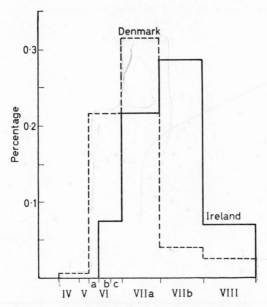

Figure 13. *The sub-fossil occurrences of the pollen of the ivy* (Hedera helix L.) *expressed as a percentage of the total tree pollen for succeeding pollen zones of Post-glacial period in Ireland and Denmark (from Godwin, 1956, after Iversen and Jessen)*

its greatest percentage representation in the Sub-boreal before declining in the Sub-Atlantic. Comparable patterns are recorded for Ireland by Jessen (1949) and in Somerset by Godwin (1956). As with ivy, and the oak, holly pollen also has relatively high values in the Sub-boreal. As the result of these facts, Iversen's work on the present day occurrence of the three species enables a considerable degree of precision to be introduced into the descriptions of the climatic conditions of this period of Post-glacial time. Iversen recorded the behaviour of the three species at sites close to meteorological stations using as his criteria the mean temperature of the coldest month together with that of the warmest. The results are shown in *Figures 12* and *14*. Upon these graphs it is possible to indicate a thermal tolerance limit. In the case of *Ilex* this curve is vertical at $-0.5°C$, suggesting that it is intolerant of winter frost. The curve for *Hedera* appears to show a bifactorial control, namely moderately high summer temperatures and temperatures not falling below $-1.5°C$ for the coldest month. This winter thermal control acts by killing the cambium, reducing fertility and restricting growth to

85

levels where snow-cover gives protection from the worst winter weather. Finally in the case of *Viscum* it seems that the plant is restricted in the northern part of its range by a high temperature requirement which is, however, rather less in the oceanic west than in the more continental east. From these values it is clear that variations in these parameters controlling the distribution of the ivy, holly and mistletoe were probably involved in the climatic conditions

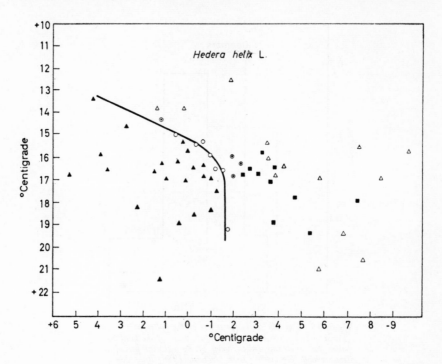

Figure 14. Thermal correlation curve for the ivy (Hedera helix *L.*) *Ordinate is the mean temperature for the warmest month; abscissa that for the coldest month. The species seems to be only slightly less susceptible to winter cold than* Ilex aquifolium *(redrawn from Iversen, 1944)*

during the Post-glacial periods in which these genera reached high values (*Figures 11* and *13*).

Amongst the trees it is *Tilia cordata* which appears to have been most responsive to the climatic conditions of this Post-glacial optimum. Among the aquatic plants the cases of *Najas marina* and *Najas flexilis* are outstanding. The former occurs today in a few Norfolk broads but it is recorded from the Boreal deposits at Skelsmergh Tarn in the Lake District and at several sites in Ireland. It was abundant in zone VI and the early phase of zone VII at Hockham Mere, Norfolk, but virtually disappeared in the later phases. The second species, *Najas flexilis*, is today a plant restricted to the extreme Atlantic fringe with a disjunct European range. Since it has a more widespread distribution in North America it has been suggested that this represents an origin in that area. However, fossil records reveal that it was widespread throughout England, Wales and Ireland during the Post-glacial climatic optimum and its present restricted distribution is therefore a product of an extremely recent climatic deterioration.

THE SUB-ATLANTIC TIME

Zone VIII of the general British scheme of Godwin (1956) is the so-called alder-birch-oak-beech period of Post-glacial vegetational history. There is a pronounced shift in the forest composition and where lime has persisted into sub-zone VIIb it now almost disappears. In England and Wales *Ulmus* values fall and in Ireland *Pinus* virtually disappears. Throughout the entire region of the British Isles the values for *Betula* increase at this time so that the pollen of this tree attains a comparable status to that of alder or oak. Simultaneously the pollen of *Fagus* reaches high values in the south and east of England and is present in values of 1–2 per cent elsewhere in the British Isles.

This period is in fact characterized by two principal effects. The first is the so-called climatic deterioration, whilst the second is the progressive deforestation by man. One general effect of the climatic deterioration was to cause a resumption of bog growth. This had come to a standstill and the surfaces of bogs were often *Calluna* covered or bore stands of *Betula*. The surfaces now became progressively waterlogged and *Sphagnum* peat was laid down in the pools on the surfaces, or, if calcareous drainage water flowed onto them, *Cladium-Hypnum* peat. In general this latter separates the older, highly humified, dark brown *Sphagnum-Calluna* peat from the upper, fresh, unhumified *Sphagnum* peat (Godwin, 1956).

PREHISTORIC HUSBANDRY IN THE SUB-BOREAL PERIOD

The role of man within the eco-system began to change quite considerably as farming cultures spread across Europe to replace the pre-existing hunting cultures of the Upper Paleolithic (see below). The migrations of the Neolithic peoples across the region brought the techniques of cultivating cereals and keeping domestic animals into the region of north-west Europe. By comparison with these changes the changes in the tools used by these people were of relatively little significance. As noted above, West (1956) has produced evidence for forest clearance by Acheulian man in the Hoxne interglacial deposits. The first documentation of similar activities during the Post-glacial period was provided by Iversen (1941). The changes involved in the pollen diagrams are a little way above the point where the pollen of *Ulmus* and *Hedera* shows a lasting decrease whilst that of *Fraxinus* the ash first establishes itself as a continuous curve. This is in fact the boundary of sub-zones VIIa and VIIb. At this level the pollen of *Quercus*, *Tilia*, *Fraxinus* and *Ulmus* undergoes a distinct, though only temporary, decline. A contemporaneous transitory increase takes place in the *Betula* pollen frequencies, a more lasting one in those of *Alnus*, and the pollen of *Corylus* has a pronounced maximum. The decline in the forest pollen is attributed to forest clearance, whilst the increase in that of *Betula, Alnus* and *Corylus* is due to the character-istic regeneration of the species of these genera in the cleared area.

This work is supported by many lines of evidence. Neolithic remains and charcoal layers occur with the onset of the vegetational changes and there is a low but constant frequency of the pollen grains of cultivated cereals. Just above the charcoal layers the non-tree pollen increases suddenly and then drops away. Indeed Iversen (1941) pointed out that the pollen of *Plantago major* and *Plantago lanceolata* acts as landmarks for distinguishing the forest clearance of European man from this Neolithic period onwards. The Danes actually take the view that *Plantago lanceolata* came to the country with agriculture. Godwin, however, draws attention to the fact that certain heliophilous plants which occur in the open vegetation of the Late-glacial period, notably *Centaurea cyanus, Euphorbia* sp., *Galeopsis* sp., *Plantago major, Polygonum aviculare* and *Sonchus arvensis*, reappear as ruderals with the onset of forest clearance. Pearson (1962b) has suggested that a similar change may have been imposed upon such heliophilous Coleoptera as *Pterostichus coerulescens, Agonum mulleri* and *Calathus melanocephalus* which occur in Late-glacial deposits and are synanthropic today.

More recently Troels-Smith (1954, 1955, 1960) has drawn attention to certain additional lines of enquiry. The early interpretation of the fall in the values of the pollen of *Ulmus* at the Atlantic/Sub-boreal transition (Iversen, 1941) pointed to a concurrent fall in the percentage representation of the pollen of the ivy. As noted above, *Hedera* is a very sensitive climatic indicator and Iversen suggested that a climatic change might be responsible for the decrease of both genera. In contrast, Troels-Smith, following Faegri (1944), suggests that the *Ulmus* fall is culturally conditioned. In support of this thesis these authors emphasize the widespread use of elm as a fodder tree for stall-feeding of cattle (Nordhagen, 1954). For this purpose the trees are pollarded and the twigs lopped every few years. Such a treatment will prevent the trees from flowering and the decline in the pollen may result from this type of animal husbandry. Troels-Smith has applied similar interpretations to the contemporaneous decrease in the pollen of *Hedera*. Even at the present time the evergreen foliage of this species is used as fodder.

This interpretation of the decline in the percentage representation of *Ulmus* pollen is substantiated by the appearance of the pollen of cultivated cereals, together with that of the ruderal *Plantago*, in minute traces before the forest clearance phases of the Danish pollen diagrams but never before the *Ulmus* decline. The same is also true of the species *Allium ursinum* which is also taken to be anthropochorous. As the result of their investigation, Troels-Smith and his collaborators have in fact been able to link up the portions of their pollen diagrams containing these minute traces of cereal pollen with the archeo-logical horizon of the A ceramics of Becker (1948). This is said to be equivalent to the classical Ertebølle culture and as such combines hunting and fishing with primitive agriculture. Troels-Smith (1954) envisages these very primitive farmers with small grain fields and their cattle stalled all the year round. This would result in the extensive use of fodder feeding. Such methods of farming would contrast sharply with that of the later Landnam culture when cattle were pastured in large numbers as indicated by the high values for the pollen of the Gramineae. Indeed, Troels-Smith pointed out that the discoid axes of the classical Ertebølle culture would be well suited to bark-peeling. Besides using the *Ulmus* for fodder they would also be selecting for *Quercus*, the acorns of which are widely used by man for food (Brockmann-Jerosch, 1936).

Iversen (1960) points out that the use of *Ulmus* for fodder as an explanation of the elm decline necessitates pollarding a very large number of trees if the pollen is to be seriously reduced in a mixed oak forest. It is difficult to imagine Stone Age man undertaking such an enormous task which would involve climbing 15 metres up the trunks. Today pollarding begins before the trees reach a great height and the same would probably be true during the Stone Age. Iversen (1960) therefore concludes that the climatic effect explains the major decrease in the frequency of *Ulmus* pollen. One may therefore conclude that there was a marked effect on the vegetation by primitive farming but that the more sensational changes are best explained climatically.

CLIMAX AND SUCCESSION IN POST-GLACIAL TIME

As the result of extensive researches, Iversen (1960) has emphasized the contribution that an extensive knowledge of plant succession can make to understanding Post-glacial vegetational history. Although the original dogmatic assertions of Clements (1916) are no longer acceptable, nevertheless, climax vegetation remains one of the fundamental concepts of dynamic plant sociology and the Anglo-American school of phytogeography (Tansley, 1949). In general terms one may say that wherever vegetation is not in equilibrium with its surroundings, succession will set in and continue until stability is reached. This final phase of stability is called the climax vegetation.

Tree species may be divided into pioneer species and climax species. The first of these groups is distinguished by a very high reproductive rate. They set their fruits at an early age and these are uniformly abundant year by year. Seed dispersal is effective and as a result trees of this kind appear readily wherever suitable conditions are created, as for example when lakes are filled in or cultivated land abandoned. On the other hand they are weak in competition since they are heliophytes and have a relatively short life. Typical of this group of pioneer trees are *Betula*, *Populus tremula*, *Salix* and *Sorbus*.

In general terms the climax species have opposite characters to the pioneer species. Their rate of reproduction and their seed dispersal are generally poor. In the initial stages of colonization they cannot keep pace with trees of the pioneer group. However, once established they stick to their ground and generally supersede the *Betula-Salix* group. The principal reasons for this are their long life and their great height which therefore provides a large amount of shade and excludes the heliophytes from below their canopy. Where *Quercus* and *Betula* occur together then after less than 150 years there will be an unmixed oak forest. 'The birch will die from old age while the oak retains its youthful vigour'. *Tilia*, *Fagus* and *Ulmus* are still stronger than *Quercus* since they have a greater tolerance of shade as indicated as long ago as 1863 by Vaupell. The generalized effect has been expressed by Boysen Jensen (1949) as the fact that heliophilous species will eventually be replaced by shade tolerant species provided the conditions of growth are favourable to the latter.

7

An application of these considerations to the study of the Post-glacial vegetational succession enhances our understanding of the principles involved. In the first place there is an early but short-lived *Juniperus* maximum followed by a well-marked *Populus tremula* maximum. Then follows a long section in which *Betula* predominates with *Pinus* present in increasing quantities. This Pre-boreal birch period terminates with the immigration of hazel. Iversen (1960) concludes that although the climatic amelioration at the end of zone III is basic to this succession nevertheless it is not just a temperature change that is causing it. He suggests that the birch phase is a pioneer stage in a protracted succession. The presence of *Cladium* in organic deposits shows that the climatic conditions were such that a forest type vegetation could have existed so that its absence was simply due to the fact that the forest elements had not yet migrated to the region of north-west Europe. There was no need for *Juniperus* to immigrate since it was present in the region even before the climatic change took place although at that time it was stunted. Aspen and birch spread from stands within the area and pine was not far off (see Pearson, 1962b however). In contrast the thermophilous species had their nearest stands south of the Pyrenees and Alps (see Oldfield, 1962). As a result it took many centuries for them to reach Denmark and, in the case of *Fagus* and *Carpinus*, millenia. Firbas (1949) has further pointed out that there is no conformity between the sequence of immigration and the warmth requirements of the species.

The fact that *Corylus avellana* is a shade-tolerant shrub enables it to thrive under the canopy of *Betula* and *Pinus*. As the result of this the latter two cannot regenerate because of the underwood of hazel. This contributed to the fall in the percentage representation of *Betula* and *Pinus*, the short-lived *Betula* succumbing first. The resulting Boreal hazel forest would therefore be the result of these factors and there is no need to consider this anything more than a seral stage in the succession. Hazel simply happened to be the first shade-tolerant tree to immigrate and therefore had no competition. Iversen suggests that the critical factors in the final reduction of the *Corylus* forest were in fact the elm and lime. These climax species are just as shade-tolerant as *Corylus* and overtake it in height. Since hazel cannot thrive in the enhanced shade of an *Ulmus/Tilia* forest it succumbs. As the result of such considerations as these Iversen therefore concludes that one cannot attach any climatic significance to the boundaries of zones IV–VII. Whilst one may not go as far as this with him it is clear that the normal seral succession is involved in the Post-glacial vegetational history.

6

ISOTOPE DATING AND FURTHER CLIMATOLOGY

ISOTOPE DATING IN GEOCHRONOLOGY

The possibilities of using the decay constants of radioactive isotopes as a method of deriving an absolute chronology of the past, with which biological and geological events could be compared, arrived with the discovery of radioactivity. In fact an investigation of the practical possibilities began about 1940 when work was initiated on the uranium/lead method. It was, however, in the post-war period, and more especially the last decade, that the improvement of analytical techniques resulted in a tremendous increase in the data available for geochronology. Actually it is only during the last six or seven years that the information has been forthcoming which permits the extensive dating of geological events on an absolute time scale.

A review of the determination of the decay constants used by geochronologists is provided by Aldrich and Wetherill (1958). More recent assessments of these constants, together with an outline of the difficulties which attend their determination, have been provided by Gast (1961); Glendenning (1961); Compston and Jeffrey (1961); Gerling *et al.* (1961); Amirkhanoff *et al.* (1961) and Libby (1963). The general principles of this method of dating the past depend upon relatively straightforward premises. These consist of assuming that (*i*) the decay rates for radioactive isotopes have been constant during geological time, (*ii*) in the case of carbon-14, that the quantities of them occurring in the atmosphere are constant and (*iii*) that when they have been incorporated into the closed system of deposits their concentration decreases with time according to their decay constants. If these premises are accepted, and work has suggested that within certain limits they are the case, the concentration of a radioactive isotope contained in a deposit bears a direct relation to the time before the present that the material in the deposit was laid down.

THE TECHNIQUES USED FOR ^{14}C AND Rb/Sr DATING

As an example of the methods which are used to determine the concentration of radioactive isotopes in geological deposits we may consider the measurement of the radioactive isotope of carbon, ^{14}C. A review of the methods involved for the other isotopic measurements can be found in the papers cited above. The theory of ^{14}C isotope age determinations depends upon the following succession of events. Atoms of nitrogen contained in the atmosphere are exposed to a continual bombardment by neutrons in the cosmic radiation. The result of this bombardment is the formation of the radioactive isotope of carbon, ^{14}C. These radioactive atoms then slowly disintegrate, generating the normal nitrogen atom with an atomic weight of 14. Experimental determinations of the period necessary for the quantity of ^{14}C to be reduced to one half of its initial concentration indicate that this period is $5,730 \pm 40$ years (Godwin 1962).

The ^{14}C produced in the atmosphere according to this scheme is rapidly oxidized to carbon dioxide and as such enters the reservoirs of this gas in the oceans. From water and air it is then incorporated into the structural compounds of plants during photosynthesis. If these plants, or animals which have eaten them, then become preserved in the organic deposits which are forming at the bottom of swamps or ponds, the radioactive carbon is virtually isolated from the atmosphere. In this closed system the proportion of the ^{14}C contained in the cellulose of plant cell walls diminishes in relation to the normal carbon isotope to reach a concentration of 50 per cent of the initial concentration 5,730 years after the time of deposition. With these facts Libby (1951; 1955) realized the potentialities of the ^{14}C system for geochronology of the more recent periods of geological time. As the result of his initial stimulus several laboratories have now developed techniques for measuring the ^{14}C content of organic deposits. These methods all rely upon the ignition of a sample of the organic material from a known stratigraphical horizon. This converts the carbon in the material to carbon dioxide or acetylene and the radioactivity of the resulting gas can be measured.

In order to measure this radioactivity several methods have been used. For convenience one may cite that described by Godwin Walker and Willis (1957) and carried out in the Radio-carbon Dating Laboratory at Cambridge by Dr. Willis. The counting chamber is a copper cylinder with a diameter of 7·6 cm and an unshielded anode length of 50·1 cm. The effective counting volume, which is taken to be the cylindrical volume surrounding the exposed wire, is 2·25 litres. The anode wire is made from a molybdenum/tungsten alloy and held in position by guard ring assemblies one of which also serves as the pumping stem for evacuating and filling the counter. A protective castle, built from 280 zinc slabs which weigh 40 lb. each, surrounds the counter and serves to reduce the gamma background. In fact this zinc shield reduced the background count rate to 273 counts per minute. From this level it was reduced further to a level of 27 counts per minute by a protecting shield of geiger counters surrounding the proportional counting chamber. Cosmic ray mesons which penetrate both the geiger shield and the proportional counter produce a pulse in each of these. The geiger pulse is therefore arranged to cancel the pulse which is produced by the internal proportional counter by means of an anti-coincidence gating device. As a result of the use of this device the only pulses which are recorded by the counting mechanism are those which originate from the ^{14}C contained within the central cylinder and which are therefore a measure of the age of the material.

The limits of this method are set by the low natural count of the atmospheric ^{14}C. In practice dating is only possible back to about 15,000 years before the present but by enrichment of the samples it is possible to extend this to approximately 75,000 B.P. The principal method of enrichment consists of placing the gas, obtained by igniting the organic material, in a temperature gradient. This principle has been used for some years in the separation of gases which differ considerably in mass and nature. It is more difficult to utilize it for the separation of isotopes which only differ slightly in mass. The method is based upon the observation of Enskog (1911), that if a gaseous mixture of molecules of differing mass is placed in a tube which is hotter at one end than at the other, the heavier molecules will tend to diffuse to the colder end. As originally used in chemistry, convection currents were avoided by having the hot plate parallel to the cold one. If these plates are placed at vertically opposite ends of a long tube the resulting convection currents can be used to enhance the separation.

A further difficulty may also be encountered from the possible incorporation into the deposit of carbon-containing material of older date. An example of this is the incorporation of coal into glacial drift and then by reworking of the drift into organic material of Late-glacial age.

It can be inferred from this summary that there are immense practical difficulties involved in the production of a pure sample of gas for analysis of ^{14}C and the building of electronic equipment which is sensitive enough to detect the minute count differences. However, other methods of isotope dating which are applicable to far older sites have other inherent difficulties. Of these one of the most important, when using the rubidium/strontium and uranium/thorium concentration to date deposits, lies in the variation which occurs in the isotopic composition of any daughter element according to the mineral used. In the early work on the determination of the rubidium/radiogenic strontium values lepidolites and muscovites were available. No one was concerned with the isotopic composition of the original strontium because the minerals had none. The strontium detected was therefore all of radiogenic origin. However, as work became more critical, and nearer to the limits of its theoretical possibility, it was also carried out upon minerals which were known to have an original strontium content. In these cases the assay of the original strontium content is clearly of considerable importance.

Gast (1961) undertook a generalized attack upon this problem and attempted to assay

(i) The distribution of radiogenic strontium in the earth's crust;
(ii) What happens to strontium which is derived from rubidium;
(iii) How it becomes distributed between various geochemical reservoirs.

In order to do this Gast and his co-workers at the University of Minnesota determined the isotopic composition of strontium obtained from a variety of igneous, metamorphic and sedimentary rocks. The principal doubts which arise from their $^{87}Sr/^{86}Sr$ ratios are related to the fractionation which has been observed in certain runs as it had previously been assumed that the $^{86}Sr/^{87}Sr$ ratio was constant within approximately 0·2 per cent.

Working within these limits it is, however, possible to age given deposits by the use of ratios such as rubidium/strontium and potassium/argon. The premises involved are once again similar to those outlined above and consist of measuring the time since the mineral under examination became a closed system for the elements under consideration. Under these conditions the age T is given, for example, by the equation

$$\lambda T = \ln (1 + {}^{87}Sr*/{}^{87}Rb)$$
$$\text{so that } T \doteqdot {}^{87}Sr*/\lambda^{87}Rb$$

where $^{87}Sr^*$ refers to the number of radiogenic strontium molecules derived from ^{87}Rb and λ = the decay constant of rubidium. The $^{87}Sr^*$ content can be calculated from the equations

$$^{87}Sr^* = {}^{86}Sr \left[{}^{(87/86)}Sr \text{ now } - {}^{(87/86)}Sr \text{ initially}\right].$$

where ^{86}Sr refers to the number of molecules of strontium-86 at the present time; $^{(87/86)}Sr$ now refers to the total strontium-87/86 ratio and $^{(87/86)}Sr$ initially represents the initial values for this ratio at the time T years ago, when the system is assumed to have become a closed system for strontium and rubidium. From these equations the age in years is therefore

$$T \eqsim {}^{86}Sr/\lambda{}^{87}Rb\left[{}^{(87/86)}Sr \text{ now} - {}^{(87/86)}Sr \text{ init.}\right]$$

This is the equation of a straight line with its gradient defined by the $^{86}Sr/\lambda{}^{87}Rb$ ratio and with $^{(87/86)}Sr$ initially its independent variable. This provides a graphical method of estimating time T. If the comparable lines for the various components of a compound deposit are plotted on a graph they will all meet at the point of the original formation of the closed system for rubidium and strontium.

TERTIARY AGES FROM SEDIMENTARY ROCKS

Reports on the dating of various Tertiary deposits have been received from widespread regions. In the case of the dating of sedimentary rocks Amirkhanoff (1957), Goldrich (1959), Kazakow and Polevaya (1958), Lipson (1958) and Wassenburg et al. (1956) have reported age determinations on glauconites of various ages. Measurements of the potassium/argon and rubidium/strontium ratios on this mineral show a uniform variation with geological age and there is relatively little scatter. The results appear to fall 10–20 per cent short of ages which were measured on micas that were associated with dated igneous or sedimentary rocks, but in no cases have glauconites yielded ages that are definitely higher than the expected limits of the time scale.

Glauconites have an interlayered structure. This lamination involves 10 layers together with expansible montmorillonitic layers. The potassium content of the glauconites appears to bear an inverse relationship to the percentage of expansible layers. Furthermore the percentage of the expansible layers is greater in younger glauconite than in older. This suggests that the glauconitic pellets continue to develop towards pure mineral grains over long periods of time. This is associated with a decrease from 30 per cent or more of expansible layers in young glauconite to 10 per cent in glauconite of early Paleozoic age (Hurley, 1961). As the expansible layers undergo some modification at depth, and over long time periods, it is to be expected that this factor alone will affect the age ratios. The result of cation exchange is that common strontium is absorbed on to the basal plane surfaces of the expansible layers. It is therefore proportional to their abundance but only affects the Rb/Sr ratio by an increase in the precision error of the analysis.

With these additional difficulties in mind it will be seen from *Table 26* that ages have been obtained from various Tertiary and Cretaceous deposits. These suggest a maximum age of 60 million years B.P. for the age of the early Paleocene and 56 million years B.P. for the beginning of the Eocene. In view of the suggestions made by Hammen (1961), which are reviewed below, that there may have been a series of major climatic cycles of approximately similar age during recent geological time, it is interesting to note that the results obtained by Folinsbee, Baardsgaard and Lipson, together with those of Holmes (1947), agree with the results in *Table 26* and suggest a maximum age for the early *Cretaceous* period of 130 million years B.P.

Table 26. A general comparison of ages of glauconite obtained by different investigators in millions of years B.P. (Hurley, 1961)

Geological age	Lipson, 1958	Wassenburg et al., 1956	Amirkhanoff et al., 1957	Kazakov and Polevaya, 1958	Goldich, 1959	Hurley, 1961	Cromier, 1956 and Herzog et al., 1958
						K/Ar	Rb/Sr
Pliocene						7	
Miocene	20–23		20–26				
Oligocene	15–21		31				
Eocene	35		42–62	35		50–58	52–56
Paleocene	46	50		56		60	
Mesozoic/Tertiary transition							
Upper Cretaceous		68	78–83	72–112	63	87–90	67
Lower Cretaceous	136		83–104	88–122		88–104	

RADIO-CARBON DATING OF THE LATE-GLACIAL PERIOD

The Late-glacial Period which was described in Chapter 5 is widely recognized in deposits throughout the European and North American regions. It in fact grades imperceptibly into the preceding Full-glacial Period and comprises a period of cool climate between the peri-glacial conditions which existed in the north temperate regions during the Full-glacial and the definitive climatic amelioration of the Post-glacial period. In recent years it has been investigated in several areas (summarized by Godwin and Willis, 1958; Gross, 1954; 1955; and Iversen, 1954). Godwin and Willis in fact record the results of dating, by the ^{14}C method, nine deposits in the British Isles and compare them with those from seven deposits on the continental mainland. In all of these cases the deposits included material which showed very clearly the succession of solifluction layers of sand and gravels enclosing a layer of organic material, or alternatively included pollen which on analysis showed the characteristic relations of open vegetation above and below with higher values for the arboreal pollen frequencies at intermediate levels. The deposits investigated in the British Isles comprise: Garral Hill, Banffshire, whose pollen content was analysed by Donner (1957); Scaleby Moss, (Godwin *et al.*, 1957); Low Wray Bay, Windermere (Pennington, 1947); a section exposed in the flank of a drumlin in the upper Ure Valley at Lunds, Yorkshire (Walker, 1955); deposits containing the remains of *Megaceros*, the Irish Elk at Neasham (Blackburn, 1952); Flixton, Star Carr, Yorkshire (Walker and Godwin in Clark, 1954); Aby Grange, Lincolnshire (Suggate and West, 1959); the china clay pits at Hawks Tor, Cornwall (Connolly, Godwin and Megaw, 1950); Helton Tarn, Lancashire (Smith, 1958); and Knocknacran, County Monaghan, Ireland (Mitchell, 1951; Libby, 1955). From this list it is quite clear that the investigations involved deposits from a wide area within the British Isles. The similarity of the results from these sites leaves very little doubt of the synchroneity of the Late-glacial zones and suggests that the principal boundaries of zones I, II and III of the general British scheme of post-glacial vegetational history are:

zones III/IV	10,300 years B.P.
zones II/III	10,800 years B.P.
zones I/II	12,000 years B.P.

These results have now been confirmed by further analyses of deposits within both the Palearctic and Nearctic regions and it is difficult to escape the conclusion that in spite of differences of altitude, latitude and degree of continentality, the boundaries of the Late-glacial period, which were erected on the basis of pollen-analytical investigations, are synchronous over Europe and North America.

RADIO-CARBON DATING OF THE POST-GLACIAL PERIOD

In 1955 a pit dug through deposits at Scaleby Moss, Cumberland, enabled Godwin, Walker and Willis (1957) to date by the ^{14}C method the organic material laid down over most of the period since the Allerød climatic oscillation. They concentrated on dating the boundaries of the zones of the general British scheme as shown by the pollen diagrams from the site. They noted some striking similarities with other datings made on the European continent. These suggest that following the end of the Late-glacial period the Pre-boreal/Boreal transition took place at approximately 9,600 years B.P., the boundary of zones V and VI lies at 9,000 years B.P., and the VI/VII boundary 7,500 years B.P.

A comparable series of analyses also exists for material associated with sea levels at different points in Post-glacial time. These comprise the careful datings carried out at Groningen by de Vries and Barendsen (1954) and others at Christchurch, New Zealand and in the Mississippi basin. The results of these suggest that following the melting of the ice-caps there was a progressive rise in sea level between 12,000 and 5,500 years before the present. This indicates that the oceans, which reached their present level during the Post-glacial climatic optimum, did so about 5,500 years ago. At approximately that date there occurred the culmination of the Post-glacial climatic amelioration and the beginning of the subsequent climatic deterioration. It is of considerable interest in this respect that archeological datings of the earliest occupation layers from sites in the Sinic, Indic, Hellenic and Syriac civilizations suggested until recently that civilization began about 5,000 years ago. If that is the case it is difficult to escape the conclusion that this development in man's social habits was associated with the climatic deterioration following the Post-glacial climatic optimum, but recent dates for the earliest Syriac communities suggest an older origin at 8,000 B.P. (Bowle, 1962).

PALEO-TEMPERATURE MEASUREMENTS

THE VARIATION OF THE $^{18}O/^{16}O$ RATIO

Oxygen is one of the most abundant chemical elements in the world's crust. In fact the atmospheric oxygen comprises three stable isotopes ^{16}O, ^{17}O and ^{18}O and the relative abundance of these isotopes varies according to the source of the oxygen. In the case of the $^{18}O/^{16}O$ ratio this variation can be as much as 10 per cent. Within this variation the lowest values have been observed in glacier ice and the highest in the carbon dioxide of the atmosphere. Since the chemical properties of these isotopes differ slightly the thermodynamic properties also vary and Si $^{16}O^{16}O$ is different from Si $^{17}O^{16}O$ and Si $^{18}O^{16}O$. However these differences are so small that in ordinary chemical considerations they can be neglected but they form the basis for the use of isotopes in the study of geochemistry.

In the world's oceans the value of the $^{18}O/^{16}O$ ratio is dependent upon the temperature of the region. From this it clearly follows that if the carbonate skeletons of marine organisms are produced in equilibrium with the sea-water, then it will be possible to measure the temperatures at which the carbonate was incorporated into the skeletons by studying their $^{18}O/^{16}O$ ratio. That this is a valid premise and that the ratio is temperature dependent was established for both organically and inorganically precipitated carbonate by experimental means (Epstein, Buchsbaum, Lowenstam and Urey, 1953; McCrea, 1950). Skeletal carbonate material was grown under constant known temperature conditions whilst carbonate was slowly precipitated out of water. Both were analysed and their $^{18}O/^{16}O$ ratios determined. As the result of these determinations, and assuming that the concentration of sea-water is homogeneous and has not changed with time, it is possible to determine the temperature of the oceans to within 1°C as far back as the Paleozoic.

In the case of modern marine organisms whose habitat water can be analysed it is possible to obtain precise temperatures in this way. The existence of heterogeneous oxygen isotope concentrations in the oceans is the most serious limitation to the usefulness of this temperature scale in the measurement of past temperatures. Studies which have been carried out on present-day waters indicate that the principal reasons for the fluctuations in the observed values of the $^{18}O/^{16}O$ ratio are associated with the presence of regions with very low temperatures. The water of snow and ice has a different isotopic composition to sea-water. Since the variation is related to salinity changes, and since these are minimal in the open oceans, one may feel reasonably confident about the temperatures determined for oceans in non-glaciated areas or times.

THE METHODS OF MEASURING OXYGEN ISOTOPE RATIOS

The measurement of the ratios between the different isotopes of oxygen involves the use of a mass-spectrometer designed by Nier (1947). This apparatus is most conveniently used to measure the isotope values of the gaseous phase of carbon dioxide. The $^{18}O/^{16}O$ ratio is determined by comparing mass 46, that is to say $^{12}C^{16}O^{18}O$, with mass 44, $^{12}C^{16}O^{16}O$.

The gas is introduced into the apparatus, through a small leak, into a source which ionizes the gas to $CO_2{}^+$. These ions are then accelerated by means of a 1,500 V electrostatic field and subsequently emerge from the final collimating slit as a well-defined beam of $CO_2{}^+$ ions with a nearly constant energy content. This beam is then passed through a magnetic analyser and the ions are deflected into paths which are determined by their mass. Collectors for each desired mass are mounted at the point of optimum focus of these derivative resolved beams and on hitting the collectors the ions are neutralized. In this neutralization the electric current of the ions is imparted to the collectors and their electronic components. These currents are then passed through high value resistors across which voltages are developed. These voltages are proportional to the ion intensities striking the collectors. The voltages developed by the signals are balanced and compared one with another in a bridge circuit. The output of the circuit gives a null point which is recorded on a sensitive potentiometer. By a simultaneous collection of the beams of ions one is able to tolerate to a considerable degree the inevitable fluctuations in the intensity of the beams of ions which result from instabilities in the beam source. As a modification of this procedure McKinney, McCrea, Epstein, Allen and Urey (1950) introduced a magnetically operated valve. This enables the worker to switch from a standard gas to an unknown in a matter of seconds so that one can undertake a rapid comparison of the two gases under approximately similar working conditions. According to Epstein (1959) the sensitivity of the method is about ± 0.01 per cent and the comparative method nullifies the effect of background impurities in the tube of the mass-spectrometer.

TEMPERATURE DETERMINATIONS ON DEPOSITS OF OLIGOCENE AND MIOCENE AGE

The results of the determinations of the oxygen isotope ratios of deep-sea cores (Emiliani, 1956) suggested that within the portions which were ascribed to the Oligocene and Miocene there were rather uniform temperatures. It would not be possible on the available data to assert that periodic changes occurred and there were certainly no changes comparable with those of the later Quaternary period.

The oxygen isotope analyses were carried out on samples of the marine foraminiferan *Globigerinoides sacculifera* within three deep-sea cores obtained from equatorial and sub-tropical regions of the Atlantic Ocean. In certain of the samples Emiliani found it necessary to add specimens of *Globigerinoides rubra* to make up the required 5 mg which were needed for each analysis. The known stratigraphical ranges of these species of foraminifera within the cores suggested that one sample was of Middle Oligocene age and the other two of Lower to Middle Miocene age. Typical *Globigerinoides sacculifera* are not found in these cores in positions which are stratigraphically below the Miocene but in these older areas there were numerous specimens which only differed from the normal ones in the absence of a broad, flattened last chamber.

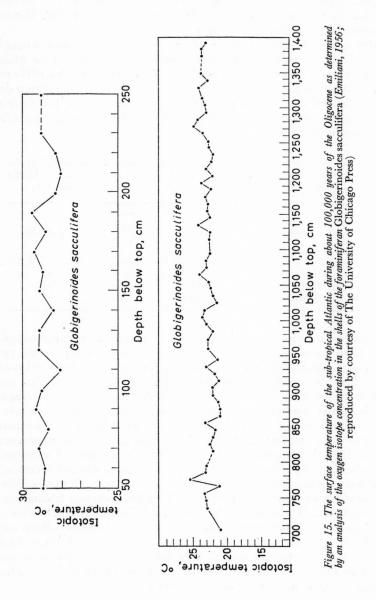

Figure 15. The surface temperature of the sub-tropical Atlantic during about 100,000 years of the Oligocene as determined by an analysis of the oxygen isotope concentration in the shells of the foraminiferan Globigerinoides sacculifera (Emiliani, 1956; reproduced by courtesy of The University of Chicago Press)

99

Two corrections were applied to the results. One of these was to take into account the smaller [18]O content of sea-water in non-glacial times (Emiliani, 1955) and the other to account for the regional differences in the isotope content of sea-water (Epstein and Mayeda, 1953). As a result of these operations the final temperatures, although they may be somewhat inexact, are thought not to have a systematic error in excess of 1–2°C. The results from one core are shown in *Figure 15*.

Although the Oligocene temperatures appear from these data to have been reasonably uniform Emiliani noted some fluctuations during the Miocene. However it is of importance to note, in relation to the discussion of the results of Van der Hammen on page 106, that these Miocene fluctuations do not seem to be periodic. The average values for the temperatures of the tropical ocean surface water during this period of the Tertiary based on these data are contained in *Table 27*.

Table 27. The average temperatures of the Tertiary as determined by the estimation of the oxygen isotope ratios of deep-sea cores compared with the average August temperatures of the regions today (Emiliani, 1956)

Age	Average temperature °C	Present August temperature °C	Difference
Lower-Middle Miocene	22·8	26·5	3·7
Lower-Middle Miocene	24·1	28·0	3·9
Middle Oligocene	28·3	28·0	0·3

It will be seen from *Table 27* that the Oligocene temperatures appear to have been the same as those pertaining in the same regions at the present time. In contrast to this the Miocene temperatures would seem to have been some three degrees lower than those at present. Indeed these data conflict with evidence from continental sources which suggest that the climate of North America and Europe during the Miocene was somewhat warmer than the present. Emiliani (1954) had already demonstrated that the superficial water of the arctic and antarctic regions was not lower than approximately 7°C during Miocene times. At that time there was a communication between the Atlantic and Pacific oceans through the region of Central America. This persisted until late Pliocene times (see Chapters 1 and 8). It may well be that this would have resulted in part of the Caribbean current flowing into the Pacific Ocean. This would have weakened the Florida current, in whose path the deep-sea cores were taken, and as a result the isotherms off the coast of eastern North America would have been displaced southwards. Emiliani suggests that this displacement was not evident in the Oligocene because of the generally higher temperatures but it became evident in the Miocene following a general decrease in temperature.

PLEISTOCENE TEMPERATURES

Prior to the publication of the data considered in the last section, Emiliani (1955) had reported the results of investigating the oxygen isotope ratios of globigerinid skeletons of Quaternary age. As the result of these investigations that author was able to state that the temperature of the superficial water of the Pacific, Atlantic and Caribbean had undergone periodic oscillations during the Quaternary. These fluctuations appeared to have an amplitude of 6°C, although the values in the Pacific, at least, seem to have been greatly affected by the local oceanographical conditions.

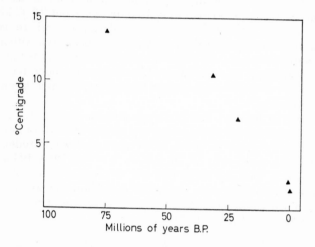

Figure 16. The decrease in temperature of the surface water at high latitudes and of the bottom water in open oceanic basins during the past 75 million years, as determined by isotope analysis of calcareous foraminifera (from Emiliani, 1961; reproduced by courtesy of The University of Chicago Press)

Within the core obtained from the Caribbean region, analysis of the oxygen isotope ratio of the shells of pelagic foraminifera suggested that there were seven complete temperature cycles. As the result of the extrapolation of the rates of sedimentation, together with data provided by ^{14}C analyses, it appeared that the earliest temperature minimum occurred at approximately 280,000 years ago. Original correlations with continental events led Emiliani to suggest that this minimum coincided with the Gunz glaciation.

In one of the Pacific cores which extended to what Emiliani took to be the Upper Pliocene there were about fifteen complete temperature cycles and by comparable calculations to those mentioned above he concluded that the Pleistocene lasted 600,000 years (see Chapter 1). Within this time-scale, which is of course at variance with that of certain other workers, the pre-Gunzian phase appeared to be at least as long in time as the post-Gunzian, classical glacial sequence. Within the complete series variations in the foraminiferal species suggested that there had been some lowering of ocean level in glacial periods, as it had previously been shown that there is a sequence of foraminifera with increasing depth. Closely placed samples from short pilot cores provided a temperature record over Post-glacial time. These measurements suggested that there had been a continuous temperature increase from about 16,500 to about 6,000 years ago. This period of climatic amelioration leading to the Post-glacial climatic optimum of the botanists

(Godwin, 1956; Godwin, Walker and Willis, 1957; Godwin, Suggate and Willis, 1958) was followed by a decrease in temperature leading to the present climate.

Analyses of the proportions of the oxygen isotopes contained within the skeletons of benthonic foraminifera showed that the temperature of the bottom water in the equatorial regions of the Pacific was similar during the glacial periods to that of the present day. In marked contrast to this the temperature in the eastern equatorial Atlantic was about 2·1°C lower than that at the moment. The complementary interglacial bottom in the equatorial Pacific was only 0·8°C higher than the glacial temperatures. Although comparable determinations for the Atlantic were inconclusive, they nevertheless suggested to Emiliani that the influx of ice melt-water along the bottom of the Atlantic from the poles was greater during certain interglacials than at the present time.

As the result of this work Emiliani suggested that there was a good correspondence in time between these temperature fluctuations in low latitudes and the successive glacial advances in the high northern latitudes. By comparison with the conclusions of Milankowitch (1920, 1930, 1938) and van Woerkom (1953) Emiliani noted that the theoretical period of maximum insolation, dated by calculation at 10,000 years before the present, would be 5,000 years ahead of the Post-glacial climatic optimum. This fact conforms with the predictions of Zeuner (1945).

ZOOLOGICAL DATA ON CENOZOIC MARINE CLIMATES

Durham (1950) reported an extensive series of analyses of the occurrence and significance of reef-building corals in Cenozoic marine deposits. These substantiate the climatological conclusions of botanists and physical chemists. In this work Durham took the 18°C February isotherm as the most conveniently definable parameter for the Tertiary climate. The selection of this particular value of 18°C relied upon the fact that it closely approximates to the minimum temperature at which reef-building by hermatypic corals occurs today. He considered that these organisms are the most sensitive indicators of thermal variations available in the region he was studying. The choice of the February isotherm was based upon the fact that this month is the coldest period of the year, at least at the present time, and is therefore the period when the isotherms of the northern hemisphere are at their most southerly point.

PALEOCENE CLIMATES

Fossiliferous strata of early Paleocene or Martinez age are not known north of 40° latitude in the nearctic region and even there are but poorly known. The most well known is that of Lower Lake California which lies at approximately 39°N. The fauna contains an organism which was originally designated ?*Stylophora* but which is, according to Durham, quite clearly a hermatypic reef coral. Together with this there occurs the solitary coral *Flabellum remondianum* Gabb, the lamellibranch genera *Crassatellites*, *Perna*, *Pinna*, *Plicatula* and *Venericardia* as well as the gastropod genera *Cypraea*, *Turritella* and *Tritonium*. Durham suggests that the whole assemblage is probably

102

a climate in which the temperature lay at about 20°C or slightly
⟨th⟩is was the case then the 18·5°C isotherm must have been some-
⟨...⟩r north. Such a suggestion for the value of the minimum tempera-
⟨...⟩borated by Durham's report of the reef coral *Haimesiastraea* in the
⟨...⟩the town of Martinez at 38°N, the ecologically similar genera
⟨...⟩ the Panoche Pass area at 36°30′N and *Siderastraea* in the Simi

⟨...⟩ecent Paleocene fauna is that reported by Clark and Woodford
⟨...⟩ the Mount Diablo region. Although the list of genera and species
⟨...⟩size it nevertheless includes the lamellibranch genera *Crassatellites*,
⟨...⟩a, *Pedalion*, *Pitar*, *Pteria*, *Venericardia* together with the gastropods
⟨...⟩, *Cypraea*, *Ficopsis*, *Oliva*, *Pseudoliva* and *Turritella*. Alongside these
⟨...⟩ere occurred the corals *Flabellum*, *Archohelia* and *Turbinolia*. Such
⟨...⟩ion is interpreted by Durham as indicating that the conditions
⟨...⟩h the remains were deposited were tropical in character and again
⟨...⟩t the 18·5°C February isotherm must have lain considerably
⟨...⟩th.

EOCENE CLIMATES

Fortunately the marine faunas of the more recent early Eocene Capay age
are known from as far north as the southern end of Vancouver Island at
49°N. An examination of the faunal lists from various sites once again led
Durham to suggest a tropical climate for their period of deposition. He
reached this conclusion in view of the presence of the reef coral genera
Astreopora, *Colpophyllia*, *Leptophyllastrea*, *Madracis* and *Montipora* together with
the orbitoidal foraminifera, mollusca, brachiopoda and calcareous algae.
This being the case the 18·5° isotherm must have once again lain some
distance to the north of the principal site in the straits of Juan de Fuca at
48°N.

Marine faunas of the more recent Eocene Domengine period are less
definitive. Nevertheless deposits of this age in the state of Washington contain
the coral *Madracis*, which, although not strictly a reef dweller, is usually
tropical. In addition there are the lamellibranchs *Corbula*, *Macrocallista*, *Pitar*
and large *Venericardia*, the gastropods *Eocernina*, *Eratopsis*, *Ficopsis*, *Harpa*,
Nerita and *Turritella* and also the cephalopod *Aturia*. The climatic characteristics of this assemblage of genera suggest temperatures comparable with
those of Capay time.

The even more recent Tejon stage, which is represented by Eocene deposits
in Washington and north-western Oregon ascribable to the Cowlitz formation,
has a marine fauna comparable with that of the Domengine stage. The genera
are largely those of a deep-water facies and the shallow water corals and
molluscs are lacking. However, Durham (1942) reported a reef coral *Astreopora* from Seattle which appeared to indicate that the 18·5°C February
isotherm could not have occurred as far south as that.

In fact the type deposits of the Cowlitz formation contain many well-
preserved fossils (Weaver, 1943). These include the lamellibranch genera
Obliquarca, *Pteria*, *Crassatellites*, large specimens of *Venericardia*, *Macrocallista*,
Pitar, *Sanguinolaria* and *Corbula*. There is also the tropical gastropod association of *Nerita*, *Neritina*, *Turritella*, *Potamides*, *Ficopsis*, *Cymatium*, *Cantharus*,

103

Pseudoliva and *Conus*, together with the nautiloids *Cimomia* and *Aturia*. Furthermore the hermatypic coral *Hydnophora* was recorded in the Lower Cowlitz formation near Balch, Washington. All these records suggest deposition of the fossiliferous material at a temperature of about 20°C or slightly higher. This corroborates the records of *Astrocoenia* and *Crassatellites* further north.

OLIGOCENE AND LOWER MIOCENE CLIMATES

Marine facies of the faunas of the Lincoln and Blakeley stages of the North American Oligocene are again best known in the region of Oregon and Washington. In the last-named region the fauna of the Quimper sandstone at 48°N includes several coral genera. One may cite *Siderastrea*, *Arcohelia*, *Tubastrea* and *Astrangea*. These occur beside the remains of various gastropods which also occur in the Gries Ranch fauna from further south. All these fossils indicate that the Quimper sandstone contains a fauna of tropical surroundings.

The most well-worked fauna of Blakeley age occurs near Seattle to the southern end of Vancouver Island at 48–49°N. The remains have been recorded by several authors and are summarized by Durham (1950). Several of the lists include the reef coral *Siderastrea* together with another genus, which seems to have similar ecological characteristics, namely *Eusmilea*. In addition the recorded fauna also includes the lamellibranchs *Antigona*, *Chione*, *Corbis*, *Crassatellites*, *Macrocallista*, *Pitar*, *Semele*, *Tivela*, and the gastropods *Actaeon*, *Ancilla*, *Ficus*, *Marginella*, *Oxystele* and *Rapana*. Using the same criteria as in the cases outlined in the foregoing sections Durham concluded that this fauna represented life under climatic conditions in which the temperature could not have fallen below 18·5°C.

Faunas of a comparable age are also known to occur in the Gulf of Alaska at 60°N. There the association of *Chione*, *Macrocallista*, *Pitar*, *Turritella* and the nautiloid genus *Aturia*, all again suggest a warm temperature of not less than 15°C. Durham notes that this is particularly striking in view of the fact that Taliaferro in Clark (1932) concluded that at least some of the sediments were apparently of glacial origin. In relation to these suggestions it was noted by the earlier workers that it was possible that the climatic conditions at the head of the Gulf of Alaska during the Upper Oligocene may have resembled those in the North Island of New Zealand today. In that region the minimum yearly temperature is about 14°C but there are extant glaciers. However, in opposition to this thesis, Durham volunteers an alternative suggestion. This is based upon the fact that the 15°C August isotherm along the Pacific coast of North America leaves the coast at about 34°N and goes out to sea. At latitudes 44–48°N it then swings back into the coast. Durham suggests that with the more northerly distribution of the isotherms during Upper Oligocene times a similar isothermal pattern occurred but further north along the coast.

MIOCENE AND PLIOCENE CLIMATES

Marine sediments of the Temblor-Briones age occur as far north as the straits of Juan de Fuca. Within these deposits fossils occur which are comparable with those in the foregoing faunas. These include the genera *Anadara*, *Aturia*, *Chione*, *Turritella* and *Trophosycon*, whilst further south at 45–47°N in south-western Washington and north-west Oregon the Astoria formation contains the coral *Lophelia*. Durham suggests that this indicates that the 13°C isotherm therefore lay at about 48°N.

The Jacelitos formation of the central Californian Pliocene, which occurs at 36°N, also includes several of the genera noted in the Miocene lists. However there are also the lamellibranchs *Dosinia, Apolymetis, Lyropecten, Tivela* and the gastropods *Forreria, Megasurcula* and *Sinum*. Durham concludes that at this early Pliocene time the minimum temperature could therefore not have been less than 13°C. Similar conclusions may also be drawn from contemporaneous faunas in the Coalinga Kettleman Hills area at 36°N.

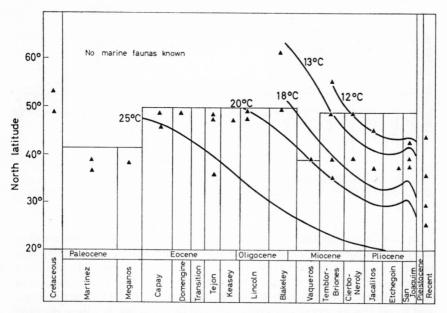

Figure 17. Diagram to show the probable past positions of the February marine isotherms along the Pacific coast of North America during the Tertiary as indicated by the occurrence of hermatypic corals (from Durham, 1950)

All these considerations therefore led Durham (1950) to conclude that the climate of the early Tertiary in north temperate latitudes was considerably warmer than that of the same regions today. This warm climate was modified with time and the isotherms moved progressively further south during the later Tertiary. These conclusions are illustrated in *Figure 17*.

UPPER CRETACEOUS AND TERTIARY CLIMATIC PERIODICITY

Whilst considering the data suggestive of climatic periodicity during the Cenozoic it will be very instructive to take account of similar evidence for the foregoing Cretaceous. Very few examples of continuous floral records through long periods of the Cenozoic are known at the present time. For this reason the information provided by investigations of polleniferous deposits in Columbia, South America are of outstanding importance.

The composite pollen diagram obtained from the sites stretches from the uppermost Cretaceous to the Lower Miocene (Van der Hammen, 1957). In these diagrams there is pollen of palms and other angiosperms and the spores of ferns. Van der Hammen considers that these can all be assigned to one of eight groups and of these eight several show maximal and minimal values for their percentage representation at rather regular intervals.

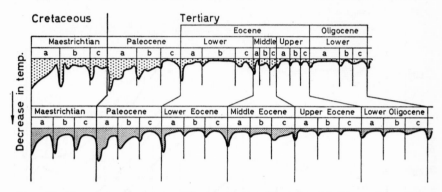

Figure 18. Diagram showing the curve of the representation of the pollen of the Monocolpites medius *group of palms in the deposits of Columbia. Below the same curve is shown redrawn on a time scale and somewhat simplified (from van der Hammen, 1961)*

In fact the outstanding fluctuations occur in the percentage representation of a group of palms known as the *Monocolpites medius* group. The maxima and minima of this group are correlated with comparable fluctuations in the representation of other groups. The result of the analysis of a collection of pollen diagrams from sites in Columbia as much as 1,500 kilometres apart and showing a variety of different ecological facies, shows that these maxima and minima are synchronous in all the sites. Owing to the widespread origins of the sites and the variety of facies Van der Hammen suggests that local influences can probably be excluded so that the origins of the maxima and minima may well lie in climatic changes.

The *Monocolpites medius* group have both short and long term fluctuations. During the Paleocene and Middle Eocene there are high values for its percentage representation and indeed if the short period maxima are removed from the diagrams the overall picture would resemble the climatic curves obtained from North America and based upon the remains of macro-fossils (Chapter 3). Earlier work by Umbgrove (1942) had suggested a low temperature for the Paleocene and for this reason Van der Hammen tentatively suggests that the maxima in the percentage representation of *Monocolpites medius* indicate periods of climatic deterioration, or at least falling temperature. A glance at the diagram in *Figure 18* will show that the maxima and minima appear to occur regularly. In the Maestrichtian, Paleocene and Lower Eocene, for example, the distances between the peaks are surprisingly constant. Following this the distances become shorter and then longer again,

106

but Van der Hammen emphasizes that they still seem to be regular and states that the long time intervals are derived from sediments laid down under conditions of quiet sedimentation whilst the shorter ones come from sediments of tectonically active times.

From *Figure 18* it can also be seen that every third maxima is greater than the former two although the increase is less in the more recent parts of the deposits. The importance of these maxima is all the greater if, as Van der Hammen suggests, they do correspond to the base of the various international

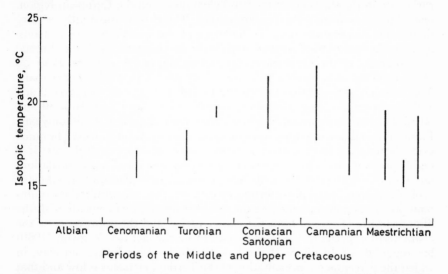

Figure 19. The temperature ranges during various epochs of the Cretaceous as obtained by analysis of the oxygen isotope concentrations in the shells of west European belemnites (from Emiliani, 1961; after Lowenstam and Epstein, 1954; reproduced by courtesy of The University of Chicago Press)

geological units of Lower Eocene, Middle Eocene etc. This would indicate that a change of climate occurs at exactly the period when there are important changes in the flora and fauna and that this climatic variation is especially marked at the bases of the Paleocene, Eocene and Oligocene. It is of course exactly at these geological horizons that many new faunal combinations occur for the first time as will be seen from Chapter 7.

If now one takes the data of *Table 26* above it is possible to estimate the duration of these climatic oscillations. In fact Van der Hammen (1961) assumed the beginning of the Tertiary to be at 60 million years B.P. and the base of the Miocene at 18 million years B.P. It is clear from *Table 26* above that this is not yet firmly established but nevertheless the conclusions of the last-named author are of considerable theoretical interest. From the two values of 60 million and 18 million Van der Hammen obtained the total length of the period represented by the Columbian pollen-diagrams as 42 million years. Dividing this into 21 intervals suggested that the time between the temperature palm minima represented by the *Monocolpites medius* group was 2 million years. The longer time interval between the higher pollen maxima is therefore 6 million years. The data in *Table 26* quite clearly show that these figures cannot in any way be considered final, but give an interesting example of the possible oscillations of climate which occurred in the early Tertiary. Although the composite diagram of Van der Hammen (1957) does not come any nearer the present than the Lower Miocene, there are several indications that similar periodicity typifies the climate during the deposition of younger Miocene and Pliocene deposits.

Taking the data outlined above, together with the results of Lowenstam and Epstein (1954) for the analysis of the oxygen isotope ratios of the carbonate in the shells of Cretaceous belemnites from the European region, one obtains extremely interesting results. There was apparently a very significant temperature drop at the base of the post-Aptian Cretaceous, again at the base of the Cenozoic, and finally of course the repetitive climatic deteriorations of the Quaternary glaciations. From the data of *Table 26* above it is clear that these periods are (a) 30 and (b) 60 million years apart. This certainly suggests that during the period in which the Cenozoic fauna and flora were evolving there were climatic cycles with periods of 30 and 60 million years and probably minor cycles of 6 million and 2 million years. From the fact that the temperature maxima and minima of Van der Hammen coincide with the base of the successive international geological units it is highly probable that they represent extensive world-wide climatic oscillations and that these probably lie at the base of the faunal replacement rhythms of geological time. This is also corroborated by the fact that within the Columbian pollen-diagrams themselves the temperature minima coincide with the disappearance of species from the earlier period and the appearance of the characteristic species of the later period. From the fact that Zagwijn (1960) has reported a cold phase at the base of the Pliocene Reuverian clay, in which the percentage representation of the Tertiary elements is low and that of *Pinus* high, it seems probable that this long-term series of climatic cycles was indeed world wide and continued into the Pliocene. It is also significant that Bürgl (1959) recognized 10 cycles of approximately equal thickness within Cretaceous deposits. On the basis of the data for the age of the Cretaceous in *Table 26* it would appear that each of these would again be 6 million years in length.

7

CARNIVORA

Arising from the insectivores of the late Cretaceous this super-order has a common origin with the other component of the cohort Ferungulata, the Ungulates. It is possible that this origin may lie amongst the deltatherioid forms of the Djadochta Cretaceous deposits in Mongolia, and certain carnivores which were initially only known from incomplete material, were in fact thought to be lepticid insectivores. The variations which occurred in the morphology of the carnivores during the Tertiary reflect differing degrees of specialization to their principally flesh-eating mode of life. The variations may indeed be correlated with the characters and degree of specialization of the herbivores upon which they preyed. As these latter animals changed in form from the ancestral plantigrade insectivore habit to cursorial, saltatorial or burrowing herbivores, so there was a concomitant modification in the characters of the carnivores. The adaptations exhibited by the modern genera consist in the development of carnassial teeth with shearing surfaces; a reduction in the post-carnassial dentition; together with a wide gape which results from the extensive vertical movement which is permitted by the mandibular articulation. The cerebral hemispheres are well developed, allowing considerable powers of learning and the cursorial or semi-arboreal life is associated with a well-developed cerebellum. Adaptations similar to these were also evolved along several lines of the early Tertiary carnivores, several groups of which had a modified dentition although the carnassial modifications took place in teeth other than the fourth upper premolar and first lower molar of the fissipeds.

During the Paleocene period in which the herbivores still included the archaic multituberculates, the Condylarthra, Pantodonta and Dinocerata, the dominant carnivores were the primitive Procreodi. Subsequently, when the hippomorph and tapiromorph Perissodactyla, the paleodont Artiodactyla and the ischyromyid rodents appear in the Eocene, the Procreodi were replaced as dominant forms by the Acreodi and Pseudocreodi. With the gradual morphological and presumably behaviouristic elaboration of the Ungulates these Eocene carnivores were themselves replaced by Fissipedia with characters similar to modern forms.

CREODONT CARNIVORES

Classifying animals from a temporo-spatial distribution into genera and species raises many problems. All the carnivores classed together as creodonts occurred during the early Tertiary period but many are forms closely related to the modern Fissipedia. Their separation from these latter forms is often the result of an arbitrary decision and the whole group show the progressive changes which took place in the placental carnivore stock in association with the evolution of the herbivores mentioned above. The principal skeletal remains of the creodonts have been found in deposits in North America and the works dealing with them discuss the various taxonomic problems in detail (Dennison, 1938; Gazin, 1946; Matthew, 1901, 1906, 1909, 1915, 1927, 1937; Matthew and Granger, 1915, 1918; Simpson, 1936, 1937a). There are also species in the Eocene and Oligocene deposits of Europe (*loc. cit*; Colbert, 1933; Dal Piaz, 1930; Martin, 1906; Piveteau, 1955).

In general the fossils suggest that these animals were rather heavily built and had a long low skull in which the facial region was developed but the brain-case small. The large size of the olfactory lobes, as seen in the cranial casts of the fossil skulls, suggests that like their modern counterparts these carnivores were macrosmatic and hunted by smell. The fact that their cerebral and cerebellar hemispheres were smooth suggests that their powers of learned behaviour and cursorial ability were not well developed. They had a complete dentition and showed several interesting evolutionary lines in which carnassial teeth were developed independently of those in modern genera (Romer, 1945; Simpson, 1945; *Traité de Zoologie*).

THE PROCREODI

All the primitive Paleocene and Eocene forms which had simple molars are classed together in the sub-order Procreodi. In fact the dentition recalls that of the early Condylarthra (Chapter 8) amongst the Ferungulata, and

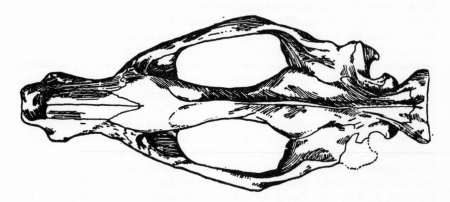

Figure 20. The dorsal view of the cranium of the aquatic creodont Apterodon from the Fayum Oligocene beds in Egypt. This genus has a particularly long muzzle but the typical small brain-case is clearly seen × $\frac{11}{28}$ (after Osborn from Viret, 1955)

also shows similarities with that of certain early Primates. All these forms having a primitive appearance and exemplified by the family Oxyclaenidae were classed together from a very early stage in their study, and constitute the family Arctocyonidae of nineteenth century authors.

During the Paleocene period some 17 genera are known to have occurred in North America and included such forms as *Deltatherium*, *Mimotricentes*, *Eoconodon*, *Tricentes* and *Triisodon*. At that time the European fauna also included similar carnivorous forms, notably the genera *Arctocyon* and *Arcto-cyonides*, whilst in Asia *Hyracolestes* seems to have filled the niche of the carnivores.

It is certain that these relatively unspecialized animals continued to exist in America during the early Eocene since both *Chriacus* and *Thryptacodon* are known from Upper Paleocene and Lower Eocene deposits in that region. However, in Europe the genera from more recent deposits are of rather questionable taxonomic affinities, and animals with the characteristics of the Procreodi do not seem to have persisted much beyond this date. Some did survive, however, and the genus *Didymoconus* occurs in Asiatic Oligocene beds.

In fact there was a considerable amount of morphological variation in these animals. Specimens of the Arctocyonidae which have been recovered from the Thanetian Beds at Cernay, and therefore dating from the Upper Paleocene, were the size of bears and had low-crowned molars which suggested omnivorous or frugivorous feeding habits. On the other hand, *Delta-therium* exhibited slight sabre-tooth tendencies, and the difficulties involved in trying to understand the habits of these creatures are exemplified by the fact that early incomplete fossils of this genus were thought to represent an icterid insectivore.

THE ACREODI

As stated above, the Paleocene Procreodi were largely replaced by more specialized genera during the Eocene period. This replacement was probably associated with the evolution of equally specialized herbivores. Of these Eocene carnivores the family Mesonychidae differ from their contemporaries by possessing blunt-cusped molars and having no carnassials. In view of this they are usually classified as a separate sub-order which comprised an isolated evolutionary line and resulted from the early Tertiary explosion of mammalian evolution.

Appearing in the Paleocene alongside the Procreodi, the Acreodi were represented at that time by *Microclaenodon* in North America and *Dissacus* in Europe. Both these genera are also known from Eocene deposits and the presence of other genera such as *Hapalodectes*, *Pachyaena* and *Synoplotherium* indicates that the family was widely distributed throughout the holarctic region at that time. In fact during this period some forms attained a giant size. In general the molars showed an adaptation to flesh-eating in their shearing talonids and the digits seem to have been flattened, fissured and hoofed in small cursorial forms. The larger species, however, may well have been carrion eaters. Certainly specimens of the type genus *Mesonyx* from the Middle Eocene Bridgerian deposits in North America had a skull nearly a foot in length, and *Andrewsarchus* from Upper Eocene deposits in Mongolia was an animal whose size recalls that of the Mesozoic reptiles.

THE PSEUDOCREODI

In contrast to the Mesonychidae which lacked carnassial teeth, the two contemporary families Oxyaenidae and Hyaenodontidae had developed marked carnassials although the actual teeth involved differed both between

111

the two families themselves and between them and the later Eucreodi and their fissiped descendants. In the Oxyaenidae it was the first upper molar and the second lower molar $\frac{M^1}{M^2}$ which were specialized in this way. In the case of the Hyaenodontidae it could be the second upper molar and the third lower molar $\frac{M^2}{M_3}$. A slightly aberrant situation occurred in the Eocene genus *Paleonictis*. In these animals the carnassials were developed on both the last premolar and first molar in the upper jaw and the first and second molars in the lower jaw. This paleonictid condition in fact combines the characteristics of the family Oxyaenidae with those of the Eucreodi (see below).

Remains of the Oxyaenidae occur in both the New and Old Worlds but until the present time the finds have been most numerous in the New World. In that region the genera *Dipsalodon* and *Oxyaena* occur in both Paleocene and Eocene deposits. At that time the contemporary European fauna contained related forms in the genera *Paleonictis* and *Paroxaena*. The earliest species retained the plantigrade gait of the ancestral insectivores and were long-bodied with short legs, but as in all carnivores this was progressively reduced to a varying digitigrade condition. The changes were most extreme in the genus *Sarkastodon*. This animal, occurring in the Upper Eocene deposits of Mongolia, had undergone a reduction in the post-carnassial dentition similar to that of the modern hyaenas *Crocuta* and *Hyaena* and in size was the equal of its contemporary *Andrewsarchus*.

The Hyaenodontidae are also first recorded together with the Procreodi, Acreodi and Oxyaenids in Paleocene deposits. At that time the European fauna knew Opisthopsalis, and during the subsequent Eocene period the genus *Sinopa* occurred both in this region and also in North America. The American fauna included a variety of other genera notably *Apataelurus, Limnocyon, Machaerodes, Prolimnocyon, Thinocyon* and *Tritemnodon* and also shared the genus *Pterodon* with the Asiatic fauna. An even more widespread distribution occurred in the later Oligocene period when *Hyaenodon* existed in Europe, Asia and North America. The late record of *Dissopsalis* from Asia during the Pliocene shows that these forms were sufficiently well adapted to be able to persist well outside the early Tertiary period during which the bulk of the Creodonts flourished. Under these conditions they would presumably have directly competed with the more specialized Eucreodi and fissipeds.

The early sinopid forms illustrate the general appearance of the family. The complete dentition included trituberculate upper molars, the body-form was small and lightly built, and the skull was elongated. Various combinations of characters occurred at this early Tertiary period and the American Eocene *Limnocyon* actually had the carnassial formula of the Oxyaenidae. As in many lines of carnivores there was a tendency for certain lines to develop sabre-teeth, for example *Apataelurus*. Since this animal occurs in North American deposits of Eocene age, when the early tachytelic phase of ungulate evolution had given rise to gravigrade Dinocerata, Pantodonta and Brontotherioids (Chapter 10), one must assume that it led a similar life, preying upon contemporary herbivores, to that later led by the sabre-toothed felids, which preyed upon the Miocene and Pliocene herbivores, and also to the marsupial *Thylacosmilus*.

112

In contrast to this development of large teeth, the small sinopid ancestors also gave rise to a hyaena-like form *Quercytherium*. As in the oxyaenid genus *Sarkastodon*, this had undergone a considerable reduction in its dentition.

THE EUCREODI

Besides the animals which have been discussed in the foregoing sections there were, during the Paleocene and Eocene, other carnivores which, although creodonts, were clearly ancestral to the modern Fissipeds. They are characterized by the presence of carnassial surfaces on the last upper premolar and the first lower molar, a condition which was partially simulated by the paleonictid oxyaenids. The primitive genus *Didymictis* is found in the Montian deposits of America but there are very few indications of the history of the group before this point in the Middle Paleocene. This early animal persisted alongside other genera during the Eocene when the early forerunners of the Fissipeds appeared. Thus alongside it there occurred such forms as *Pleurocyon, Tapocyon, Vulpavus, Miacis* and *Viverravus*. The morphology of the genus *Miacis*, which retained three molars in both jaws and is recorded from throughout the holarctic region at that time, shows that it is very close to the basal stock of the Canoidea (Arctoidea auctt). As such it was the forerunner of the mustelids, canids, ursids and procyonids. In contrast the contemporaneous *viverravids* had lost one molar in each jaw, and from their general form are thought to be the ancestors of the Feloidea (Aeluroidea auctt) and therefore gave rise to our modern felids, hyaenids, and viverrids with whom they are indeed classified by some authors.

The characters of all these genera classed together as the Eucreodi are fairly well exemplified by the two Oligocene genera *Cynodictis* and *Pseudocynodictis*. In fact their appearance was very similar to that of the modern mustelids. They were of small size and the relatively long body was slung low on the ground by the short legs which retained all five digits, each of which was probably clawed. The early forms seem to have been relatively unimportant components of the fauna but with the advent of the advanced ungulate and rodent herbivores the stock became the most important of the carnivores and the fissiped descendants eventually replaced all the other creodont stocks.

FISSIPEDIA

As indicated above, this order represents a spatio-temporal classification of the genera which evolved from the Miacidae and the Viverravidae. They are characterized by the ossification of the auditory bulla in which the component bones vary. In the typical Feloidea this structure is compound and includes contributions from both the endotympanic and tympanic bones (Gregory and Hellman, 1939). In the majority of genera there is a wide communication between the orbit and the temporal fossa. The digits are free and although in some, notably the Ursidae, Mustelidae and Viverridae, the ancestral plantigrade gait is retained, most members are digitigrade or at least semidigitigrade. The fact that in the modern forms the young are born at an early and immature stage explains the building of lairs by many of the smaller genera and the use of caves for this purpose by the larger Hyaenidae and Ursidae. The diet is in fact subject to a fair range of variation, and although the larger Feloidea are completely carnivorous the smaller genera of both Feloidea and Canoidea and the larger Ursidae are omnivorous opportunists, and will eat plant material if necessary.

CANOIDEA

The families which possess a long carotid canal and a homogeneous auditory bulla are classed together as the Canoidea (Simpson, 1945). The limbs are terminated by non-retractile claws in modern forms and there is always a penial bone. As in the case of the feloidea the origin of the sub-order lies in the mustelid-like forms of equivocal taxonomic position which date from the Oligocene.

Mustelidae

As noted above, this family comprises a group of genera which have retained the general appearance of the fossil forms from Oligocene deposits. The modern forms are characterized by the combination of carnassial teeth

Table 28. The approximate numbers of mustelid genera from the Cenozoic deposits of the world

	Europe	North America	Asia	South America	Africa
Quaternary	6	7	6	4	1
Pliocene	12	15	14	—	1
Miocene	10	15	2	—	—
Oligocene	3	2	1	—	—
Eocene	?	—	—	—	—

with reduced molars and no alisphenoid canal. As a result of the reduction in the dentition there is a pronounced shortening of the facial region in modern forms, but amongst the earlier genera which lie near the base of both the feloid and canid stocks there is a fairly generalized appearance which recalls both evolutionary lines.

The genus *Plesictis* occurs in Stampian deposits. During the Miocene and Pliocene numerous genera existed in the northern hemisphere, but, as can be seen from *Table 28*, the numbers were reduced by the beginning of the Quaternary. These late Tertiary mustelid carnivores probably had similar habits to their counterparts at the present time. For example, the genus *Melodon*, which is known from the Miocene Tung Gur deposits in Mongolia and the contemporaneous deposits in north China, is very suggestive of the modern badgers, although the mongolian specimen is larger than other fossil badgers and lacks the characteristic polybunodont dentition of later forms.

Various records are scattered through the literature showing mustelids in the subsequent Quaternary deposits. *Pannonictis pilgrimi* and *Pannonictis pliocenica* occur in the Tiglian deposits of north-west Europe and *Proputorius nestii* and *Proputorius olivolanus* are included in the carnivores of the Late Villafranchian fauna of the Val d'Arno.

Canidae

The cosmopolitan dog family is characterized by the large size of the cerebral hemispheres, the well-developed tympanic bulla, elongated facial region, long limbs and a semi-digitigrade gait. The family is diphyletic according to Matthews, who distinguishes between a line developing from the Oligocene genus *Cynodictis*, and including the modern canids, and an entirely separate line, which gave rise to the bear-dogs and true bears, and originated close to the Oligocene *Daphaenodon*.

During the Eocene various early forms seem to have occurred in the European region. *Amphicynodon*, *Paracynodon* and *Pseudamphicyon* occur in deposits of both Eocene and Oligocene age in this last-named part of the world and *Pachycynodon* which occurred with them in the Eocene had reached the Asiatic region by the Oligocene. The genera which appear in these early Tertiary deposits are generally replaced during the Middle and Upper Miocene by numerous genera which occurred at that time in the whole of the holarctic region.

By the beginning of the Oligocene the early canids showed a marked development of the brain and it is probable that many of the genera had habits which were broadly comparable with those of the wolf today. There was, however, considerable morphological variation. Wolf-like habits are indeed usually accorded to the Amphicyoninae which preserved a complete dentition, but in the lower Pontian deposits species occur which have a dentition comparable with that of the sabre-toothed felids. Thus this habit, already noted amongst the creodonts, occurred again, possibly in association with some pachydermatous herbivore prey (Chapter 11). Amongst the wolf-like Amphicyoninae there was a progressive increase in size. By the Lower Miocene this had become noticeable and in the Aquitanian there occurred specimens with the proportions of a lion. By the Burdigalian these were replaced by the larger *Amphicyon giganteus* and *Daphaenodon*, the so-called Bear-dogs.

During the Miocene the speciation is somewhat complex and disagreement exists as to the degree of polyphyletic evolution occurring in the canids at that time. For example, *Gobicyon macrognathus* from the Wolf-camp quarry site of the Mongolian Tung Gur formation is, according to Colbert (1939), a large tomarctid, but growing to a large robust size it paralleled the comparable *Aelurodon* line of North America. The similarity between the two genera *Gobicyon* and *Osteoborus* is considerable, but the North American genus *Osteoborus* had certain specializations, notably the reduction of the anterior premolars. These specializations suggest that it was partway along the evolutionary line which culminated in the later hyaenognathid dogs *Borophagus* and *Hyaenognathus*. Colbert, in distinction to Simpson, suggested that the Mongolian genus *Gobicyon* had diverged away from the American genera and had emphasized the elongation of the lower premolars without the

115

corresponding transverse growth and reduction of the anterior premolars characteristic of the typical hyaenognaths. It is certainly the case that the American and Asiatic faunas interchanged at the time, since the spoon-tusked mastodon (*Platybelodon*) and the beaver (*Amblycastor*) occur in both the Miocene deposits of North America and also in the Mongolian Tung Gur.

Besides this complex speciation other variations at that time involved developments away from the predominantly carnivorous habits. The genus *Simocyon* for example, which is related to the modern *Speothes*, is a short-muzzled form from the European Pliocene. It has been suggested that this animal represented a modification toward an omnivorous habitus.

The European Quaternary deposits have provided a number of species of canid. These were summarized by Zeuner (1945). As in the case with the felids, hyaenids and the proboscideans the general picture shows that more genera were present at the beginning of the Quaternary than at later periods. In the Late Villafranchian fauna from the early Pleistocene there are five species of *Canis*, *Canis etruscus* Maj., *Canis majori* D.C., *Canis olivolanus* D.C., *Canis urvernensis* D.C. and *Canis falconieri* Maj. There were also two foxes *Vulpes alopecoides* D.C. and *Vulpes megamastoides* Pom. From later deposits, the wolf *Canis lupus* has been recorded in the Cromerian interglacial and *Canis mosbachensis* from the subsequent Lowestoft glaciation. The wolf and *Canis suessi* lived during the last interglacial and are known from deposits which contain *Thuja* and walnuts at Ehringsdorf near Weimar, Thuringia, Central Germany.

Ursidae

The modern bears are canoids of large size with thick set limbs and only a rudimentary tail. As in the other canoid families the limbs bear strong non-retractile claws. The family is typically omnivorous and has retained the plantigrade gait of the ancestral Cretaceous and early Tertiary insectivores. An alisphenoid canal is present and the carotid canal opens into the rear of the tympanic bulla. The dentition is characterized by strong canines, reduced premolars and a similar reduction in the carnassial surfaces in association with the omnivorous diet. The molars have accessory tubercles and imitate the polybunodont herbivores in principle.

The bears are the last of the canoid carnivores to appear in the fossil record. Depending upon the criteria used to define the family they first appeared in the Miocene or the Pliocene (Frick) and it has been suggested that their origin lies in the Amphicynodontinae of the European Eocene and Oligocene deposits. It has also been suggested that they evolved from the Oligocene and Pliocene genus *Cephalogale*. Whatever the precise origin, by the Pliocene, some forms, notably *Indarctos* and *Hyaenarctos*, had attained a considerable size. Giant bears did in fact exist in much more recent periods and the most accurately dated specimen is that from the Lagoa Funda, Minas Gerais, Brazil. This is a specimen which occurred during Post-glacial time and ^{14}C analyses show that it lived at $3,000 \pm 300$ years before the present (Martin, 1958).

As with the late Tertiary canids the taxonomy of the early ursids is some-what controversial due to the various limits and criteria used by different authors to designate families and genera. Thus the species *Hemicyon teilhardi*

Colbert from the Tung Gur formation of the Mongolian Miocene deposits is a form in which the molars are more canid-like than are those of other species of *Hemicyon*. The frontalia and braincase are more expanded by comparison with those of *Hemicyon ursinus* and the auditory bulla is relatively large and oval as in the canids. The Mongolian specimen is unusual for mid-Tertiary carnivores as it is well preserved, and although the skull is slightly compressed, the dimensions are sufficiently well established to show that although the skull is smaller than those of *Hemicyon ursinus*, the teeth are larger. The alisphenoid canal, as in *Hemicyon ursinus*, is longer than that of the canids and

Table 29.   The ursid genera from the Cenozoic deposits

	Europe	Asia	North America	Africa	South America
Quaternary	Ursus	Melursus Ursus Holarctos Hyaenarctos	Tremarcto- therium Arctodus Ursus	Ursus	Pararcto- therium Arctotherium
Pliocene	Holarctos Hyaenarctos Indarctos Ursavus	Hyaenarctos Indarctos	Hyaenarctos Indarctos Plionarctos		
Miocene	* Hemicyon Ursavus	* Hemicyon	* Hemicyon		

* Indicates Amphicynodonts of Simpson (1945)

shorter than that of typical ursids. The bulla is intermediate between the dogs and bears. In canids, the bulla is, as noted above, inflated, of ectotympanic origin and has a short tube for the external auditory meatus. In ursids the bulla is flattened and has a long tube for the external auditory meatus. The bulla of *Hemicyon teilhardi* is rather flat and has a tube of medium length. This suggests that if the Hemicyoninae originated from *Daphoenodon* as Matthews suggests, then the inflated bulla of *Hemicyon teilhardi* must be a secondary condition paralleling the condition in the dogs, because the genus *Daphaenodon* has a small bulla.

It will be seen from *Table 29* that this cosmopolitan family has clearly been widespread in the holarctic region since the Miocene. On the other hand, few African ursid fossils are known, and these from the Quaternary and recent deposits. The inadequacy of this record may be representative of the lesser number of investigations or may reflect virtual absence. Certainly, as *Table 29* shows, the ursids only entered South America along with the raccoons (page 119) and other advanced placentals in relatively recent Pliocene and also Quaternary times.

Ursus remains are fairly numerous in Quaternary deposits and are well-known as the cave-bears. A magnificent survey of recent European bears is given by Couturier (1953). As in the case of the canids and the felids, there is a gradual morphological change throughout the Quaternary, resulting in a series of forms in successive periods. These changes, as they are represented in fossil European faunas, are summarized in *Table 30*.

Table 30. The occurrence of ursid species in the Quaternary deposits of Europe
(after Zeuner, 1945; Van der Vlerk and Florschütz, 1950)

	Ursus etruscus Cu.	*Ursus arvernensis* Cr. & Job.	*Ursus deningeri* V. Reich.	*Ursus savini* Andr.	*Ursus speleus* Ros.	*Ursus arctos* L.
Last glaciation					Found	Found
Eemian interglacial					Found	Found
Saale glaciation						Found
Holstein interglacial					Found	Found
Elster glaciation		Found	Found		Found	
Cromerian interglacial		Found		Found	Found	
Tiglian Clay	Found					
Late Villa-franchian	Found	Found				

Table 31. The genera of the Procyonidae from Cenozoic deposits (after Simpson, 1945)

	North America	South America	Asia	Europe	Africa
Quaternary	*Procyon* *Bassariscus*	*Brachynasua* *Nasua* *Procyon*	*Ailuropoda*		Not Known
Pliocene	*Procyon* *Bassariscus* *Cynarctus*	*Cyonasua* *Amphinasua* *Pachynasua*	*Sivanasua*	*Parailurus*	Not Known
Miocene	*Aletocyon* *Bassariscops* *Bassariscus* *Cynarctoides* *Cynarctus* *Phlaocyon* *Zodiolestes*			*Sivanasua*	Not Known

Procyonidae

The eight modern genera ascribed to this family by Simpson (1945) are characterized by the absence of an alisphenoid canal. The fossil genera are tabulated in *Table 31* and from this it can be seen that the family seems to have had a North American origin. In the Miocene seven genera existed in that region and radiation from this source is indicated by the occurrence of the remains ascribed to *Sivanasua* in European Miocene deposits and Asiatic Pliocene formations. Invasion of the South American continent took place at the end of the Pliocene as is shown by the occurrence there of *Cyonasua*. It seems probable that the family has a common ancestry with the ursids which dates from early Miocene times, and since then a considerable parallel evolution has taken place. The modern genus *Ailuropoda* has, in fact, a bear-like appearance and is specialized for a vegetarian existence in the bamboo areas of eastern Asia.

FELOIDEA

As stated previously, this sub-order includes all those forms which have a compound auditory bulla in which there are endotympanic components. The earliest animals which suggest this evolutionary line are the fossil Viverravidae. As amongst the canids there is a progressive tendency to evolve large forms of varied habits from the initial, small, plantigrade stock. This tendency is epitomized in the stocks leading to the large sabre-tooths such as *Machairodus* of the holarctic Pliocene deposits.

Viverridae

The small feloid genera classed together in this family are restricted to the warm regions of the Old World at the present time. An alisphenoid canal is present in the long, low cranium and the dentition is often reduced by loss of the premolars. The carnassial teeth are less developed than in the Felidae, the lower one often being short and having a less pointed talon. The fore limbs are always pentadactyl although the hind may be tetradactyl. In its typical form the dentition recalls that of the Eucreodi and in some classifications a vertical arrangement is used which includes both the Viverridae and these ancestral fossil forms. Similarly disagreement exists on the other side and the genus *Cryptoprocta* has been referred to the Felinae because of felid characters. Simpson (1945) reiterated its viverrid characters and suggested a close relationship with the Eocene felid ancestors such as *Paleoprionodon*. The difficulty lies of course in the intergeneric similarity between the viverrids and felids during the period in which the felids began to evolve away from the ancestral habitus of the Oligocene epoch. A similar feline form also existed in the Oligocene genus *Stenoplesictis* according to Gregory and Hellman (1939), whilst *Tungurictis* from the Mongolian Miocene deposits had primitive, strongly shearing carnassials, but a specialized inflated bulla.

The known genera from Cenozoic deposits are indicated by *Table 32*. From a probably Eocene origin in the European region the family spread to Asia in the Oligocene and only reached Africa in the Miocene. A subsequent reduction in the number of palearctic genera took place during the climatic oscillations of the Quaternary resulted in the modern distribution which is limited to the Old World tropics.

Table 32. The viverrid genera from Cenozoic deposits (after Gregory and Hellman (1939) Romer (1945) and Simpson (1945))

	Europe	Asia	Africa	Madagascar	North America
Pleistocene	Herpestes	Paguma Herpestes	Genetta Atilax Crossarchus Herpestes Suricata Viverra	Cryptoprocta Fossa	
Pliocene	Progenetta Herpestes Viverra	Vishnuictis Viverra	Herpestes		
Miocene	Progenetta Semigenetta Leptoplesictis Viverra Herpestes Proaelurus	Tungurictis	Herpestes		
Oligocene	?Herpestes Paleoprionodon Proaelurus Stenogale Stenoplesictis ?Viverra	Amphicticeps Paleoprionodon			
Eocene	Paleoprionodon Proaelurus Stenogale Stenoplesictis				

Felidae

This family includes those genera which are the most purely carnivorous of the living Fissipedia. They are the best adapted amongst living forms for flesh eating and for hunting living ungulate, rodent or avian prey. The short face and rounded head has well-developed facial muscles. The upper molar is rudimentary and the first premolar can be lost. The carnassial surfaces are well developed and there are similar structures on the premolars.

There are some irreconcilable differences of opinion about the taxonomic status of various genera. Matthew suggested that the sabre-toothed feline line arose in or near to the genera *Nimravus—Pseudaelurus—Dinictis* which are known from the European and North American Miocene deposits. In contrast to this it has been suggested that since the genera *Nimravus* and *Pseudaelurus* are a distinct group—the nimravines—which are only distantly related within the Feloidea to the machairodontines and felines, there were in fact two waves of felines each with sabre-toothed genera. As noted above it is probable that the sabre-toothed machairodonts evolved in association with the contemporary ungulates and proboscideans in a similar way to that suggested for the sabre-toothed creodonts in the early Tertiary. In fact until recently almost all the Old World forms were gathered into a single genus which denied the degree of individual speciation which has occurred amongst these animals. Simpson (1945) attempted to rectify this and to differentiate between the well-defined groups.

Table 33. The genera of Felidae from Cenozoic deposits

	Europe	Asia	North America	Africa	South America
Pleistocene	Felis Machairodus	Felis Machairodus	Felis Smilodon Machairodus	Felis	Felis Smilodon
Pliocene	Acinonyx Epimachaerodus Felis Homotherium Machairodus Megantereon Paramachaerodus	Aeluropsis Dinofelis Epimachaerodus Felis Machaerodus Megantereon ? Mellivorodon Metailurus Paramachaerodus Propontosmilus Pseudaelurus Sansanosmilus Sivaelurus Sivasmilus ? Vinayakia Vishnufelis	Felis Ischyrosmilus Machairodus		
Miocene	Hyaenaelurus Machairodus Pseudaelurus Sansanosmilus	Hyaenaelurus Megantereon Metailurus Pseudaelurus	Archaelurus Dinaelurus Hoplophoneus Nimravus Pogonodon Pseudaelurus		
Oligocene	Alurictis Dinaelurictis Eusmilus		Dinictis Eusmilus Hoplophoneus Nimravus		
Eocene	Alurictis Eusmilus				

As in the case of other fissiped carnivores the cats flourished in late Tertiary times when they underwent a considerable amount of speciation. It can be seen in *Table 33* that from the small number of genera in the early Tertiary there is a progressive increase in the genera known from the holarctic deposits which reaches a maximum during the Pliocene. One may assume that this late Tertiary speciation was associated with the contemporaneous speciation of the herbivores. Under the influence of the changing climatic and vegetational conditions with progressively more open vegetation, the herbivores underwent an outstanding tachytelic phase prior to the extensive

Table 34. The occurrence of felids in the European Quaternary deposits (after Zeuner, 1945 and Van der Vlerk and Florschütz, 1950)

	Acinonyx elatus Brav.	Machairodus cultridens Cuv.	Machairodus latidens Owen	Machairodus meganthereon Cr. & Job.	Felis lunensis Mart.	Felis arvernensis Cr. & Job.	Felis leo-spelea Goldf.	Felis pardus L.	Felis catus L.
Tubantian							Found	Found	Found
Eemian							Found	Found	Found
Saale glaciation									
Holstein interglacial							Found		Found
Elster glaciation			?				Found	Found	Found
Cromerian interglacial			Found				Found		
Norwich Crag		?	?	?	Found				
Late Villa-franchian	Found	Found		Found	Found	Found			

extinction which resulted from the climatic deterioration of the early Quaternary glaciations. In a similar way the explosive phase of feline evolution during the late Tertiary was followed by extinction during the Quaternary. The genera persisting to the present day are largely components of the fauna of the Old World tropics. If Piveteau's suggestion that there were two waves of feline evolution, the nimravine line and the feline line *sensu stricto*, is correct, then in this late Tertiary fauna, before the climatic oscillations of the Quaternary depleted it, there were unrelated sabre-toothed forms in both lines, e.g. *Smilodon* and *Eusmilus*. The genus *Hyaenaelurus* is an aberrant Miocene form considered by Pilgrim to represent a divergent line.

As in the case of the Ursidae, Canidae and Hyaenidae amongst the carnivores, and the rhinoceroses and elephants amongst the herbivores, there was a progressive replacement of genera and species by other genera and species during the Quaternary series of climatic oscillations. These replacements are tabulated in the faunal succession of *Table 34*. It will be seen that the machairodonts may have persisted until as recently as the Cromerian interglacial or even the early part of subsequent Elster glaciation in the European area. In the faunal associations of the Late Villafranchian the cats themselves were represented by *Felis lunensis* which is not known from more recent deposits which contain *Felis catus*. The body form of *Felis arvernensis* which is also from the Late Villafranchian suggests that at that time it filled a niche which was later occupied by *Felis leo*, the large 'cave-dwelling' form of this species being known from the Cromerian interglacial together with the subsequent Hoxnian and Ipswichian interglacials. This replacement series in which the early *Acinonyx*, *Machairodus* and *Felis lunensis* are succeeded by other genera and species is also parallelled by the remains of the fossil lynxes. In the Late Villafranchian fauna of the early Pleistocene the genus *Lynx* is represented by *Lynx issiodorensis* Cr. and Job. This species, which has been recorded from the deposits of the Elster glaciation (Zeuner, 1945) is absent from more recent deposits. During the last or Eemian interglacial it was replaced by *Lyns* cf. *pardus* and *Lynx lynx* which has persisted through Tubantian and Post-glacial times up to the present day.

Hyaenidae

The relationship between the Hyaenidae and the Viverridae is comparable to that which exists between the Ursidae and Canidae. The hyaenas are a late off-shoot of the viverrid/feloid stem (*Table 36*) and the intermediate condition is suggested by genera such as *Ictitherium* in a similar way to the suggestion of the canid/ursid transition by *Hyaenarctos*. This hyaena *Ictitherium* was in fact classified as a viverrid by Dietrich, Schlosser and Zdansky. In a comparable way the genus *Proteles* also appears to be intermediate between the two families, but the work of several authors, which was reviewed by Simpson (1945), suggests that it is probably best considered an hyaena.

In their typical form these carnivores have a reduced dentition and compare in this character with the hyaenoid-like genera amongst the early Tertiary creodonts, *Sarkastodon* in the Oxyaenidae and *Quercytherium* amongst the Hyaenodontinae, and amongst the Late Tertiary canids—e.g. the Borophaginae. The large head and sturdy body is carried on long digitigrade legs and in the skull the alisphenoid canal is lost. At the present time

123

these animals are restricted in their geographical distribution to the Old World. In the fossil record the family appears in Europe in the Pliocene and in Asia in the Upper Miocene. The genus *Ictitherium* which was discussed

Table 35. The characters of the modern hyaenids

Hyaena	Crocuta
1. Occiput low	1. Occiput high
2. Braincase restricted	2. Braincase expanded
3. Bulla strongly inflated	3. Bulla less inflated
4. Premolars slender	4. Premolars robust
5. Carnassial shears short	5. Carnassial shears long
6. P^4 protocone small	6. P^4 protocone large
7. M^1 present	7. M^1 absent
8. A metaconid on M_1	8. No metaconid on M_1
9. Talonid large and basined	9. Talonid small and trenchant

above has a dentition which is closely comparable with that of the Middle Miocene viverrid genus *Progenetta*. Characters which occur in the hyaenas in the strict sense and this somewhat controversial form *Ictitherium*, occur in the genus *Hyaenictis* from the European Pliocene deposits.

The modern hyaenas are in fact separated into two genera and, as was the case in the canids and ursids, there are late Tertiary species which combine the characters of both these genera. These combinations can be most easily understood by outlining the characters of the modern genera as in *Table 35*.

Table 36. The genera of Hyaenidae from the Cenozoic deposits of the world

	Asia	Europe	Africa
Pleistocene	Crocuta Hyaena Hyaenictis	Crocuta Hyaena	Hyaena
Pliocene	Hyaena Ictitherium Lycyaena	Hyaena Hyaenictis Ictitherium Lycyaena Crocuta	
Miocene	Crocuta		

The species *Crocuta tungurensis* which occurs in the Wolf-camp quarry site of the Tung Gur formations of the Mongolian Miocene was a large robust form with the typical short facial region. It was predominantly a *Crocuta* and named as such, but the protocone of the fourth upper premolar was small—a *Hyaena* character. Similar considerations apply to the two *Hyaena* species *Hyaena variabilis* and *Hyaena eximia* which also show intergeneric similarities but are classed in the one genus on the result of the overall combination of characters but more especially because of the hyaenoid auditory bulla.

In *Table 37* are grouped the fossils which are known from the European Quaternary sites. Once again there occurs the typical pattern in which an early species *Hyaena arvernensis* is replaced by another, *Hyaena crocuta*, in more recent deposits, and at the same time the family is reduced from a widespread distribution in Europe and Asia during the Pliocene and early Quaternary to its restricted distribution in the Old World tropics at the present time.

Table 37. The occurrence of hyaena remains in European Quaternary deposits (after Zeuner, 1945)

	Hyaena perrieri Cr. et Job.	*Hyaena arvernensis* Cr. et Job.	*Hyaena hyaena cf. intermedia*	*Hyaena hyaena antiqua* Lank.	*Hyaena crocuta spelea* Goldf.
Tubantian					
Eemian interglacial					Found
Saale glaciation					Found
Holstein interglacial					
Elster glaciation		Found		Found	?
Cromerian interglacial			Found		
Tiglian Clay	Found				
Late Villafranchian	Found	Found			

8

CONDYLARTHRA AND SOUTH AMERICAN UNGULATES

CONDYLARTHRA

As noted in Chapter 7, these forms, together with their descendants, are considered to have a common ancestry with the carnivores. Actually the protoungulates were very similar to the Procreodi amongst the early Paleocene carnivores, and both carnivores and ungulates are united in the cohort Ferungulata by modern taxonomists.

Some of the condylarthran genera had retained the plantigrade gait of the ancestral insectivores. Although the dentition always exhibited at least some bunodont tendencies it was in fact very similar to that of the Procreodi. The order was restricted to the Paleocene and Eocene and during the latter period was gradually replaced by the hippomorph and tapiromorph Perissodactyla, the paleodont Artiodactyla and the ischyromyid rodents in the Old World and nearctic region. In the neotropical region which was isolated from the nearctic region in Eocene time it was further replaced by an elaborate series of forms relegated to the endemic Notoungulata, Litopterna, Pyrotheria and Astrapotheria. Taxonomic difficulties arise when considering these early placentals and the genus *Protogonodon* has been variously ascribed to both the creodont carnivores and the condylarthran ungulates. Matthew (1937) suggested that there is no satisfactory method of separating all condylarthran from all creodont genera and similar difficulties are involved in the taxonomy of the subsequent ungulate forms of late Eocene age.

Some of the hyopsodontid condylarthra are very similar to the early artiodactylous genera and some of the phenacodontids are like the contemporary perissodactylous genera. The didolodonts are similarly close to the Litopterna of South America, whilst early amblypods are differentiated from their condylarthran ancestors only on the grounds that the latter were never, by definition, gravigrade.

Throughout all these herbivorous ungulates there is a tendency to modify the dentition to produce molars suitable for grinding the vegetable food. This results in a progressive fusion of the cusps on ancestral tuberculosectorial molars to produce either the lophodont dentition comprising an ectoloph, protoloph and metaloph, or alternatively to produce the analogous crescents of the selenodont dentition in the Camelidae. The production of the lophodont molars and premolars has taken place along several independent lines to produce a similar result. A summary of these ancestral bunodont condylarthran ungulates may be obtained in Ameghino (1936), Granger (1915), Gazin (1941), Lavocat (1955), Matthew (1937), Simpson (1937, 1945) and Chardin (1922). The best known genus is undoubtedly *Phenacodus* which occurs in deposits of Lower Eocene age in both Europe and North America. There was a variation in size but specimens often reached the size of a tapir although in superficial appearance the animal resembles a carnivore more than an ungulate. The fore and hind limbs were pentadactyl and short whilst the tail was long. Both hind limb and fore limb seem to have been about the same size and there was virtually no elongation of the metapodials. In fact the third toe was elongated so that although pentadactyl the foot was functionally mesaxonic. The clavicle had already disappeared and as in the mesonychid creodonts the digits seem to have borne hooves.

Forms similar to *Phenacodus* seem to have been widespread during the early Tertiary period and their evolution during the Paleocene and Eocene periods, together with the replacement by more advanced forms at the end of the Eocene, is probably associated with, and may have actually resulted in, the comparable evolution of the carnivores. The forms of the herbivores were probably adapted both to the changing vegetational conditions which led to the jungles of the Eocene London Clay and Goshen deposits, and also to the subsequent reduction in the arboreal genera of plants leading to the parkland of later Cenozoic times. Although only the former climatic and vegetational change affected the Condylarthra themselves it is interesting that amongst the carnivorous fauna there are predominantly Procreodi in the Paleocene but Acreodi and Pseudocreodi in the Eocene.

During the Paleocene the genera *Pleuraspidotherium*, *Orthaspidotherium* and perhaps the equivocal *Tricuspidion* occurred in Europe. However, the main habitat of the Paleocene Condylarthra was without doubt in North America. In that region there were some 30 genera although this number had been considerably reduced by the time that the hippomorph and tapiromorph perissodactyls appeared in the Eocene. By this time the invasion of the neotropical region resulted in the presence there of the endemic genera *Ernestokokenia* and Couto's *Lamegoia*. It is probable that they are in fact the ancestral forms from which the six South American Eocene genera evolved. Although, generally speaking, all these genera became extinct with the appearance of the later ungulates and carnivores, certain conservative forms persisted for a considerable period of time. *Didolodus* noted above as close to the basal genera of the Litopterna was still present in South America during the Miocene. It is perhaps significant that creodont carnivores are absent from the South American fauna. Instead the carnivores were the endemic borhyaenid marsupials which in many cases may not have been so markedly specialized, judging by their rapid extinction when the placental carnivores entered the region in the Pliocene.

In this assemblage of condylarthran genera there seems to have been a considerable degree of morphological variation. The genus *Hyopsodus*, and the perhaps related *Asmithwoodwardia*, although having a dentition which suggests a comparison with the Eocene artiodactyl genus *Diacodexis*, were similar in size to the modern hedgehogs. The Didolodontidae have been the subject of a controversy comparable with that which has occurred over the taxonomy of the Litopterna. Ameghino (1904, 1906) referred 2 genera from the Casamayoran deposits to this family. Roth (1927) placed them in the Didolodia and opposed any Litoptern relationships. Scott (1913) called them condylarthra-like but placed them in the Litopterna. The fact that Winge placed them in the Macraucheniidae (see below) suggests that he opposed their condylarthran status.

LITOPTERNA

This is a family of South American ungulates which, like the Notoungulates, Astrapotheres and Pyrotheres, evolved from the condylarthran genera which invaded the neotropical region in the early Paleocene, or perhaps the Late Cretaceous (Paulo Couto, 1952). From this early origin the family flourished alongside the Hyopsodontidae and the perhaps ancestral Didolodontidae. Indeed, as in the case of the other ungulates, the Litopterna are nothing more than advanced and highly specialized condylarthrans. There has been a good deal of confusion as to their exact relationships. Ameghino (1904–1906) ascribed them to the Perissodactyla. This view, negated by Scott (1910), has not been reiterated by any future workers. Most subsequent workers have agreed that they are closely related to both the condylarthran didolodontids and also the Notoungulata. Simpson (1945), accepting these relations, places both the litopterns and the other South American ungulates together with the Condylarthra. The family persisted until Pliocene and Pleistocene times in Argentina where they occur in the Pampean Beds. However, the most well-known remains are in the Middle Miocene Beds of Santa Cruz, although the early Tertiary Rio Chico and Deseado formations contain a large and somewhat heterogeneous group of probable Litopterns of very primitive especially condylarthran appearance.

All the genera are usually grouped into the two families Proterotheriidae and Macraucheniidae, a grouping which is followed by Simpson (1945) and the *Traité de Zoologie*. The early forms of both families have a complete dentition with brachyodont molars and a cranium which is similar to that of the Condylarthra *sensu stricto*. During the period in which they flourished there was a considerable development of a digitigrade gait with elongated limbs and a reduced number of digits. This evolution, comparable with that of the Perissodactyla, was also accompanied by morphological variation suggesting divergent evolution to fill the available ecological niches.

PROTEROTHERIIDAE

Within the Proterotheriidae the genus *Diadiaphorus*, which occurred during the Miocene and Pliocene, was rather like the tapiroid genera of the perissodactyls. It had a small head with a marked sagittal crest and a short facial region. The forelegs were tridactylous but owing to the relative length of the digits were functionally mesodactylous. In the dentition there was a single upper caniniform incisor on each side and the absence of the true canines resulted in a diastema in front of the first premolar. There was an increase in the size of the crown of the last premolars and the molars resemble those of the early artiodactyls.

In the related *Proterotherium*, which is also of Miocene and Pliocene age, the increased size of the nasal bones resulted in a longer facial region and a corresponding increase in the length of the limbs suggests a more equid-like gait than that of *Diadiaphorus*. However it is in the Miocene genus *Thoatherium* that this increase in limb length was carried to its extreme. This genus was completely monodactylous and the splints were much more reduced than in the modern equids although the carpus and tarsus retained some primitive characteristics.

MACRAUCHENIIDAE

Remains of the other litoptern family, the Macraucheniidae, are found in the Paleocene. They are however best known from the Patagonian Miocene and persisted until the time of deposition of the Pampean Beds of the Upper Pliocene in Argentina. The Paleocene remains ascribed to the genus *Victorlemoinea* were thus the contemporaries of the Proterotheriid genera *Wainkia*, *Josepholeidya* and *Riccardolydekkeria* as well as the condylarthran genera *Ernestokokenia* and Couto's *Lamegoia*. During the Eocene and Oligocene periods there was a considerable flowering of the genera to give such forms as *Amilnedwardsia*, *Ernestohaeckelia*, *Lambdoconus*, and *Rutimeyeria* in the Eocene deposits and *Cramauchenia Notodiaphorus*, *Proadianthus* and *Proheptoconus* in the Oligocene deposits.

The remains of the genus *Theosodon* from the Upper Oligocene and Miocene suggest that it was an animal with the proportions of a llama. There was a long neck which carried a narrow head on which the nasalia were very short. The dentition was complete, showed very little heterogeneity, and was largely brachydont. These characters exhibited by *Theosodon* were carried to a further stage in its contemporary, the genus *Scalibrinitherium*. This latter creature seems to have persisted, along with forms like *Proterotherium* and *Diadiaphorus* amongst the Proterotheriidae, into the Pliocene. The shortening of the nasalia which gave *Theosodon* its peculiar appearance resulted, in *Scalibrinitherium*, in the nostrils being placed right back at the rear of the facial region. This condition reached its apogee in the type genus *Macrauchenia* which had long limbs, a short neck and therefore a rather ungainly appearance to our eyes. In this animal the position of the nostrils was high up on top of the cranium due to the extreme foreshortening of the nasal bones. Various explanations have been put forward to explain this unusual evolution but whether the animals lived almost totally submerged under water, or, like the Pyrotheria and Astrapotheria mentioned below, had probosces compensating for short necks it is impossible to decide.

NOTOUNGULATA

The principal and most abundant ungulates represented within the Cenozoic deposits of South America are grouped together in this order. It has the distinction of having been collected by Darwin on his *Voyage of the Beagle*, and the genus *Toxodon* which was discovered by him was actually described by Owen in 1840. Although they occurred in the neotropical region from the Paleocene to Pleistocene they are also known from Asia in the Paleocene and from North America in the Eocene. Lyddeker (1894) placed the genera which were then known into the four families Pachyrucidae, Typotheriidae, Toxodontidae and Homalodotheriidae. The first three of these families he grouped together as the Toxodontia and the last he associated with the Astrapotheria. When Ameghino (1906) came to consider them he failed to appreciate the homogeneity of all the forms involved although there was a far larger number of specimens available to him than to Lydekker. As a result he ascribed them to several holarctic families. In fact the principal characters which they have in common lie in the tympanic bulla and the auditory region. This last was considerably dilated by a gigantic enlargement of the tympanic bone and had a very large epitympanic sinus. The skull was generally short and flattened above and had heavy zygomatic arches. The dentition, which was brachyodont in the early forms, shows many lines along which there is a progressive development of lophodont molars, and in many genera the presence of accessory cusps on the molars achieves a similar result. The large size of some Toxodontidae, the Isotemnidae and Homalodotheriidae, which was comparable to that of the amblypods and Dinocerata in the holarctic region, suggests a mode of life comparable with that of the living pachyderms. On the contrary the relatively primitive Notostylopidae which occurred during the Eocene were similar in size to, and probably had the habits of, the rodents.

The basic descriptions of all the genera and species are contained in the collected works of Ameghino (1913–1936) although, of course, this author distributed them amongst a number of holarctic families. Further works which provide a summary of our knowledge of these still only incompletely understood animals are those of Cabrera (1939), Kraglievich (1934), Patterson (1932, 1934a, 1934b, 1936, 1937), Roth (1903), Scott (1913; 1937a), Simpson (1933a, 1933b, 1934, 1935, 1948) and Sinclair (1909).

The early genera which are known only from Mongolia during the Paleocene and North America during the Eocene are grouped together in the family Arctostylopidae. The most primitive forms of the South American notoungulates are the Henricosborniidae. These occur in the Riochican and Casamayoran. None occur in the Musters or later formations and Simpson suggests that even in the Riochican they are conservative survivors rather than actual ancestors.

Groups which were less divergent in the Eocene than in the Miocene seem to be near the base of the notoungulate line. Of the 13 families 9 occur in the Casamayoran and/or the Musters. 5 occur in the Santa Cruz Beds and are namely the Homalodotheriidae, Toxodontidae, Interatheriidae, Mesotheriidae and Hegetotheriidae. Only the Toxodontidae, Mesotheriidae and Hegetotheriidae survived until the end of the Tertiary. Each of these was represented by fairly stereotyped genera by the Pliocene, and during the Pleistocene were reduced to one or two closely related genera.

At their peak during the Eocene and the Oligocene not only were there many genera and species within the various families but the actual populations comprised a wide variety of forms. These highly variable populations result in a very intricate assemblage of species and genera and it is only really in the Miocene that they are replaced by the clearly defined lines which characterize the various families.

PRIMITIVE NOTOUNGULATES

The molar structure of the primitive Henricosborniidae is very reminiscent of that of small condylarthran genera such as *Asmithwoodwardia*. Really the only essential difference lies in the rather more lophodont dentition, a change which, as noted above, occurs along several lines of the ungulate herbivores.

The Paleocene Arctostylopidae are quite clearly more advanced than the South American Henricosborniidae in this respect, the teeth in the two genera *Paleostylops* and *Arctostylops* having a more lophodont trend and a trigonid specialization which is absent in the South American genera. The Henricosborniidae are themselves similar to the other early family the Notostylopidae but lack the definite metacone fold and the more pronounced separation of the protocone and hypocone.

The present views about the three genera *Henricosbornia*, *Othnielmarshia* and *Peripantostylops* which comprise the family Henricosborniidae are the result of the study of a relatively large population of animals recovered from a single horizon at Canadon Vaça. These specimens which were collected by Simpson and Williams comprise 2 associated upper and lower jaws, 7 lower jaws and about 100 molars. The results of the biometrical studies made on these specimens enabled Simpson to distinguish between the 3 genera of the family originally described by Ameghino (1906) but confused by that author with several non-valid species.

The upper and lower dentition of the genus *Paleostylops*, occurring as they do in the Paleocene deposits of eastern Asia, suggest that at that time the Notioprogonia, which comprises the three primitive families Arctostylopidae, Henricosborniidae and Notostylopidae, either:

(1) Had a widespread distribution with the henricosbornids in South America and *Paleostylops* in Asia;

(2) Originated in Asia or elsewhere in the Holarctic region and spread from there to South America where they subsequently became isolated; or

(3) That the opposite is true and these animals having originated in the neotropical region later spread north to the holarctic region where the later evolution of holarctic genera resulted in their extinction.

In the absence of definitive early material from one region only it is clearly impossible to differentiate between these three alternatives.

The Lower Eocene genus *Notostylops* is quite the best known of the complete notoungulate fauna. It had in general terms a similar anatomy to that of the rodents and as the result of the study of endocranial casts it is clear that this similarity extended to the relative proportions of the brain. As the Arctostylopidae, Henricosborniidae and Notostylopidae are absent from deposits of Oligocene or Miocene age it seems probable that they were replaced by the Typotheria and Hegetotheria in an analogous manner to the replacement which took place in the other ungulate lines in the holarctic region.

TYPOTHERIA

These small mammals are grouped together on the basis of the auditory bulla which was only incompletely separated into a tympanic cavity and epitympanic sinus. This last named structure was filled with spongy tissue. As noted above the habits, size and brain seem to have been similar to those of the rodents and also to the more primitive Notioprogonia. Although they became separated off at a fairly early day the two families Interatheriidae and Mesotheriidae of Simpson (1945) are therefore naturally associated together. However this is not the case with the Hegetotheriidae considered below. The typothere-like appearance of these latter seems to be only a superficial similarity resulting from analogous habits, a fact that is also true of other lines of notoungulates (Patterson, 1936).

The absence of roots to the incisors in certain genera has resulted in the erection by many authors of the two families Typotheriidae and Interatheriidae without and with roots respectively. These are families which seem to have evolved from the Eocene genera *Notopithecus* and *Transpithecus*, and to have persisted until the Oligocene and Miocene. With the exception

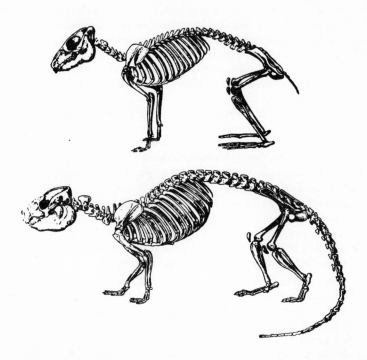

Figure 21. Skeletons of (*top*) the hegetothere Pachyrukhos moyani *Ameg and* (*bottom*) the Miocene typothere Interatherium robustum *Ameg. Both from the Santa Cruz formation (after Scott, from Lavocat, 1955)*

of the genus *Protypotherium* the Interatheriidae did not persist beyond that date but the Typotheriidae continued to be represented in the Pliocene by *Pseudotypotherium*, *Typotheriopsis* and also others. Even during the Quaternary period they were still represented by *Bravardia*, *Typotheriodon* and *Typotherium*.

During this relatively long temporal distribution the body form and presumably the habits as well, underwent a number of variations comparable to those of the rodents. The Miocene genus *Interatherium*, one species of which is represented in *Figure 21*, was partially digitigrade. This trend was carried further in *Protypotherium* which had a lighter body and was higher on the legs. Both these genera therefore contrasted with the Pliocene and early Pleistocene genus *Typotherium* which although having hypsodont and rootless cheek teeth and incisors which were comparable with those of rodents was the size of a bear.

HEGETOTHERIA

Although similar in anatomy and probably therefore also in ecology to the Typotheria, the similarities of this sub-order to the last one are apparently superficial. Each succeeding author who has investigated them has produced results which emphasize the sharp separation of the hegetotheres from both the typotheres and toxodonts. For this reason Simpson classed them as a separate evolutionary line and in his review of mammalian classification erected the new sub-order to contain them.

They existed alongside the Typotheria during the period of the Eocene and Oligocene and the principal anatomical differentiation of the genera lies in a vertical separation of the tympanic cavity from a hypotympanic sinus. The early Eocene forms all comprise such genera as *Eohegetotherium* and *Eopachyrukos* and are replaced in deposits of Oligocene age by others such as *Prohegetotherium* and *Propachyrukos*. The later genera seem to have persisted for a rather longer period and both *Pachyrukos* and *Hegetotherium* which appear for the first time in the Upper Oligocene existed well into the Miocene. The actual chronology of the Pliocene and Quaternary deposits of South America is still not clearly defined but the pachyrukine genus *Paedotherium* seems to have survived the initial invasion of the region by fissiped carnivores and advanced holarctic ungulates to occur during the early Pleistocene period. The typical form of these pachyrukids is similar to that of the lagomorphs and it is probable that both *Pachyrukos* and *Hegetotherium* were saltatorial and filled the ecological niche of these glirids and were replaced by these latter animals during the Quaternary.

TOXODONTA

The families Toxodontidae, Isotemnidae, Leontiniidae and Homalodotheriidae are all similar to one another in several respects. They are generally of large size and characterized in the auditory region by a large hypotympanic sinus separated by a horizontal partition from the tympanic cavity. Owing to a gap in the knowledge of the early faunas the ancestry of these Toxodonts is not clearly known. There are several families of the Eocene notoungulate fauna which have structural similarities to the later true Toxodonts. However the relationships of these animals, the Oldfieldthomasidae, Archeopithecidae and Archeohyracidae to the later forms cannot be precisely stated. This inadequacy of the available information is due to the absence of any faunal remains which are intermediate in age between the Eocene Musters formation and the Oligocene Deseado fauna.

The Lower Eocene *Thomashuxleya* is a sufficiently primitive form for it to be suggested as a possible ancestor of the group. From some such ancestral form evolved the later families and these show several groups of relationships, Both the Isotemnidae and the Homalodotheriidae are sometimes removed and grouped together as the Entylonychia. They are aberrant and very specialized forms which, like the Chalicotheres amongst the Perissodactyla, had claws instead of hoofs. The limbs of the type genus *Homalodotherium* were also disproportionate in size so that although the forelimbs were digitigrade and long the hind ones retained a plantigrade form and were short. The Isotemnidae seem to have been a heterogeneous assemblage and persisted

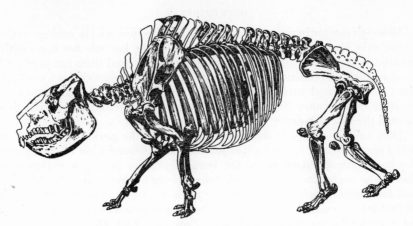

Figure 22. The skeleton of the Miocene toxodont Nesodon imbricatus Owen (after Scott, from Lavocat, 1955) Original ca. 7 ft. long

from the Paleocene, e.g. *Isotemnus* and *Eochalicotherium*, to the Upper Eocene— *Rhyphodon* and the Lower Oligocene—*Pleurocoelodon*. As the name of the genus

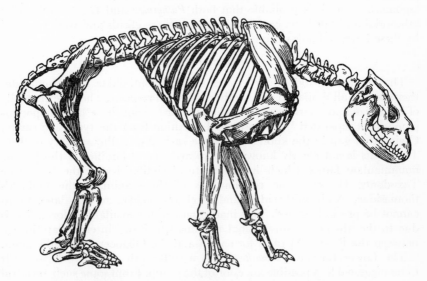

Figure 23. The skeleton of Homalodotherium (after Scott, from Lavocat, 1955) Original ca. 6 ft. long

Eochalicotherium suggests, several authors have been struck by the similarity of some of these animals to the chalicotheres, and Romer (1945) has suggested that they may have had comparable and perhaps root-digging habits.

134

As the result of the work of Patterson (1936) it is clear that the Leontiniidae are related to the other Toxodonta on the basis of tympanic structure. However, the precise inter-relationships are not clear. They comprise four genera of Oligocene age *Ancylocoelus*, *Leontinia*, *Scarrittia* and *Colpodon* best considered as a related and parallel evolutionary group. Although all these genera were of large size *Toxodon* of the Pleistocene was truly gravigrade and probably simulated the living pachyderms.

ASTRAPOTHERIA

Besides the toxodontids there were other genera which attained a large size in South America during the early Tertiary. The astrapotheres differ from the Notoungulates principally in the presence of a normal auditory region and the absence of an epitympanic sinus. Derived from the early condylarthran fauna which also gave rise to the Notoungulates it seems probable that this group, together with the Litopterna, are more directly related to the Condylarthra than are the Notoungulate genera.

All the astrapothere genera were originally considered by Ameghino to be South American Amblypoda, a fact which emphasizes the size and appearance of these animals. However, this concept has since been abandoned in favour of the relationships outlined above. Although Scott (1928) drew attention to similarities with the Notoungulates, these are probably also the result of convergent evolution. Lavocat (1955) includes together the two differing groups represented by the Trigonostylopidae, with simple incisors and a large tympanic bone, and the Astrapotheriidae with bilobed incisors and a small tympanic bone. The information available concerning the anatomy of *Trigonostylops* was very much increased by the work of Simpson (1933a) and this emphasizes that although both groups have a common condylarth or Litoptern-like ancestry, they are evolutionary lines which have remained separate from a rather early date.

The Eocene genus *Trigonostylops* is really rather peculiar. The neurocranium was low, elongated and armed with a sagittal crest, the palatine region had an unusual structure and there were tusks.

The contemporary astrapotheriid genera *Albertogaudrya* and *Astraponotus* are known only by their dentition. However it is probably from these forms that the enormous Miocene species *Astrapotherium magnum* Burn. of the Santa Cruz Beds evolved. In this animal the cranium was elongated and had a short high sagittal crest. The orbit was small and incompletely closed posteriorly but placed well forward on the facial region. The occipital region was narrow and since the nasalia were extremely short it is probable that like the Macraucheniidae amongst the Litopterns, and also the Pyrotheres, there was a prehensile proboscis. Indeed the forelimb had also a superficial resemblance to that of both the elephants and *Uintatherium*, whilst the absence of upper incisors and the presence of markedly developed canines in the form of tusks, enhance this similarity. The length of these large Miocene animals exceeded 2·8 metres and in height they were about 1·4 metres. In fact during the Oligocene and Miocene there were five principal genera of similar appearance, *Parastrapotherium*, *Astrapotherium*, *Astrapothericulus*, *Uruguaytherium* and *Xenastrapotherium* (Kraglievich, 1928a; Paulo Couto, 1952; Scott, 1937; Riggs, 1935; Simpson, 1933a, 1934).

PYROTHERIA

The exact relationships of the four genera *Carodnia, Propyrotherium, Pyrotherium* and *Griphodon* are not accurately known. *Carodnia* has been removed by Couto, *Propyrotherium* is of Upper Eocene and *Pyrotherium* of Lower Oligocene age. *Griphodon,* which occurs in undated deposits in Peru, is of equivocal age but probably comparable to these other early Tertiary genera.

Together the four genera form the smallest although one of the most distinctive and isolated orders of the mammals. Although it has a wide range,

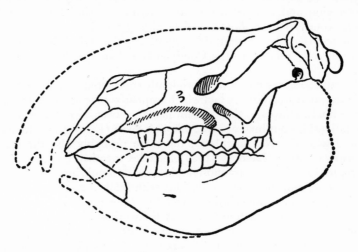

Figure 24. The skull of Pyrotherium *(after Lavocat, 1955)*
Original ca. 2 ft. long

occurring in sites over a considerable area of South America, the actual number of specimens is never great. The principal works relating to the order are those of Ameghino (1902c), Anthony (1924), Gaudry (1906), Loomis (1914), Patterson (1942) and Simpson (1945).

The type genus *Pyrotherium* which occurs in the Patagonian Oligocene deposits is a very large animal with a gravigrade form. The head is long and narrow and as in the Astrapotheres and *Macrauchenia* the fact that the nasal bones are abruptly shortened suggests that in life there was a prehensile proboscis. This last suggestion is given extra probability in these particular forms as the nostrils although far back on the face are disposed vertically. There were short stout tusks and the molars were markedly bilophodont and separated from the anterior teeth by a well-defined diastema. The occurrence of primitive forms of uncertain but probably pyrotherioid relationships in South American Paleocene deposits suggest that these forms evolved from bunodont ancestors in South America and that their considerable similarities to the proboscideans are simply the result of convergent evolution.

136

9

ARTIODACTYLA

Following de Blainville (1816) the even-toed ungulates are distinguished from both tapiromorph and hippomorph perissodactyls (Chapter 10) by the fact that the axis of the limbs passes through digits three and four. Linneus, together with all subsequent workers, recognized the homogeneity of the ruminant groups, and classed both the Cameliformes and Boviformes as Pecora (Ruminantia of other authors). However, Linneus considered that the pigs were not related to these forms and it was de Blainville (1816) who first ascribed these animals to the taxa which are broadly recognized today. Once these inter-relationships were established it was clear that amongst the modern forms the taxonomic problems were relatively small. Since the time of these taxonomists the discovery of many fossil forms has tremendously complicated the group. Most fossils can certainly be ascribed to sub-orders originally based on modern forms, but they greatly increase the number of families and also render it extremely difficult to draw distinct boundaries between groups that would be well defined on the basis of modern forms. Other fossils do not conform to the definitions of any of the classical taxa of de Blainville. As a result of this situation there are several irreconcilable differences of opinion which prevent any system of artiodactyl classification being universally accepted (Simpson, 1945). The principal taxonomic works dealing with the group were reviewed by Simpson (1945) together with those of all other Mammalia. The most notable earlier workers were Matthew (1929), Osborn (1910) and Scott (1940).

As stated above, the axis of the limbs passes through digits three and four in modern forms. This is accompanied by a reduction in size of the lateral metapodials, which are, however, still represented externally. The principal skeletal element of the forelimb is the radius, and in all modern forms, with the exception of the camels, the limbs are unguligrade. In the camels, which have progressed a long way from the ancestral plantigrade condition, the limbs are in fact still digitigrade. This is probably an adaptation to desert life. The cranium is elongated and the orbit is separated from the temporal fossa to form a complete ring. However, the outstanding pecoran character is the possession of horns. The order comprises several evolutionary lines considered to be ascribable to two sub-orders by Simpson (1945).

In the primitive early Tertiary fossil forms there is a complete dentition which includes normal incisors and large carnivore-like canines. Even as early as the Eocene, however, forms occurred which already possessed such typical artiodactyl characters as the double-pulleyed astragalus. These genera, with their bunodont molar dentition, have given rise to several lines of evolution. Progressive modifications resulted in large plains-dwelling, grass-eating herbivores in the late Tertiary and Quaternary periods. The upper incisors are often lost and, in contrast to the conditions which exist in most mammals, the postero-internal molar cusp is not the hypocone but the metaconule. The Artiodactyla are probably best considered as comprising the two sub-orders of Simpson (1945). In this classification the Suiformes are contrasted with the ruminant artiodactyls from which they differ in not regurgitating their food. The stomach in both sub-orders however comprises several regions.

SUIFORMES

The animals included in this sub-order have been recognized as related for a considerable period of time. Except perhaps for the oreodonts, there is little doubt that they have a common origin. The earliest Paleodonta approximate to the generalized artiodactyl form expected in the common ancestor of all fossil and living genera. On the contrary, the later Paleodonta, the Suina, and the Ancodonta, represent three major lines of specialization from this early Eocene and Oligocene origin. By the Miocene at the latest they are found to comprise distinct assemblages, but the earlier genera are difficult to separate. This difficulty is shared by the genera of other major placental orders during the early Tertiary tachytelic phase of mammalian evolution. The major works in connection with the Suiformes are those of Osborn (1910), Scott (1937a), Weber (1928) and the *Traité de Zoologie*.

PALEODONTS

As implied in the previous paragraph, the Suiformes underwent an early tachytelic evolutionary phase during the Eocene and Oligocene periods which is comparable with that of the tetradactyl hippomorphs. These early forms are classed in several discrete families. Some of these families appear to be close to the evolutionary line of the later Suiformes, whilst others are probably abortive evolutionary lines. The extinction of these early forms may be the result of the more advanced forms of later periods supplanting them, the later carnivores preying on them, or their inability to withstand the successive climatic oscillations, as suggested by van der Hammen (1957; 1961) (Chapter 6). The earliest of them were in fact closely comparable with many other early placentals. They had a complete dentition with no diastema and, although the molars had blunt cusps, they were not so markedly bunodont as later forms.

Amongst the European genera of the family Dichobunidae, the facial region was comparable in size to the cranial region and the muzzle was very narrow anteriorly. In fact the plan of the basicranial region was very similar to that of the creodont carnivores. In the lower jaw the tubercles of the molars were conical and in the absence of the artiodactyl-like double pulleyed astragalus would suggest affinities with the primate, creodont or insectivore stocks. The American genera of the family are perhaps more closely allied to the artiodactyl line. Several other groups of primitive forms also occurred at this early Tertiary period. The Choeropotamidae had a long muzzle, a long vertical canine in the upper jaw and a caniniform first premolar in the lower jaw. The Cebochoeridae of somewhat doubtful relationships, had, on the contrary, incisiform canines and the complete dentition was retained in a truncate muzzle. An even more characteristic group, the Leptochoeridae, which occur in the Oligocene deposits of North America, retained the primitive trituberculate pattern on the upper molars. These families are removed from the paleodonts in some more recent classifications (notably Colbert, 1938a) but for a complete review of the group it is necessary to assess the results of several authors (cf. Simpson, 1945).

ENTELODONTS

As noted above there were several lines of evolution amongst the early Tertiary Suiformes. The genera of most uncertain lineage are those of the Achaenodontinae and Entelodontinae. Simpson placed them in a separate super-family of the paleodonts but despite many studies there is still no satisfactory basis for their classification (Colbert, 1938a). The factors commonly considered are the relative development of the jaw, the jugal bones and

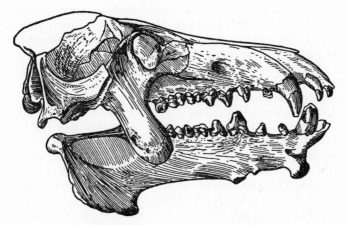

Figure 25. The skull of the North American Oligocene entelodont Archeotherium marshi *Trox. to show the pendant apophysis of the upper jaw (after Troxell, from Lavocat, 1955) Original size ca. 1½ ft.*

their processes. As Simpson (1945) pointed out, these are subject to a considerable amount of variation which may be, at least in part, sexual. In any case of questionable validity for the definition of a species, Matthew (1934) has suggested that many of the types may be relegated to a single variable genus. Obviously this is a question of definition.

The representatives of the two sub-families flourished during the Upper Eocene and the Oligocene periods. It is possible that an incomplete dentition known from the Lower Eocene deposits of Mongolia is also ascribable to an entelodont. The known genera were rather variable in size, and *Achaenodon* of the Upper Eocene of North America was very similar to, and only slightly lighter than, a hippopotamus. The massive jaws were armed with well developed canines, and the body was carried on short tetradactyl limbs. In contrast, the Entelodontinae, which also had crania and skeletons comparable in size with those of modern hippopotamuses, had slim elongated limbs. In these the radius and cubitus were ossified together, the peroneus was free, and the hands were didactylous with short digits. In the skull, the proportions were again variable. The genus *Archeotherium*, which persisted through both

139

Lower and Upper Oligocene periods in North America, had a post-orbital region which was short by contrast to the facial region. It seems, therefore, to have had a relatively small brain, and cranial casts reveal that the large olfactory lobes and the cerebellum were not covered by the cerebral hemispheres. However, the most outstanding characteristic of the skull was the presence of a large flat apophysis which hung down from its source on the upper jaw to the level of the bottom of the lower jaw. In view of the heavily built body combined with the lithe limbs it has been suggested that they were semi-aquatic in life.

SUINA

During the Oligocene there also occurred forms which are exactly comparable with our modern pigs and peccaries. The bunodont dentition comprised molars, which were often armed with accessory tubercles, and well developed canines. It is probable that, even at an early stage in their evolution, the suids were becoming divided into lines. Of these, one probably stems from genera similar to the European *Doliochoerus* and the American *Perchoerus*, and leads to the New World peccaries (Pearson, 1927). The other, originating from forms similar to *Paleochoerus* of the European Lower and Middle Miocene, leads to the pigs. All these fossils have been reviewed by Colbert (1935), Pearson (1927, 1928), Pilgrim (1926) and Stehlin (1900).

The European *Paleochoerus* had a rather short face and the basicranial region retained a slight angle with the palate. The cranium bore a sagittal crest. The dentition was complete with no marked diastema, and alongside these primitive generalized characters there were similarly primitive tetradactylous limbs. The genus occurred with similar but perhaps descendant forms of larger size, for example *Hyotherium*. Also in Miocene times *Listriodon* developed defensive canines, comparable to those of the wart hogs.

The other group of genera, at the base of the Tayassuidae, were similar to *Paleochoerus*. In the genus *Hesperhys*, from the North American Miocene deposits, there is an incipient molarization of the premolars. This condition was carried further in *Prosthenops*, and in *Milohyus* resulted in a secondarily homodont dentition in which the premolars and molars compare with those of the horses in the Perissodactyla.

CAENOTHERES

During the period from the Upper Eocene to Lower Miocene in which these various suid lines were flourishing, there were also a number of other lines whose relationships are not clearly understood. These side lines exhibit primitive characters and have been ascribed to both suid and tylopod assemblages. The caenotheres were reviewed in considerable detail by Hürzeler (1936) who concluded that there were 6 valid genera, although in the case of *Procaenotherium*, from the Lower Oligocene of Europe, and the later *Caenotherium*, from the Middle Oligocene and Lower Miocene periods of Europe, the distinctions are relatively slight.

Simpson (1945), probably influenced by Matthew, included these forms within an infra-order which contained the anthracotheres, anoplotheres and hippopotamuses. Grassé suggests that this is perhaps not warranted, and that these animals should be considered as separate units possibly allied to the ancodonts. The caenotheres were in fact small, being about the size of rabbits. They were apparently limited to the European region where they appear for the first time in deposits of Upper Ludian age. Like the groups already discussed they underwent speciation during the Upper Eocene to Middle Oligocene periods. The cranium included large inflated auditory regions and the jaw contained a complete dentition in which the lower incisors pointed forwards as in the suids. The forelimbs were pentadactyl and the hind ones tetradactyl. The family presumably had a common origin with the Eocene suids and with the tylopods. During the Upper Eocene and Oligocene periods

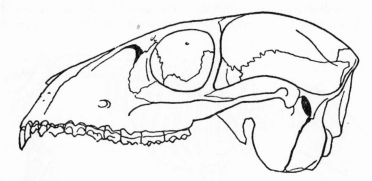

Figure 26. The skull of Cainotherium *from Europe (after Hürzeler, from Lavocat, 1955). × ca. 2*

they probably filled the ecological niche of the modern lagomorphs. At that time it is of interest that the contemporary South American fauna also included the typotheres and hegetotheres which occupied this self-same ecological niche and which, in the absence of rodents or lagomorphs, persisted into the Pliocene and Pleistocene periods respectively (Chapter 8). Since the hind legs of the caenotheres were longer than the forelegs it is also possible that they further paralleled the lagomorphs by being saltatorial.

ANCODONTS

Simpson (1945), in his study of mammalian taxonomy, placed the two families Anthracotheridae and Anoplotheriidae alongside the caenotheres and the hippopotamuses. Other workers on these forms include Stehlin (1910), Deperet (1908), Hurzeler (1936), Colbert (1938b) and Pilgrim (1940). The ancodont genera were in general tetradactylous, but occasionally pentadactyl, for example *Bothriodon*. They had a complete dentition with four principal tubercles on the upper molars. In contrast the lower molars were armed with conical tubercles internally, whilst the outer tubercles were enlarged to crescents, this condition being known as buno-selenodont. It has been suggested that the infra-order was derived from the Eocene Dichobunidae and *Anthracobune* is cited as a genus which shows similarities with both the anthracotheres and anoplotheres. It is probably sufficient to say that the ancodonts are further examples of the early flowering of the suids during the Tertiary. Throughout the regions of China, Mongolia and America there are several Eocene genera similar to the anthracotheres and to the paleodonts, and at the end of the Middle Eocene the true anthracothere *Anthracosenex* is known from Mongolia and China. The genera *Anthracotherium* and *Bothriodon* flourished in Europe at the end of the Eocene and during the Oligocene period, and it is possible that they were descended from the foregoing forms.

It has been suggested that the Anthracotheres are polyphyletic. Simpson suggests that the two lines are typified by *Bothriodon* and *Anthracotherium* whilst, following Colbert, he also suggests that the hippopotamuses have evolved from the anthracotheres. The early genera from Eocene deposits were of small size and are principally represented by dental remains. These small forms were succeeded by larger species in the Oligocene period, the

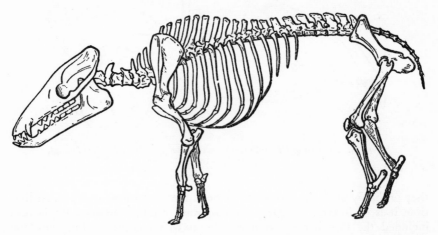

Figure 27. A reconstruction of the skeleton of the Tertiary suiform species Anthracotherium magnum *(after Khowalevsky from Lavocat, 1955)*

change in size being accompanied by the change from a bunodont to a buno-selenodont dentition. The evolutionary trend from small to large forms is very common in early Tertiary mammalian lines and the conditions in which the fossil remains of these larger Oligocene forms occur suggest that they may have lived in the vicinity of water. In view of this it is possible that they were semi-aquatic like the hippopotamuses and entelodonts. The facial region of the skull was longer than the cranial portion and there were well developed parietal crests. Further similarities with the modern hippopotamuses lay in the form of the cubitus. However, unlike the hippopotamus condition, this bone was not fused to the radius. Nevertheless, Colbert and Simpson suggest that, in view of the other similarities, the ancestry of the Quaternary hippopotamuses lies in the anthracotheres.

During the Oligocene period the ancodonts appear to have undergone a considerable amount of evolution in the region of North Africa and the Middle East. The remains of *Bothriogenys* have been recovered from deposits in Egypt dating from that time. This is a genus which persisted into the Miocene, when it occurs with several other genera. The two genera *Hyoboops* and *Merycopotamus* which occurred in contemporaneous Indian deposits, had expanded snouts similar to those of the hippopotamuses. During the Miocene/Pliocene periods in India there occurred genera of doubtful validity such as *Gonotelma* and *Hemimeryx*, whose relationship with other genera has been the subject of discussion. It has been suggested that many of these forms are genera endemic to the area around Pera Bugti where their remains are found; this fauna would include the earlier genus *Hyoboops*. In the Siwalik deposits themselves the ancodonts are chiefly of this *Gonotelma* and *Hemimeryx*-like stock, but the genera known from the Oligocene are still present. Since *Merycopotamus* and *Hyoboops* occurred throughout the Indian and Middle East areas at this late Tertiary time, it has been suggested that the entire region, from Tunisia to the site of the Siwalik deposits in Pakistan, comprised an extensive region of savanna. Grassé suggests that the ancodonts evolved in this region in a tropical aquatic habitat. This suggestion is corroborated by the presence of only small numbers of them in the New World, where their remains are scarce.

OREODONTS

Alongside the ancodonts, paleodonts, entelodonts, and caenotheres, there occurred another group of suids. These had a selenodont dentition and appeared in the Eocene deposits, persisting through most of the later Tertiary and disappearing during the Pliocene. Although they were abundant, their origin, like that of the others, is not precisely known. By the time of their appearance in the late Eocene they were not only separated from other artiodactyl groups but also divided by the form of their digits into two distinct families. As a result of the absence of any evidence about the related and ancestral genera they have at various times been placed in several of the suid groups. The less specialized genera seem to resemble the anthracotheres of the previous section and this is taken by Simpson (1945) to indicate their relationships. Matthew (1929) actually considered the oreodonts as ancodonts but some conception of the lack of conviction that his hesitant arguments induce may be gained from the fact that Scott, as late as 1940, asserted that these animals were in fact tylopods and not suids at all.

In fact the genera of the Agriochoeridae, namely *Protagriochoerus*, *Mesagriochoerus* and *Diplobunops* of the Upper Eocene in North America, and *Agriochoerus* of the Oligocene and Lower Miocene in the same region, are outstanding in their characteristic clawed digits. These organs were so unusual that the various parts of the body were originally described separately. The teeth were thought to be those of Artiodactyla, the fore limb that of a carnivore and the hind limb that of a chalicotherioid perissodactyl. It was not until 1894, some forty years after they had first been described, that finds of associated material revealed that the various parts were all those of the same genus. The more recent discovery of the Late Eocene genera has confirmed their artiodactyl nature and suggested the affinities with the merycoidodonts.

This last-named family is represented by some dozen genera which existed during the Oligocene, Miocene and Pliocene periods. The genera are exclusively North American and all seem to be derived from the probable stem genus *Merycoidodon*. Many skeletons of this genus are known and indeed the Merycoidodontidae are among the more numerous of the late Tertiary fossils in North America. Thorpe (1937) reviewed the bulk of the previous work and following his paper Scott (1940) and Schultz and Falkenbach (1940–1950) have added to our knowledge of these animals.

In the skull these artiodactyls had a narrow muzzle with long nasals and a small orbit. The brachyodont dentition was complete, and in the lower jaw there were incisiform canines and caniniform first premolars. It has been suggested that the analysis of the structure of vertebrae, and also that of the limbs, indicates a mixture of ancodont and ruminant features.

Subsequent evolution gave rise to a series of evolutionary lines which terminate in genera such as *Ustatochoerus*, *Brachycrus*, *Merychyus* and *Cyclopedius* of the Miocene and Pliocene periods. This evolution from the central merycoidodont stock took various forms. For example, shortened nasals accompanied by an increase in the size of the dentition leads to the Miocene genus *Ticholeptes* and an even greater reduction in the size of the nasalia gives rise to the brachycephalic condition of the contemporaneous *Brachycrus*.

HIPPOPOTAMUSES

As indicated above these large amphibious artiodactyls have many features which they share with the Ancodonta. Matthew and Colbert therefore have suggested both by implication and directly that these two groups of graviportal animals are related and that the hippopotamuses are derived from ancestral ancodonts. The modern forms live upon succulent aquatic plants and occupy well marked out territories, each of which has equally well-defined regions for sleeping, defaecating and entering the water. At the present time they are limited to Africa but were considerably more widespread during the Quaternary and foregoing Pliocene periods. *Hexaprotodon* is known from the Middle Pliocene and probably also Pleistocene deposits in Asia whilst the modern genus *Hippopotamus*, which was already occurring in Africa during the Pliocene, existed in both Europe and Asia during the various interglacial periods. During this time it is thought to have occurred in the Netherlands at least in the Tiglian, Taxandrian (see Chapter 4) and Needian periods (van der Vlerk and Florschütz, 1950).

TYLOPODA

The camels, like the giraffids, proboscideans and Suiformes, have very few survivors today. The group is extremely distinctive and was already recognizable in the Middle Eocene, and by the end of the Eocene they were well characterized. Simpson (1945) suggests that they are incorrectly placed within the ruminants and considers them to represent an individual evolutionary line comparable in status with these and the Suiformes. In fact the Ruminantia as a whole seem to have evolved from a prototypal traguline, and the tylopods from a closely related group. Lavocat (1955) suggests that the Xiphodontidae, comprising the three genera *Dichodon*, *Xiphodon* and *Haplomeryx*, are selenodonts close to the base of the ruminant stock. Simpson classed these animals within the Tylopoda and so emphasizes their camel affinities. Early Tragulina, and especially the hypertragulids, are very similar to contemporaneous Tylopoda and Scott (1940) suggested that they were in fact tylopods. Colbert (1941) disagreed with this concept and asserted that they were distinct Tragulina.

XIPHODONTIDAE

This family of selenodont Eocene artiodactyls was discussed by Stehlin (1903–1916). There are three principal genera which date from the Middle Eocene to Lower Oligocene. *Dichodon*, which includes the genus *Tetraselenodon*, occurs from the Middle Eocene to Lower Oligocene of Europe, and *Xiphodon* and *Haplomeryx* from the Upper Eocene of the same region. *Xiphodon gracile*, from the Ludian near Paris, was an animal of about 70 cm in height and similar in build to the modern chamois. In the skull, as in that of the ruminants, the orbits were closed posteriorly. The metapodials were very elongated and in both fore and hind limbs only a vestige of the lateral ones persist, so that the creatures were didactylous. The anterior dentition was uniform, there was no diastema, and the premolars were long and had cutting surfaces. In fact the series graded uniformly from the incisors to the cheek teeth, and in the upper jaw the molars retained the ancestral five cusped pattern with the protoconule distinct. It is probable that the xiphodontids represent a European line which, evolving from early Eocene anoplotheres, paralleled the American camelids (Lavocat, 1955).

CAMELIDS

The surviving members of the Tylopoda are the camels and llamas. These modern camelids have a cropping mechanism similar to that of the ruminants but the loss of the upper incisors has not been carried to such an extent as in these latter forms, the lateral ones being retained. Similarly the division of the stomach into several chambers has not reached the degree of development found in the ruminants. The available studies on all the fossil and living forms are largely old. These are summarized by Hay (1929–30) and Scott (1937). Matthew recognized a central line of evolution in post-Oligocene time which, with a few abortive offshoots, leads to the Pleistocene and modern forms. Besides this there are, according to Simpson (1945), three other divergent lines represented by the sub-families Pseudolabidinae, Alticamelinae and Stenomylinae.

The genera of the Oligocene and Eocene periods probably include the ancestors of all the later lines but, as in the early Tertiary perissodactyls and Suiformes, these early genera include a variety of types whose phyletic affinities are not clearly understood. Amongst these early fossils the genus *Protylopus* from the Ludian Uinta beds of America was a contemporary of the European *Xiphodon*. Together with the related genera *Camelodon* and *Eotylopus* it is considered to be an early camelid sufficiently distinct from the later Upper Oligocene, Miocene, Pliocene and Recent Camelinae to be considered a separate sub-family, the Poebrotheriinae. In *Protylopus* the limbs were short and the fore limbs were still tetradactylous. Although the upper molars no longer retained the five cusps of the Xiphodontidae, the protocone is a peculiar forked shape, suggesting that it incorporates the missing protoconule. In fact the genus is in many respects similar to the contemporaneous anoplotheres, caenotheres and oreodonts. Indeed Lavocat (1955) suggests

145

that *Eotylopus* is structurally a hypertragulid, although also related to the camelids on the basis of the cranial proportions.

Poebrotherium of the Lower and Middle Oligocene had the general body proportions of the South American llama, although smaller and with lighter legs. The head was long and pointed with the cranium short and the muzzle long and narrowed anteriorly. With large prominent orbits the cranium resembles that of living Camelidae. The neck was long and the construction of the tarsus at the end of the thin legs resembled that of the llama. In contrast to the continuous dentition of the xiphodontids, the canine of this genus was situated between two diastemas, but the premolars and molars both retained a relatively primitive structure.

The evolutionary changes which resulted in the camelids include the elongation of the limbs and the co-ossification of the radius and cubitus, the formation of cannon bones, modification of the phalanges and development of hypsodonty in the teeth. Of the genera which appear to lie in an ancestral position to the modern genera, *Protolabis*, from the Middle Miocene to Lower Pliocene of Wolf Fork, had reduced first and second incisors. In *Procamelus* of the Upper Miocene they are no longer present. In the Pliocene *Pliauchenia* the second premolar had disappeared whilst in *Camelus* itself there were only two lower premolars and in certain North American Pleistocene forms there was even more specialization. It has been suggested that the llamas of South America have evolved from a Pliocene ancestor perhaps somewhat similar to *Pliauchenia*, and in early Pleistocene deposits they are represented by *Paleolama* (Lavocat, 1955).

In his studies of the tylopods, Matthew, whose conclusions were never published in one summarizing work, suggested that a group of brachyodont forms joined together in the subfamily Alticamelinae represented an evolutionary line leading to a giraffe-like condition with a markedly elongated neck. These animals occur in beds of Middle Oligocene to Lower Pliocene age in North America. There are probably four genera involved, *Paratylopus*, *Oxydactylus*, *Miolabis* and *Alticamelus*. The cranium of *Paratylopus* shows similarities with that of the modern *Camelus*, but differs from it in its longer nasalia and narrower muzzle. The Lower Oligocene *Oxydactylus* was an outstanding camelid since it had evolved to a condition in which it stood on long thin legs. A comparable increase in length of the limbs also took place in *Alticamelus*, but here the condition was also enhanced by the long giraffoid neck which resulted from an elongation of the anterior cervical vertebrae. As a result the animal stood about 12 feet in height.

The other side-line of the camelids from the *Poebrotherium*-like forms comprises the two late Tertiary genera *Stenomylus* and *Rakomylus*, which are joined by Simpson (1945) into the family Stenomylinae. *Stenomylus*, from the Lower Miocene in North America, had a short skull with a narrow muzzle, in which there was retained a complete hypsodont dentition. The head was carried at the end of a neck which showed a slight trace of elongation, and although the body was small it was carried on long legs. The hypsodont condition of *Stenomylus* also occurred in the other genus *Rakomylus*, but the facial features were probably modified by the possession of a prehensile upper lip, giving an appearance reminiscent of that of the pyrotheres and astrapotheres of South America, and also of the probocispeans.

Although the Camelinae itself was the only sub-family to persist until the present day, and is now only a very insignificant feature in the world fauna, its present numbers have been reduced when compared with the conditions during various stages in the Quaternary period. Martin (1958) records camelids in the North American region during Post-glacial time at $11,200 \pm 250$ and $10,902 \pm 440$ B.P. in Nevada, and $2,040 \pm 90$ B.P. in Florida.

RUMINANTIA

During the Eocene period the herbivorous fauna living in the northern temperate region, which was then covered by a tropical jungle vegetation, was predominantly a perissodactyl fauna. However, although the Perissodactyla were still numerous in the fauna, by the end of the Eocene the Artiodactyla, characterized by being paraxonic not mesaxonic had increased in number and by the Oligocene it was this latter group that had become the dominant ungulate herbivores. This condition has persisted until the present time. Actually, the perissodactyls continued to exist in a variety of forms up until the end of the Pliocene, but after this period they declined. In contrast the artiodactyls remained numerous and varied until the present time. As stated in the previous sections the dominant artiodactyls of the early period, during late Eocene and Oligocene times, were in fact the Suiformes. Since that date the predominant artiodactyls in both the present northern temperate region and the Old World generally have included progressively more ruminant forms and these latter are the most widespread genera at the present time. Many authors, summarized by Simpson (1945), have considered these creatures, both living and fossil, and it is quite clear that the group comprises a taxonomic unit. Certain authors have also considered that the tylopods of the previous section should be considered as closely allied and have classed them as Pecora accordingly. Other authors also exclude the Tragulina from the Ruminantia. However, following recent workers, both Simpson (1945) and Lavocat (1955) class them as ruminant forms closely related to the ancestral group from which all ruminants have evolved.

TRAGULINA

This group was originally erected to include the primitive living tragulids or chevrotains which were recognized as surviving relics of an artiodactyl facies current during middle Tertiary times. Despite this initial concept it is clear today that these forms are considerably removed from the fossil forms known from that date. In the group as a whole the outstanding anatomical characteristic is the fact that the bones of the feet are not fused into a cannon bone. The tragulids appear at a period roughly contemporaneous with the early tylopods of the previous section. In fact the modern forms cannot be traced further back than the late Miocene, but the family Gelocidae, which occurs in the Eurasian region in deposits of Upper Eocene and Lower Oligocene age, includes a number of forms which resemble modern ones in their anatomy.

Lavocat (1955) has suggested that the ancestral genus is *Archeomeryx*, which occurs alongside the more specialized selenodont hypertragulids.

However, as is usual with the late Tertiary forms there has not been an all-embracing general review of all traguloid forms, the principal sources of information being Carlsson (1926), Colbert (1935, 1941), Flerow (1931), Frick (1937), Matthew and Granger (1925), Milne Edwards (1864), Petersen (1919), Pocock (1919), Scott (1940) and Stehlin (1910). As the result of this scattered literature it is not surprising that differences of opinion persist and Simpson (1945) follows Colbert (1941) in considering *Archeomeryx* a definite hypertragulid. This latter author suggests instead that the ancestry of the tragulid line may be represented by *Amphimeryx* and *Pseudamphimeryx* of the Upper Eocene and Lower Oligocene periods. The incomplete remains of these genera show a primitive dentition.

The genus *Archeomeryx*, which Lavocat suggests represents an ancestral form, is in fact considerably better known than is *Amphimeryx*. Indeed, virtually the whole skeleton of the former genus is known. The skull is primitive and of a size comparable with that of Javanese chevrotains. The cerebral hemispheres were small and on the top of the cranium there was only a low sagital crest in contrast to the prominent occipital crests. The radius and cubitus were separate and the cuboid co-ossified with the naviculare. The metapodials were also separate. In the dentition the reduced canine was isolated from the incisors by a small diastema and from the premolars by a larger one. In fact the lower canine is very modified, as in the oreodonts, and is virtually incisiform, being replaced functionally by a caniniform first premolar. The first premolar thus differed very much from the remaining premolars which were shearing teeth. Dental remains which some authors consider intermediate between this genus and the other early hypertragulids are considered by Simpson as definitive tragulids, and classed as *Indomeryx* in the Gelocidae.

Amongst the other hypertragulids the bulk of the early forms are not essentially different the one from the other. Many of them have distinctive features which prompted some authors to separate the group into sub-families. Simpson (1945), whilst recognizing these divergencies, prefers to unify the group into a more coherent whole classifying distinctive types as tribes. Amongst the fossil forms there are five principal groups, namely the tribes Leptotragulini, Hypertragulini, Leptomerycini and Hypisodontini of Simpson's Hypertragulinae together with his family Protoceratidae.

The hypertragulids, with the camelids, represent the principal lines which have undergone a modification of the bunodont molar to a selenodont condition in which crescentic ridges contrast markedly with the lophodont condition in elephants. The genus *Leptomeryx* is one of the best known representatives. In size it would appear to have been a small animal about 55 cm in length. It resembles the modern *Tragulus* but, because the fore limb is relatively longer, lacks the arched back. In the small, low and narrow skull, the orbits are situated about midway along its length, the dentition having the caniniform first premolar and incisiform canine. Although none of the early genera were large, *Hypisodus* was a tiny animal. This contrasts very markedly with the larger size of some later forms Lavocat (1955).

The relationship of the protoceratids with the hypertragulids is not completely clear, and has been denied by some authors. The principal champion of this point of view was Schlosser, who suggested that these tragulids were in fact ancestors of the giraffes. However the consensus of opinion at the

148

present time places them in the Tragulida, and suggests that the giraffe-like appearance is the result of evolutionary convergence. The earliest member is the type genus *Protoceras* from the Oligocene deposits at White River in America. The skull of this genus had three pairs of apophyses, one on each of the maxillary, frontal and parietal bones. These protuberances seem to have exhibited sexual dimorphism and were smaller in females. In the limbs the radius and cubitus were co-ossified, and four digits were retained. In the dentition, as in the Bovidae, the upper incisors are lost. The three pairs of cranial protuberances of this early genus *Protoceras* were replaced by the much larger horns of the later Miocene *Syndioceras*, and the two Pliocene genera *Paratoceras* and *Synthetoceras*.

The Gelocidae of Simpson are, as stated above, early forms which are similar in appearance to the later chevrotains. In the limbs the metapodials are incompletely fused and in the dentition the first lower premolar is not caniniform. Gelocidae occurred in both America and Eurasia in contrast to the later tragulids, which were apparently restricted to the Old World. The modern tragulids were represented in the Miocene and Pliocene by several genera, for example *Dorcabune* and *Dorcatherium*, comparable with *Tragulus* and *Hyemosuchus*, the oriental and African chevrotains of today. These are small animals about a foot in height and weighing only half a dozen pounds. They resemble large rodents such as the South American agoutis. Although they chew the cud and are therefore comparable with the larger and more well-known ruminants, their stomachs lack the complexity of the bovids and other Pecora. In the upper jaw the incisors are lost as in pecorans generally, and the typical ruminant cropping structure of lower canines and incisors is well developed. As the limbs of most of the later genera are long and functionally didactylous, they are more advanced than in any of the forms considered above, with the exception of the xiphodonts and later camelids. On the other hand the fibula is complete although fused to the tibia, and the lateral toes are short but complete structures. Since the meta-carpals are never complete in higher ruminants, and the toes themselves often reduced, it is clear that these animals are on a less specialized plane than the typical ruminants. In fact the absence of horns and large upper canines in the males, together with unspecialized limbs, are characters to be expected in the ancestral line of all pecorans.

PECORA

As was noted in the relevant sections, the exact taxonomic relationships of the fossil and living Tylopoda and Tragulina is still in dispute. In contrast the remaining groups of the Artiodactyla, the cattle, deer and giraffes, are un-animously considered to represent a closely linked assemblage which is not unduly modified as the result of the study of fossil forms. Nevertheless the relationships of the genera within these three super-families Bovoidea, Cervoidea and Giraffoidea do raise some still unsolved problems.

The earliest forms which are assignable to the group as a whole are the Blastomerycidae from the Chinese and Mongolian Stampian deposits. These were presumably derived from an Asiatic hypertragulid ancestor and although they are definitely cervoid in appearance it is actually difficult to demarcate the exact limits of the two groups.

Cervoidea

The general consensus of opinion is that most of the cervoids can be traced back to the Oligocene forms which were referred to above. Amongst living forms the muskdeer are perhaps the closest analogues of this Oligocene ancestry which is epitomized by the genus *Eumeryx* from the Asiatic deposits. From these ancestral forms several independent evolutionary lines occurred during the Miocene to produce the modern giraffids and cervids and also a rather different assemblage of animals classed as Dromomerycinae by Frick (1937) and Simpson (1945).

The early genera which are grouped together in the sub-family Blastomerycinae comprise forms which lack antlers. A number of these, for example *Dromotherium* and *Parablastomeryx*, had the upper canines enlarged to form

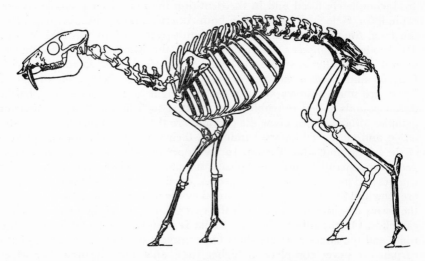

Figure 28. *Restoration of the skeleton of* Blastomeryx advena *Matthews, from the North American Miocene deposits (after Matthew from Lavocat, 1955)*
Original ca. 2 ft. long

stout tusks which are comparable to those existing in the modern chevrotains. In the limbs there were four digits but since the two median ones were longer than the others the animals were functionally didactylous. As in the later giraffes the teeth were low-crowned and adapted for a browsing existence. In general these forms occur in Oligocene deposits in Eurasia and appear rather abruptly in America during the Miocene. In fact, however, the American genera such as *Blastomeryx* are less specialized than their Eurasian confrères because they retain the well-developed lateral metapodials which were referred to above. It is extremely interesting in this respect to note that the modern North American fauna includes forms which have a relatively primitive limb structure.

In contrast to the foregoing the European *Dromotherium* was a medium sized animal about 90 cm in length. It had a long skull bearing a low sagital crest and in the limbs there were thin but complete lateral metapodials.

The principal papers which are concerned with both these early genera and the subsequent late Tertiary cervoids are Cabrera (1941); Colbert (1936); Frick (1937); Kraglievich (1932); Matthew (1908); Pilgrim (1941); Schlosser (1924); Stehlin (1928; 1937); Teilhard de Chardin (1939) and Lavocat (1955). In general one may conclude that forms most closely related to the modern deer appeared in the European region during the Miocene. It is, however, difficult to relate all these to a single hypothetical or actual ancestor. Indeed Pilgrim (1941) considered that certain of the aberrant genera, the Dromomerycinae, were in fact giraffes. Since, as already stated, both the cervoids and giraffoids are presumed to have a common ancestry it is clear, as Simpson (1945) points out, that this is largely a terminological difference. Nevertheless there was certainly considerable variation during the early phases of the evolution of the deer.

Figure 29. The skull of Cranioceras skinneri *Frick from the Pliocene deposits of North America (after Frick from Lavocat, 1955) Original ca. 1 ft. long*

The unusual Dromomerycinae were very inadequately known until the thirties of the present century. Indeed some were actually classified with the Antilocapridae. In fact they comprise a number of genera with large and branched horn-cores. The principal ones are *Barbouromeryx* from the Lower and Upper Miocene, *Drepanomeryx* and *Dromomeryx* from the Middle Miocene and *Rakomeryx* and *Cranioceras* from the later Upper Miocene, and, in the last case, Pliocene times. Of these genera the most aberrant by comparison with our modern experience are the Cranioceratinae. These, besides having paired frontal processes which presumably bore giraffoid horns in life, also had an unpaired occipital process. Although thought to be exclusively

151

American, a skull from the Spanish Miocene has a comparable condition but is even more unusual because its unpaired occipital process is forked.

In the past the late Cenozoic and living deer were all referred to the single genus *Cervus*. Today this name is usually reserved for the European red deer, the wapiti and related forms. During the Quaternary the speciation within the stock allied to the modern species produced the giant moose *Cervalces* of North America and *Megaceros* the Irish Elk of north west Europe. As the result of recent palynological investigations of the stratigraphical layers of bogs which contain sub-fossil *Megaceros* remains, it is now known that they occurred together with *Bison* and other bovid species up to and during the Allerød climatic oscillation. This suggests that they were animals of open-vegetational conditions, and that they became extinct during the Post-glacial afforestation. In zone IV of the general British scheme of Post-glacial vegetational history, it is possible that they fell an easy prey to late paleolithic and mesolithic man, owing to their total size and that of their horns, which would render them very cumbersome in the encroaching forests.

Giraffoidea

In view of the fact that some of the Dromomerycinae (page 151) show parallel adaptations to the giraffids, they perhaps support the suggestion of Colbert (1935b), and implication of Matthew, that the giraffes are late Tertiary, perhaps Miocene, offshoots of the cervid stock. However, it must be noted that Crusafont (1952) considers the Dromomerycinae are giraffids. The former consideration would mean that from *Paleomeryx* and its allies there evolved in North America animals closely paralleling the related evolutionary line of the giraffes which were their contemporaries in the Old World. As the result of this relatively close taxonomic relationship it is not surprising that the exact position of certain early forms along one or other of the three principal evolutionary series is not precisely known. The outstanding examples of such genera of doubtful status are *Lagomeryx* and its allies. Simpson (1945), following Pilgrim (1941), ascribes them to the giraffid line. However he is careful to emphasize the fact that they are also closely allied to *Paleomeryx* and *Dromomeryx*. As in the case of the cervid *Paleomeryx*, the remains of *Lagomeryx* are of Upper Miocene age in Asia, and somewhat earlier in Europe. The related *Procervulus* also occurred alongside it in Europe, whilst in Africa the remains of *Climacoceras* seem to be of another lagomerycid.

From these Miocene animals there evolved during the subsequent Pliocene period a group of aberrant genera. Only the Giraffinae in this group underwent the increase in height resulting from lengthening of the limbs and neck, a trait already noted in the camelid *Stenomylus*. The ancestral forms of these aberrant genera may well lie within the paleotragids. These consist of three genera *Paleotragus*, *Giraffokeryx* and *Samotherium* from the Lower Pliocene of Eurasia, and also the present day okapi of the Belgian Congo. They are smaller forms and have a more normal build. From these genera with a normal appearance the evolution of *Sivatherium* and its allies involved a considerable increase in size. *Sivatherium* was an enormous Pliocene form found in India and Pakistan. *Sivatherium giganteus* Falc. and Caut. itself had a skull measuring three-quarters of a yard in length and carrying two large horns. Of these, the anterior pair, which were borne on the frontalia, were conical, whilst in contrast the posterior pair on the parietalia were palmate. This species is known from the upper region of the Siwalik freshwater deposits, and is probably the result of orthogenetic evolution in an herbaceous open-vegetational or parkland habitat, which presumably existed in the region during Miocene and Pliocene times. It is probable that such a savanna-like habitat stretched well into North Africa during some part

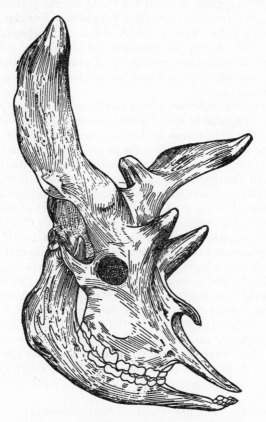

Figure 30. The skull of the giraffid Sivatherium giganteum *Falc et Caut. from the upper deposits in the Siwalik series (after Colbert from Lavocat, 1955) Original skull ca. 2 ft. long*

of the period, because by the end of the Pliocene the Sivatheriinae had penetrated to Africa. In the late Pliocene or perhaps Villafranchian fauna of Algeria they are represented by *Libytherium*, whilst in South Africa the genus *Griquatherium* appears to be a Pleistocene relic of this late Tertiary Asiatic group. As in the case of so many genera, this region is in fact the sole place in which the sub-family have persisted until today.

Bovoidea

As noted in Chapter 10, the Perissodactyla were apparently the more dominant herbivores during Eocene and Oligocene times. Subsequently the Artiodactyla became the numerically dominant forms, and of these it is the genera of the super-family Bovoidea which today outnumber all other ungulates. Simpson (1945) points out that, having arisen in their present form at a recent period, they are now at their apogee. In fact in the northern temperate regions they appear to be the animals which, together with the equids and the Irish Elk, *Megaceros*, composed the herbivorous ungulate fauna of the open-vegetational phases of the Quaternary. Numerous workers have recorded their remains from Allerød deposits and similar considerations would suggest that they were probably dominant herbivores in the late-glacial phases of the earlier interglacials, and also during the open-vegetational phases at the end of the interglacials. In the British Isles it is probable that all these animals were reduced in numbers during the Post-glacial period of afforestation.

The hypertragulid *Archeomeryx* from the Upper Eocene deposits of China and Mongolia, suggested as the ancestral form of the Tragulina above, may well represent the appearance of the common ancestor of the Bovoidea. However, no known bovoid fossils occur in the Oligocene, and the true forms only appear doubtfully at, and more probably above, the basal Miocene deposits of both the Palearctic and Nearctic regions. Even at this early period the bovoid stock was reasonably clearly differentiated into lines. One of these culminated in the antilocaprids or prongbucks of the modern New World fauna, whilst the others led to the predominantly Old World Bovidae.

Owing to the gap which exists in the fossil record of the Oligocene bovoid forms it is impossible to obtain a precise picture of the early stages of this differentiation into two types. It is possible, however, that the predominantly New World distribution of the antilocaprid line and the Old World distribution of the bovid line was present at an early stage. A summary of the geological history and taxonomy of the former is provided by the works of Colbert and Chaffee (1939), Frick (1937), Matthew (1924) and Stirton (1938). The literature on the bovids is immense and records of sub-fossil occurrence in Quaternary deposits widespread. One may cite with Simpson (1945), Bohlin (1938), Frick (1937), Pilgrim (1937), Pilgrim and Hopwood (1928), Pilgrim and Schaub (1939), Pocock (1919), Schlosser (1904) and Schwarz (1937).

The Antilocapridae—The prongbuck of North America, which is the only living representative of the antilocaprid evolutionary stock, is an isolated type. In its high-crowned teeth and absence of lateral metapodials it is similar to the antelopes. However the horns of these creatures are quite different. The horn is actually forked, in a way which is reminiscent of the early Cervoidea, and the horny covering is shed annually. Since this is in such marked contrast to the condition in the bovids it is a corroboration of the suggestion that the two lines have had a separate ancestry for a considerable period, and probably since Oligocene times.

It has been suggested that the Upper Miocene and Pliocene *Merycodus* is a possible fore-runner of the genus *Antilocapra* itself. However, the merycodonts are a controversial group whose exact taxonomic affinities were in dispute for a considerable time. Winge (1924) considered that they were not bovoid at all but simply hypsodont deer. Matthew (1924) ascribed them to the Antilcapridae and most subsequent writers have followed him in this. There were three genera, *Merycodus* itself and *Meryceros* and *Ramoceros* from the Lower Pliocene of North America. Although the dentition shows a pattern similar to that of the antilocaprids, the horn formations were very variable. Those of *Ramoceros*, for example, were trifid and, as noted above, similar to those of early deer.

In the Lower Pliocene the definitive antilocaprid genera *Proantilocapra* and *Hexabelomeryx* occur. From forms similar to these and occurring in the Middle and Upper Pliocene fauna of North America the genera of the American Pleistocene evolved. These comprise the four extinct genera *Osbornoceros*, *Ilingoceros*, *Texoceros* and *Ceratomeryx*, together with the modern *Antilocapra* itself. The exact temporal relationships of these forms is unfortunately difficult to assess as Frick in his works quotes a stratigraphy which is different from that of other authors.

Besides wholly nearctic fossils, reports have been made of antilocaprid remains in South America, Europe and Asia. The evidence for these is in general very slender but it should be remembered that the known connections between Eurasia and North America which permitted the interchange of *Bison* and equids between the two regions would have provided at least a potential route for such an invasion.

The Bovidae—These animals are the most recent and evolved of the ruminants. They are characterized by the presence of true horns borne on a bony horn core. They appear in the Old World fauna at a late period in the Miocene and from that date have speciated to produce literally dozens of genera in the Pliocene deposits of the Palearctic. With the climatic deterioration of the Quaternary period they were greatly reduced and many disappeared from the European region. As in so many other cases a reduced but still extensive living fauna, reminiscent of the conditions which probably prevailed on the late Tertiary grasslands, is preserved in the Old World tropics.

As a result of their relatively recent appearance and speciation there has presumably not been sufficient time to allow any extensive evolution along a particular line. Whether this is or is not the reason, one may certainly note that many difficult taxonomic problems exist in the consideration of these animals. Many attempts have been made to represent the inter-relationships of the known genera and these are summarized in Simpson (1945). A review of the actual characters of the genera is provided by Sokalov (1954). The individual genera have been considered by a multitude of authors in an immense number of small and often relatively uninformative papers. A brief introduction to this list will be provided by Freschkop (1955) and the authors cited on page 154.

The earliest forms which suggest bovid affinities are the remains of *Eotragus*. This animal occurs in deposits of late Miocene age. Since it is known only in the Eurasian region it has been suggested that it was in this region that the family emerged. Slightly conflicting suggestions based on the supposed antelope affinities of *Strongulognathus* and *Propaleoryx* would put the site of origin in Africa. This line of thought indicates a later migration northwards to colonize first Eurasia and then the New World (Lavocat, 1955).

Whichever of these two suggestions is correct one thing is certain and that is that from the ancestral chevrotain-like tragulids there evolved during the late Miocene period a group of large artiodactyl genera which were adapted for life on plains supporting a predominantly open vegetation. A group of these genera are classed in the Tribe Strepsicerotinae and include *Paleoreas* from the Upper Miocene and numerous genera of Pliocene age.

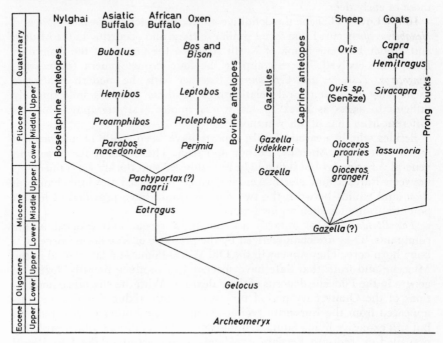

Figure 31. The probable evolutionary inter-relationships of the Bovidae and Antilocapridae (simplified from Pilgrim, 1946)

Alongside these animals the ancestors of the modern cattle appear to have occurred in the shape of *Proamphibos*, *Proleptobos* and *Leptobos* from the Asiatic Pliocene. A large number of these fossil genera such as *Protragelephas*, *Gazellospira* and *Antilospira* of the Eurasian Pliocene outline the extensive speciation which had taken place by that time.

156

10

PERISSODACTYLA

The relationships of the large variety of fossil and recent odd-toed ungulates have been the subject of a considerable amount of discussion. Linneus did not recognize the relations which are accepted today. It was de Blainville (1816) who saw the significance of the division of the ungulates into odd-toed and even-toed groups, and the former group, the Perissodactyla, have since then been subject to a variety of arrangements. Later workers, notably Wood (1937), Scott (1941) and Simpson (1945), have concluded that these odd-toed herbivores may be considered to be of two types, the hippomorphs with W-shaped ectolophs, and the ceratomorphs. The groups probably had a common pentadactyl ancestor in the early Tertiary period.

In the modern cursorial forms there is no clavicle, the usual condition in the ungulates. The relatively primitive tetradactyl condition was common in the Eocene, but more recently the digital formula has been reduced in association with the cursorial habits. Although in tapirs this ancestral tetradactyl condition has been retained, no other genera have had more than three digits on each foot since the Oligocene period. The dentition, which was complete in the early forms, has also been subject to a variety of specializations. Together with reductions in the incisors a diastema often occurred in the later Tertiary forms.

In the early Tertiary the molar already had a hypocone and was equipped with six bunodont cusps. An ectoloph was developed in later genera and a metaloph and protolophs are present in tapirs. The teeth may remain low-crowned as in the early Tertiary families or, alternatively, they may become hypsodont. In the most advanced forms there tends to be complete molarization of the premolars. This tendency is carried to its extreme in the Pleistocene and Recent caballine and zebrine horses in which the entire series of premolars and molars are similar to one another. In association with this development of the grinding teeth there is also a tendency to lengthen the facial region in order to accommodate them.

HIPPOMORPHS

EQUID HIPPOMORPHS

The members of this sub-order fall naturally into three major groups. The most modified of the hippomorphs are the Quaternary horses. These forms are highly adapted to a cursorial herbivorous life on open grass or parkland. There is no loss of teeth, and the incisors are retained as cropping organs. In the upper molars the ectoloph is represented by two crescents. One of these is homologous with the paracone and one with the metacone. Small projections represent the parastyle and metastyle.

The cursorial mode of life presumably evolved in association with several factors, including the development of advanced carnivores and the increase in the herbaceous open vegetation in the late Tertiary. As a result of this evolutionary trend, the humerus and femur comprise short driving segments with the long pendulant radius and tibia hanging from them. The third toe has a much elongated metapodial but short phalanges, the last one carrying a hoof.

Out of the extensive literature on the Equoidea one may cite Haughton (1931) on the African fauna, and Filhol (1888), Loomis (1926), Matthew (1926), Matthew and Stirton (1930), Osborn (1918), Sefve (1927), Stehlin (1928) and Stirton (1940).

Tetradactylous Equid Hippomorphs

In the Eocene deposits of Europe and North America remains of small perissodactyls occur which were about the same size as a fox terrier. In the New World these forms are represented by *Eohippus*, *Orohippus* and *Epihippus*. In the Old World these genera do not occur, but there is a very similar animal *Hyracotherium*, which Simpson synonomizes with *Eohippus*. In the skulls of all these Eocene hippomorphs there was a short facial region and the orbits were placed about halfway along the length. All the teeth were present and only a slight diastema represented an evolution away from the hypothetical ancestral form. However, the low-crowned molars had already acquired the herbivorous appearance. They were square and each had six cusps in the upper jaw and four below. Although there are indications of loph formation, the form is nevertheless bunodont. Considering the limbs, the forelimb was tetradactylous but the hindlimb was already functionally tridactylous although a splint bone indicates the remains of the fourth digit. In the Upper Eocene these early tendencies towards a cursorial and herbivorous life had advanced further. The hind leg lost its splints and became both functionally and actually tridactylous. Alongside this development the dentition underwent a change, the last two premolars becoming molariform.

Paleotheres

During the Upper Eocene no true representatives of the equid evolutionary line appear to have occurred in Europe. However, there were instead a series of evolutionary lines of hippomorphs in which the transition from bunodont to bunolophodont molars took place separately from that which occurred in the American equid lines. *Lophiotherium*, *Paleotherium* and *Plagiolophus* are typical of these forms. A related genus, *Propaleotherium*, is known from the Eocene deposits of China.

The evolution of these genera had already begun in the Lower Lutetian, and in the Middle and Upper Eocene there evolved, from animals whose general appearance resembled that of *Eohippus*, genera whose skeletons were like those of modern tapirs. At the same period large forms also occurred, notably *Paleotherium*, which were comparable in size to modern rhinoceroses. In these animals the early tetradactylous limbs had been superseded by tridactylous ones, and three premolars were molarized. In contrast to the evolution in the equid line, this decrease in the number of digits was not accompanied by the development of long legs. The limbs were short and stout. This difference in limb structure suggests that in contrast to the cursorial horses the larger paleotheres were forest-dwelling animals and probably comparable with modern tapirs. Following this early tachytelic phase these animals became extinct by the end of the Oligocene, and in this and sub-sequent periods the characteristic and most numerous ungulates were in fact artiodactyls.

Tridactylous Equid Hippomorphs

In the Lower Oligocene deposits of North America remains of animals are found which were larger than the earlier and more primitive *Eohippus*. These genera were similar in size to a collie. As exemplified by *Mesohippus* and *Miohippus*, they comprise the tridactylous phase of equid evolution.

In the foreleg the outer toe had largely disappeared although traces still remained. The metapodials of the remaining toes were elongated, and the central toe was somewhat larger, although all three reached the ground. A larger diastema occurred in the mouth and although the premolars were molariform in appearance the cheek-teeth were in fact still low-crowned. The combination of these dental and digital characters suggest that these creatures were browsing forest-living animals like their Eocene ancestors. Indeed their splayed toes were probably associated with movement over the soft ground of forest glades in which they fed upon the leaves of bushes and shrubs.

Some of the genera underwent a considerable increase in size comparable with that of *Paleotherium* amongst the paleotheres. For example, *Anchitherium* was about the size of a pony, but it retained the primitive tridactylous limbs and low-crowned molars. This genus occurs in Europe which suggests that during the Oligocene these forms invaded this region, and as noted in the previous section, Europe had been free of equid hippomorphs since the Early Eocene period.

In some regions certain genera of the tridactylous forest horses persisted into the Pliocene period. Indeed during this period another genus attained a considerable body size. This animal, *Megahippus*, was the size of a rhinoceros and perhaps lived in the increasingly large areas of herbaceous vegetation which the vegetational remains suggest were encroaching progressively upon the Tertiary forest. In contrast the species of the Miocene genus *Archeotherium* and its conservative allies retained the small size of their early Tertiary ancestors (Romer, 1945).

Mesodactylous Equid Hippomorphs

During the Miocene period many of the tridactylous forms which were discussed in the previous sections became progressively more reliant upon a single digit. It is, however, improbable that they were truly one-toed and more probable that the lateral toes still reached the ground. In association with this development, the herbivorous adaptations were increased. The cheek-teeth were longer and there was an increase in the length of the diastema. These changes resulted in a longer facial region and the orbita now lay behind the mid-line of the skull. The teeth were still low-crowned and, besides being longer, had developed a cement covering. This was deposited in the depressions which separated the hypocone, ectoloph, protoloph and metaloph. Indeed in the Upper Miocene genus *Merychippus* the teeth were no longer low-crowned and had a thick cement covering. Although it is possible that these hypsodont teeth were an adaptation to eating siliceous grass which would abrade the low-crowned teeth, Simpson has drawn attention to the fact that these animals were larger than the earlier forms and as such needed larger teeth.

The varied Pliocene equid fauna arose from these Miocene types. In America the genera *Calippus*, *Megahippus*, *Nannipus* and *Neohipparion* all flourished at this late Tertiary period. *Hipparion* occurred in North America, Europe, Asia and Africa, and in fact persisted into the Quaternary period.

It was probably from the Pliocene form *Pliohippus* that the modern horses evolved. As indicated above these animals exhibited a tendency to be of larger size and stouter build than the *Hipparion* stock. Simpson (1951) drew

Table 38. The probable occurrence of known equids in Quaternary deposits in north-west Europe (after Van der Vlerk and Florschütz, 1950)

	Equus stenonis Cocchi	*Equus robustus* Pomel	*Equus sussenbornensis* Wurst	*Equus caballus* Linn.
Tubantian				Found
Eemian				
Drenthian				
Needian			Found	
Taxandrian				
Tiglian		Found		
Pre-Tiglian	Found			

attention to the fact that the modifications of the limbs do not necessarily result from a change in habitat from jungle or forest to life on plains. They may be the necessary outcome of an increase in size. Whilst *Eohippus* could run like a terrier, it is a fairly general rule that the mechanics of locomotion in large animals do not result in a simple scaled up form of the condition in smaller related species, but involve a greater or lesser degree of modification.

In the Pliocene period the main invasion of South America by the holarctic Eutheria began. Together with carnivores, this resulted in the appearance of equids in the region. By the Pleistocene this stock had changed sufficiently from the ancestral forms to result in several genera which are known only from the South American Quaternary deposits. Of these one may cite the genera *Hippidion*, *Onohippidion* and *Parahipparion*. In view of this speciation one may assume that the region at that time offered adequate congenial parkland habitats for these forms. Indeed it is highly probable that they contributed to the extinction of the indigenous ungulate fauna, an extinction which has today resulted in the complete absence of any of the Tertiary forms. The last members of this ungulate fauna, if they survived the climatic oscillations of the Quaternary, would appear to have been extinguished by the early pre-western human settlement of the area.

During the period in which equid genera were contributing for the first time to the South American fauna, a parallel speciation was occurring in the Old World. In a comparable manner to the succession already noted in the case of the hyaenas, lions, dogs and lynxes, the equid stock shows a series o species replacing each other in the European Quaternary deposits. This temporal speciation is summarized in *Table 38*. For many years these forms were considered to be caballine horses but a close study of the dentition has shown recently that many of the specimens are not caballine but zebrine. We know nothing, of course, about their external appearance. One can only conjecture that the presence or absence of stripes may have varied in relation to different open vegetational savanna or forest habitats.

BRONTOTHERIOIDS

These hippomorph perissodactyls are first found in the Wasatch deposits of the Lower Eocene. They are particularly well represented in North American deposits and a specimen of the group first drew attention to the great series of rich faunas in the White River deposits. Although this remarkably full sequence of brontotherioids exists in the North American region they are, nevertheless, also known from Mongolia, and occurred in Europe during the latter part of the Eocene. Most of the literature consists of the reviews of Granger and Gregory (1943), Osborn (1929), Scott (1941) and Simpson (1945).

The skull of these animals was long and low, and bore a large pair of horns which exhibited a sexually dimorphic size variation. In the dentition both the incisors and a premolar could be absent, and the premolars slightly molarized. The molars were only partially lophodont, but had a large surface area. In these teeth a W-shaped ectoloph lay outside isolated cones. The appearance of the whole animal was, in the larger forms, that of a gravigrade herbivore with tetradactylous forelegs and tridactylous hind ones. They appear to have evolved from a tetradactylous hippomorph similar to *Hyracotherium* or *Eohippus* of the holarctic Eocene deposits.

Lambdotherium, an early genus, was a small lightly built animal of cursorial habits. It is known from fossil remains of both cranium and limbs. The skull is similar to *Eohippus*, but the first premolar is lost, and the upper molars, although still retaining a low-crowned appearance, have V-shaped ridges formed by the paracone and metacone. This animal may be considered as an intermediate stage between the tetradactyl equids like *Eohippus* and the true brontotherioids. The genus *Eotitanops*, which occurred alongside *Lambdotherium*, was larger, of heavier build, and suggested the graviportal form of later genera. In the hind leg of these animals the lateral digits were more developed than in *Eohippus*.

From these early hippomorphs the later titanotheres evolved. In this development the skull underwent changes and the body assumed a graviportal appearance. The facial region was shortened so that the orbita became progressively more anterior. At the rear the cranium contained a brain of small size, and was covered by a flattened supra-temporal region. Above the whole towered the horns which in the males of the more recent genera were often a considerable size.

161

Even in the most modified and recent forms, for example the Oligocene Embolotheriinae and Brontotheriinae of North America and Asia, the

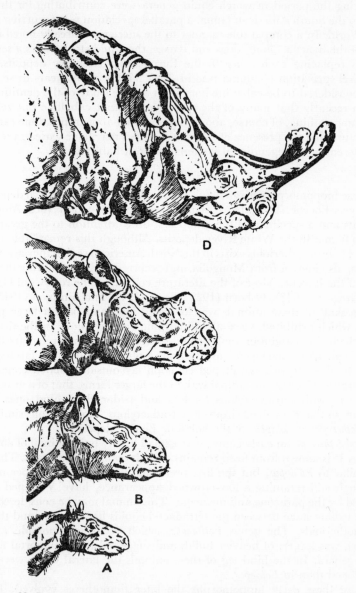

Figure 32. Restoration of various Brontotherioids according to Osborn (from Lavocat, 1955)
    (A) *the Lower Eocene* Eotitanops
    (B) *the Upper Eocene* Manteoceras
    (C) *the Upper Eocene* Protitanotherium
    (D) *Lower Oligocene* Brontotherium

dentition remains simple. In *Brontops* from the Lower Oligocene of North America and possibly Europe, the omoplate of the sternum was long, the pelvis large, and the hand had four large digits. The fact that the development of horns took place along several distinct lines is perhaps correlated with the contemporaneous evolution of the Acreodi, Pseudocreodi and Eucreodi amongst the creodont carnivores. On the other hand it may of course be related to the sexual behaviour in the males and the most probable explanation would combine both these suggestions. As the teeth would not have been able to withstand an excessive amount of wear, these creatures probably fed on soft vegetation. Their small brains suggest that they were not able to modify their behaviour to any great extent. In view of this it is probable that their extinction resulted from the combination of the effects of advanced carnivores, climatic changes causing changes in the vegetation, and the development of the more adaptable early artiodactyls.

CHALICOTHERES

Pentadactyl Chalicotheres

When they were first discovered, the dental remains of chalicotheres were thought to be those of perissodactyls, whilst the claws were ascribed to an unknown edentate. Only when later finds included both sets of organs together did paleontologists allow themselves to be forced to repudiate Cuvier's so-called law of correlation. For a time this resulted in the chalicotheres being separated as a distinct order on the supposition that claws must have preceded hooves. However, a trend from hoof to claws is also known today in two other groups, the South American notoungulates (Chapter 8) and the artiodactyls (Chapter 9) (Simpson, 1945).

Appearing in Eocene deposits of North America, Mongolia and China, these creatures seem to have persisted in these regions during the Oligocene. They were about the size of sheep and retained the primitive pentadactyl limbs together with a relatively unspecialized complete and bunodont dentition. These early forms are usually grouped in the two genera *Eomoropus* and *Grangeria* of the sub-family Eomoropinae in contradistinction to the later and more specialized sub-family, the Chalicotheriinae. The anterior region of the skull of *Eomoropus* is unknown, to date, but in the genus *Grangeria* the whole skull has characters indicative of an early perissodactylous condition comparable with that suggested by the limbs and teeth (Colbert, 1935a).

Tridactylous Chalicotheres

In the Miocene deposits of Europe, Africa, Asia and North America there are remains of large tridactylous chalicothere perissodactyls, which probably originated from relatively unspecialized genera such as the Eocene *Eomoropus*. These later forms appear in the Oligocene and some persist until the Pleistocene period in Africa and Asia. Although the anterior limbs were longer than the hind ones, they were similar to the horses in general characters. The cropping teeth resembled those of the titanotheres, and had a W-shaped ectoloph on the upper molars and a double V on the lower ones. However, the functionally tridactyl feet of these later Tertiary chalicotheres are their outstanding characteristic. In association with buno-lophodont teeth indicating an herbivorous evolutionary line, there occur digits armed with strong retractile claws on the terminal phalanges, the inner one being particularly large. In spite of this unorthodox digital construction the animals

163

were probably perissodactyls, as indicated in the case of the Eomoropinae. In the skeleton the omoplate is similar to that of the odd-toed ungulates *sensu stricto*, and indeed the limb bones show resemblances to those of the Brontotherioidea. However, in view of the claws, the habits of these animals must have been very different from those of the titanotheres. In general the suggestions advanced to explain the clawed digits fall into three groups, as follows:

(1) The retractile claws were used for digging up roots or tubers.

(2) They were used for pulling down branches to browse upon the leaves, whilst living in a forest habitat.

(3) They were used leaning against tree trunks to browse.

It is immediately apparent that no single one of these speculative explanations is inherently superior to the others. Indeed it may be that the claws were used for all three purposes by a generalized herbivore.

CERATOMORPHS (TAPIROMORPHS)

In contrast to the dental structure of the foregoing hippomorph Perissodactyla in which the upper molars have a W-shaped ectoloph, the tapiromorph genera have a simple ectoloph. In the place of the compound structure of the hippomorphs, there are transverse protolophs and metalophs on the upper molars. Primitive forms which have some resemblances to the modern tapirs of tropical America and the Orient are found in Eocene deposits, but the true tapirs appeared in the Oligocene. Unlike the hippomorphs which include several fossil lines not found at the present time, the ceratomorphs can all be included in the two super-families Tapiroidea and Rhinocerotoidea, both of which have living representatives. However, most of the members of both groups are extinct and the two super-families have produced more varied lines than the modern forms would perhaps suggest. The early Eocene genera were probably broadly ancestral to both the tapirs and the rhinoceroses and it is probable that the modern rhinocerotid forms arose from a tapiroid stock. These rhinocerotids, which resemble the swine amongst the artiodactyls, are relatively conservative in morphology and have perhaps retained many of the habits of their early Eocene forebears. The ancestral stock was in all probability closely related to the isectolophids from the Lower and Middle Eocene period of North America and the Upper Eocene of Europe.

EOCENE CERATOMORPHS

During the Eocene, the European fauna included tapiromorph animals of a rather aberrant form. These were the lophiodonts. Included together in one family they were, nevertheless, of a variety of morphological and presumably ecological types. The type genus *Lophiodon* was a heavily built animal, but in contrast the other genera were lightly built, and presumably cursorial, herbivores. As an example of the latter forms one may cite the Middle Eocene *Chasmotherium*.

Although the development of lophiodonts is analogous to the evolution of the later tapirs, and indeed to several quite unrelated groups of early Tertiary herbivores, there are only indirect similarities with recent true tapirs. The premolars are more simple than the molars and the forelimbs were tetra-dactylous. The group does not appear to have persisted unchanged after the end of the Eocene, but if the genera *Lophialetes* and *Schlosseria*, which were reported from the Irdin Manha beds of Mongolia and comparable deposits in Korea, are lophiodonts, then the family must have had a widespread distribution during the Eocene period.

There were in America at that time animals which are classified in the family Helaletidae. These were similar to the European lophiodonts and also to the early Eocene isectolophids. The early genus *Homogalax*, classed as an isectoloph, had feet very similar in appearance to the tetradactyl hippo-morphs, but the teeth already suggested a ceratomorph trend. The type genus *Helaletes* had an elongated nasal region and a large facial depression. In all these holarctic forms there was a tendency to increase the transverse ridges of all the teeth, and to revert to a secondary homodont condition comparable to that of the recent hippomorphs.

LATER TERTIARY CERATOMORPHS

The ancestors of the true tapirs which occurred in the Oligocene had already acquired a tapiroid appearance (Hatcher, 1896; Schaub, 1928; Schlaikjer, 1937). Although the premolars were not entirely molariform, these forms showed a trend towards the secondary homodont tapiromorph cheek teeth. The European and North American *Protapirus* occurred at this time, although, as with many of these presumably forest-dwelling animals, there is a dearth of fossil specimens. Along with the American *Miotapirus* and Eurasian *Paleotapirus*, animals of this genus persisted into the Miocene fauna over a wide area. Although some species were restricted to the New World, for example the poorly defined *Tapiravus*, the principal remains during the later Tertiary period are known from deposits in Eurasia. During the Quaternary, the fossil remains of the modern *Tapirus* are recorded from Eurasia and the Americas, and it is by a reduction of this widespread Quaternary distribution that the modern disjunct distribution in South America and the Orient has arisen.

CURSORIAL RHINOCEROSES

The family Hyrachyidae from the Eocene deposits of America, and possibly also Asia, is the earliest group of cursorial rhinoceros genera. It is in fact near to the base of the ancestral tree of the Rhinocerotoidea of Simpson (1945), and was represented by four genera *Colonoceras*, *Ephyrachyus*, *Hyrachyus* and *Metahyrachyus* (Wood, 1934, 1937). The family seems to have persisted throughout the Eocene and its species seem to have been of a similar build to that of the contemporary horses. The complete dentition presented simple premolars and rhinoceros-like molars. The various genera varied in size from that of an Alsatian dog to that of a pony, and, like the eohippids and other Eocene perissodactylous genera, had tetradactyl forelimbs and tridactyl hind ones. A cursorial habit is suggested by the generally light build, whilst the long neck suggests browsing, perhaps semi-giraffe-like, feeding habits.

A further tendency towards cursorial adaptations is shown by the related hyracodonts *Triplopus*, *Epitriplopus*, *Prothyracodon* and *Hyracodon*. These animals, which occurred from the Middle to Upper Eocene in Asia, and Middle Eocene to Upper Oligocene in North America, were of a heavier build than the Hyrachyidae. However, in spite of this increase in bulk, they still resemble the Middle Tertiary tridactylous hippomorphs in appearance rather than the modern rhinoceroses. Further evolution towards a cursorial equid-like form did not take place, and the family became extinct at the end of the Oligocene.

AMYNODONT RHINOCEROSES

In contrast to the cursorial rhinoceroses discussed in the previous section there was another short-lived branch of the Rhinocerotoidea, the amynodonts The various genera included in this family, for example, *Amynodon, Amyno-dontopsis, Mesamynodon*, and *Cadurcotherium*, seem at the present time to be a relatively homogeneous assemblage. They occurred in both North America and Eurasia during the Upper Eocene and the Oligocene periods and underwent an early development to produce extremely heavily built animals. In view of this large body-size it seems very probable that they led semi-aquatic lives similar to those of hippopotamuses. In the limbs the ancestral tetradactyl digital formula was retained anteriorly whilst the hind limb was tridactylous.

In the skull the nasalia were short and their structure suggests a prehensile upper lip. The molars are markedly hypsodont. This molar modification may well be indicative of abrasive, perhaps siliceous, foods, such as would be afforded by the Gramineae of tropical regions at the present time. Thus the relatively primitive and unspecialized limbs are combined with an advanced form of dentition. In the later genera of this evolutionary line, such as *Metamynodon* from the Lower and Middle Oligocene beds of northern America and the Oligocene deposits of Asia, a further modification of the dentition and jaw structure resulted in a reduction in the number of premolars.

RHINOCEROSES

The fourth rhinoceros family includes approximately 31 genera, spread in time from the Eocene to the present day, together with the true rhinoceroses of the holarctic Pliocene and the African and Asian regions. They have been considered by numerous authors, those of principal interest in this context being Abel (1910), Breuning (1923), Forster Cooper (1934), Granger and Gregory (1936), Matthew (1931, 1932), Osborn (1900), Petersen (1920), Ringstrom (1927), Roman (1911), Scott (1941) and Wood (1941).

The Rhinocerotidae are first suggested by the remains of *Prohyracodon* obtained from the Eocene beds of Transylvania. At the same time, or slightly later, the American fauna contained a similar genus *Eotrigonias*. Apart from these early genera of the sub-family Caenopinae, the bulk of the rhinoceroses date from Oligocene and more recent deposits. It is highly probable that these forms have evolved from the early Eocene tetradactyl tapiromorphs, and perhaps via animals similar to the cursorial rhinoceroses (page 165).

During the Oligocene period the family showed a tendency to increase in size as in the American genera *Caenopus* and *Trigonias*, and also the European *Allocerops* and *Eggysodon*. It is in fact highly probable that not only does the sub-family Caenopinae contain the general source of all later rhinoceroses among its more primitive genera, but that it also includes the forebears of at least two divergent groups. These two groups lead to the genera *Diceratherium*, *Aphelops* and *Peraceras*.

The heavier Oligocene rhinoceros genera with their larger size and gravi-portal limbs contrasted with the amynodont rhinoceroses. The premolars had undergone a considerable degree of molarization at a fairly early date. During the period in which many closely related genera existed, it is difficult to evaluate the relationships. Almost all authors consider that the gigantic *Baluchitherium* and its relatives, from Upper Oligocene and Lower Miocene beds of Asia, are sufficiently far removed to merit a separate sub-family. This presumably indicates an isolated evolutionary history originating at an early date in rhinoceros evolution.

Another aberrant line comprised *Teleoceras* and the possibly related *Brachypotherium*, which occur in late Tertiary deposits in the New World and Old World respectively. Actually the true rhinoceroses became remarkably rare in America after the Oligocene period and do not seem to have persisted following the climatic deterioration of the Pliocene. This may perhaps be explained by their inability to follow the example of the raccoons and horses, and invade South America. As the result of this they could not have escaped the considerable vegetational changes that must have preceeded and accompanied the early Quaternary Pre-Tiglian glaciation. It is however of interest that the European Quaternary genera occurred in the temperate vegetation of the various interglacials. As in the case of the bears, lions and horses, the successive interglacial periods have different species of rhinoceros. During the Tiglian interglacial both *Dicerorhinus merckii* and *Dicerorhinus etruscus* probably occurred in north-west Europe. The latter is also recorded from the Needian interglacial by Van de Vlerk and Florschütz (1950) whilst during the Eemian interglacial and Tubantian period the species *Coelodonta antiquitatis* was widespread in the region (*idem.* and West and Sparks, 1960).

11

PROBOSCIDEANS

The unique and outstanding characters of the living elephants were recognized at a very early date but they have at various times been classified alongside a variety of other forms. Linneus placed them in his 'Bruta' together with anteaters, sirenians, sloths and pangolins and in 1945 Simpson associated them in his Paenungulata along with the Dinocerata, Pantodonta, Pyrotheria (Chapter 8), Embrithopoda, Hyracoidea and Barytherioidea.

In a similar way the fossil proboscideans were probably the first fossils to attract the attention of man. Lying in superficial deposits their huge size resulted in the ancient Greeks observing them and the numerous more recent works are summarized in the momentous production of Osborn (1936, 1942). This monumental treatise has caused considerable difficulty because Osborn used different taxonomic principles to all other taxonomists. Comparisons of the various conflicts arising out of this work are summarized by Simpson (1945) and Vaufrey (1955, 1957). Although the later Tertiary and Quaternary forms are of the characteristically large size they appear to have evolved from smaller earlier genera. The large derivative genera in fact include the largest of all the late Cenozoic and living land mammals and they have typical graviportal adaptations. These include an expanded ilium, columnar legs, a long humerus and femur, contrasting with relatively short lower limb segments, and broad five-toed feet. These last bore nail-like structures on the outer side of the digits and had a pad beneath. The skull is of a very large size and its roughly rounded shape results from a swollen pneumatic top. Although the brain in the living genera is relatively heavy, eleven pounds in the Indian *Elephas*, it is very small by comparison with the size of the skull. As in *Pyrotherium*, *Astrapotherium* and the macraucheniid litopterns of Chapter 8, the nasal orifices are high up in the facial region between the small eyes. Below this opening, from which the prehensile trunk extends, the premaxillae descend vertically and bear the roots of the enlarged second incisors or tusks. Besides these the remaining dentition is also remarkable since there are no other anterior teeth. As in the various other herbivorous lines of the Perissodactyla, Artiodactyla and rodents the cheek teeth are highly modified in association with the need to triturate the diet of vegetation. In fact six teeth develop in each half jaw and comprise three milk premolars and three permanent molars. All of these are markedly hypsodont and covered by many high transverse ridges. The area between these is filled with cement. The number of ridges increases in the later teeth and instead of all the teeth being in position at once only four are exposed at any one time. As these become worn down by the abrasive action of the food they become pushed forward and replaced by the next teeth which have meanwhile been forming in the maxilla or dentary. Much of the taxonomy of the fossil species relies

168

upon a consideration of the form of the various teeth. In view of the great variation in ontogeny as well as the variation from animal to animal or species to species it is not surprising that considerable difficulties have been experienced by workers on fossil proboscideans.

MOERITHERIOIDEA

The American expeditions under Beadnell and Andrews (1901–1905) and Osborn and Granger (1907) which investigated the fauna of the Fayum Beds of Egypt resulted in the discovery of many interesting mammals. Of these *Moeritherium* (Andrews 1901, 1906) from both Upper Eocene and Lower Oligocene horizons is of immense significance to our knowledge of the evolution of the proboscideans. These remains were extracted from the so-called 'Bone Bed' at Qasr-el-Sagha, and according to Andrews represent several species which seem to have been much the same size as the modern tapir. As such they are seen to be comparable with the Eocene equid hippo-morphs and early Tertiary Artiodactyla of Chapters 9 and 10. The Eocene fossils were considered by Andrews to represent two species *Moeritherium lyonsi* and *Moeritherium gracile*. Two further species are known from the more recent Oligocene deposits of the same region in which they occur alongside the two mastodons *Paleomastodon* and *Phiomia*.

The skeletal remains of the moeritherioids show analogies with the sirenians and also the hippopotamuses (Vaufrey, 1955, 1957). This led Vaufrey to suggest that they were perhaps amphibious. Indeed, as the pelvic girdle is more reduced, he suggested that they were more specialized in this respect than the hippopotamuses. There was an almost complete permanent dentition in which the third and fourth upper premolars have a principally tritubercu-late form whilst the molars had a fourth tubercle. This quadrituberculate condition was further modified by the formation of transverse lamellae joining the pairs of tubercles. Unlike the condition in the more recent ele-phantoids these premolars and molars all appear to have been in use at once. However, resemblances between the moeritherioids and the more recent genera, especially the Oligocene mastodons, lay in the heavy form of their long low skeleton, the form of their tarsalia and their large incisors. However, the crania still lack the general form of the later animals and there was no epicondylar crest to the humerus although this is present in *Paleomastodon*.

MASTODONTOIDEA

For the reasons given above, the genera related together in this sub-order by Osborn (1936) are grouped by Simpson (1945) within his sub-order Elephantoidea. In re-organizing them in this way Simpson followed the laws of priority for names so that the already complex literature is now even more confused. Generally speaking the Oligocene genera from Egypt, namely *Phiomia* and *Paleomastodon*, are closely related and probably close to the common ancestor of all the later proboscideans. The more specific evolution of the various genera, for example *Mammut* from *Paleomastodon* or *Ambelodon* from *Phiomia*, is questionable. There are also several genera whose relationships are even more obscure and *Gnathobelodon* and *Eubelodon*, for example, resemble both *Gomphotherium* and the Anancinae. In fact Simpson considers that most of the other sub-families erected by Osborn (1936) comprise aberrant derivatives of an essentially gomphotheriine ancestry and he includes all of them, with the exception of *Mammut, Stegodon, Mammuthus* and the living forms on the one hand and *Deinotherium* on the other, in one family, the Gomphotheriidae.

The Mastodontoidea of Osborn (1936) include genera dating from Oligo-cene to Pliocene and Pleistocene times. By comparison with *Deinotherium* and the elephants the mastodonts had long bodies and short legs. There was a low cranium with a poorly-developed pneumatic sinus and the single incisors were developed into tusks. The molars show various stages in the transition from the bunodont to the zygolophodont condition. In fact the intermediate molars have three, four or five transverse lamellae and it is on the basis of these differences that Vaufrey (1955), following Osborn, subdivides the sub-order. This progressive increase in the size and number of the lamellae is of course correlated with the increase in size which took place within the Mastodontoidea during the Tertiary. As noted in the case of the hippo-morphs, increased body-size would have involved the consumption of larger quantities of the herbaceous food and put a premium on the development of efficient grinding surfaces. Associated with this there is a development of the masticatory masseter muscles and the area of their insertion on the parietal region of the skull.

TRILOPHODONT MASTODONTOIDS

Following the conclusions of Lortet and Chantre (1879), Vaufrey (1955, 1957) considers that the mastodontoids which have trilophodont molars can be further subdivided into two lines of evolution. The first of these has the presumably primitive bunodont dentition and the second a true lophodont dentition with transverse crests running across the teeth. Within the bunodont group he further distinguishes between a group of genera which possess incisors in their mandibles (notably *Paleomastodon, Phiomia, Trilophodon* and *Serridentinus*) and the Stegomastodontinae which lack them.

The long-jaw or longirostrine group comprises the early genera men-tioned above from the Fayum Beds of Egypt. Generally speaking both *Paleomastodon* and *Phiomia* occur in the Oligocene strata which are of more recent origin than those Upper Eocene and Lower Oligocene ones which contain the moeritherioid remains although these latter do occur alongside the mastodontoid remains in the intermediate Lower Oligocene. The remains of *Paleomastodon*, which had only two lamellae on its upper molars, antedate those of *Phiomia* which have three lamellae.

In the skull there are most of the characters which are later found on the more recent mastodons. The frontalia are small when compared with the parietalia and the posterior region of the skull is raised. The orbits are well back and level with the first molars. On *Phiomia*, and perhaps *Paleomastodon*, the upper incisors are well developed and down-curved. The presence of a strongly developed epicondylar crest on the humerus of *Paleomastodon* shows that even by this early Tertiary period the animals had the form of true proboscideans. The actual height of the animals varied but nevertheless could be around 6 feet.

170

The genus *Trilophodon* (= *Gomphotherium*) is also a representative of this relatively unspecialized morphological and dental facies although in the form of various sub-genera it persisted until Middle Pliocene times in the Asiatic region and Lower Pliocene times in Europe and North America. In the Eurasiatic region it seems to have appeared somewhere in the Middle Miocene but in North America not until the Upper Miocene. It then produced an array of species in the latter region comparable to those in the European and Afrasian arenas.

The principal sub-genera of this highly polymorphic genus are *Megabelodon*, *Choerolophodon*, *Genomastodon* and *Tatabelodon*. The further sub-genera *Eubelodon* and *Gnathobelodon* considered to be of uncertain taxonomic status by Simpson (1945) are also classed as *Trilophodon* by Vaufrey (1955, 1957). The fact that this latter author also considers that *Rhynchotherium* is a sub-genus of *Trilophodon* gives some idea of the difficulties which are involved in such considerations since Simpson removes the genus to a separate sub-family within his Gomphotheriidae.

All these animals had a relatively broad but short cranium with orbits situated at a comparable level to those of *Phiomia*. The upper incisors were however developed into striking tusks which were less strongly curved than those of the earlier genus. In the lower jaw there were considerable variations in the form and size of the symphysis, exemplified by the conditions in *Trilophodon fricki* Peterson, *T. giganteus*, *T. paladentatus* and *T. lulli*. Both the fourth milk molar and first two permanent molars had 3 bunodont lamellae.

The genus *Serridentinus* is considered to be closely allied to *Trilophodon* and as such classed by Simpson (1945) and Vaufrey (1955, 1957) in close proximity to it. However, the remains of the two genera are rarely found associated although with its sub-genera *Ocalientinus*, *Serbelodon* and *Trobelodon*, *Serridentinus* occurs during the same period as *Trilophodon*. The remains of *Serridentinus* are rarely found outside 50°N and therefore Vaufrey following Watson suggests that they may have inhabited a different bio-geographical or ecological niche. Since it is on the molar morphology that Osborn originally distinguished them it is quite probable that they were parallel forms adapted for eating different vegetation. In view of the known increase in the herbaceous component of the northern temperate floras it is tempting but obviously unproven to suggest that *Serridentinus* inhabited a region with different vegetational conditions to those in which *Trilophodon* existed.

The short-jawed or brevirostrine group of the trilophodont mastodons lack incisors in the lower jaw. They are classified in the two sub-families Anancinae and Cuvierioninae by Simpson (1945) but Vaufrey (1955, 1957) considers that they represent a more homogeneous collection and classes all in the sub-family Stegomastodontinae. Appearing in the Upper Pliocene of Arizona, Texas and Nebraska, they persisted well into the Pleistocene in both this region and South America.

In the skull both the cranial region and the mandibular symphysis are short. The frontalia are convex and the tusks borne by the upper jaw are divergent. Indeed in South America *Cuvieronius* had thick tusks which could be 6 feet in length.

Arising from these bunolophodont long-jawed forms such as *Paleomastodon*, are the second principal division of the Trilophodonts—the zygolophodont mastodonts. They differ considerably between themselves although Simpson following Hopwood (1935) includes them all in the single genus *Mammut*. In support of this he draws attention to the fact that the variations observed do not exceed those which exist between different species at the present time. In contrast Vaufrey prefers to assign them to the various genera of Osborn.

They are trilophodont mastodonts but in place of the bunodont or bunolophodont molars of *Paleomastodon*, *Trilophodon* or *Stegomastodon*, there are molars with a relatively wide crown and bearing well-marked transverse crests. There are two principal morphological groups which may be represented by the sub-families Zygolophodontinae and Mastodontinae.

The former of these includes the genus *Zygolophodon* which has several species in the Eurasian region. Of these one may cite *Zygolophodon tapiroides* Cuvier from the Burdigalian deposits in France, and *Zygolophodon borsoni* Hays which persisted into the Villafranchian fauna. In these animals the last molars had only four lamellae at the most, and occasionally only three. These lamellae comprise up to 9 tubercles fused together and the median sulcus which separated the bunodont crests of earlier ancestral forms remains only as the vestigeal sulcus of *Zygolophodon pyrenaicus*.

In the genus *Zygolophodon sensu stricto* the mandibular symphysis was short and with tusks, which lacked enamel, small.

In the genus *Miomastodon* which is a representative of the second morphological group the Mastodontinae, there was again a short lower jaw. The genus is best known from Colorado where it appears to have existed until the Pliocene. It is exemplified by *Miomastodon merriami* Osborn which besides occurring in the Barstovian of Colorado is also known from the Middle Pliocene of Nevada. The remains are not, however, very extensive and consist principally of two series of molars of which only one, a lower series, is *in situ* in the mandible. They have a low crown and also retain the longitudinal median sulcus of the early bunodonts.

TETRALOPHODONT MASTODONTOIDS

As their name implies, several genera differ from the foregoing genera in the prevalence of a molar structure involving four transverse lamellae. Although this condition occurs in the posterior molars of *Zygolophodon* it is only in the genera *Tetralophodon*, *Platybelodon* and *Anancus* that it extends to the intermediate molars.

In association with his general unifying principle Simpson considers that *Tetralophodon* is in fact a gomphotheriine closely allied to *Serridentinus*. *Platybelodon*, however, together with *Amebelodon*, he considers to comprise a distinct sub-family distinct from both *Tetralophodon* and *Anancus*. For convenience one may divide them into longirostrine and brevirostrine groups comparable with the similar divisions of the trilophodont mastodontoids.

Within the longirostrine group are *Tetralophodon sensu stricto*, *Platybelodon* and its sub-genus *Torynebelodon*. All these forms have short and elevated crania bearing tusks in both the upper and lower jaws. Those in the upper jaw are sub-circular in cross-section and exceed in length those in the lower jaw which are oval in cross-section. The four transverse lamellae of the intermediate molars are increased to 5, 6, 7, or 8 in the more posterior ones.

But in all cases the crowns still show individual tubercles reflecting their bunodont ancestry.

The genus *Platybelodon* has certain outstanding features. Two species are known, one, *Platybelodon grangeri* Osborn, occurring in the Upper Miocene deposits of Mongolia, and the other, *Platybelodon danovi* Borissiak, occurring in contemporaneous deposits in the U.S.S.R.

Only a female skull is known which is sufficiently complete for extensive reconstructions to be undertaken, but it is quite clear that the region of the inter-maxillary plate is enlarged, the upper incisors comparatively small, and the mandibular symphysis narrow in front and enlarged posteriorly. The posterior molars are small in *P. danovi*, wider and more elongated in *P. grangeri* and in both cases are tetralophodont (Vaufrey, 1955).

The sub-family Anancinae which comprises the brevirostrine tetra-lophodonts (Vaufrey, 1955, 1957) consists largely of the single genus *Anancus* although Simpson adds to this both *Stegomastodon* and *Synconolophus*. The cranium of *Anancus* shares the same general appearance as *Tetralophodon* but there is a certain amount of variation between the species.

PENTALOPHODONT MASTODONTOIDS

Vaufrey groups together the genera *Pentalophodon* and *Stegolophodon* on the grounds that their intermediate molars possess five lamellae. However, both are representative of monogeneric sub-families and it is possible that Simpson is correct in ascribing the former genus to a sub-generic status within *Anancus* and removing *Stegolophodon* from the mastodontoids, his Gompho-theriidae, and aligning it with *Stegodon* amongst the elephants.

Pentalophodon consists of Asiatic forms with short, wide and elevated crania. The condyles are situated in a position above the line of the palate and the lower jaw which always lacks any sign of incisors resembles that of elephants. Various species have been recorded from the Pontian deposits of China and from what have been considered Villafranchian deposits within the Siwalik series in the Himalayan region.

The remains of *Stegolophodon* are reported from deposits dating from the Upper Miocene to Pleistocene in Asia and the Middle Pliocene in Europe. It appears that the adult molars were at least pentalophodont and by the further multiplication of the lamellae they suggest relationships with the Stegodontinae. It is on grounds such as these that Simpson allied them with his elephants. It would therefore appear that whatever the exact inter-relation-ships, pentalophodont forms occurred in the later part of the Tertiary which showed affinities with the earlier trilophodont and tetralophodont genera on the one hand and with the Pleistocene and Recent elephantoids on the other.

ELEPHANTOIDEA

As noted previously, genera such as *Stegolophodon* are of uncertain taxonomic status, Osborn having difficulty in assigning it to any particular stegodontine or mammutid group. In fact it seems highly probable that the elephants evolved from the stegodontines and the stegodontines from zygolophodont forms, but one must concur with Osborn who emphasized very strongly the absence of any known fossils which link one group directly to another.

Among the actual elephantine genera it is difficult to decide whether to follow the system of early taxonomists and link them all in the single genus *Elephas* or to follow the more complex system of Osborn. As was stressed above it is often extremely difficult to distinguish between the various Quaternary forms. The succession of these forms follows a pattern which is comparable to that outlined for the felids, ursids and equids of Chapters 7 and 10. It appears that here again speciation occurred between one interglacial and the next, producing the series tabulated in *Table 39*. This culminated in the last glaciation in the woolly mammoth, specimens of which have been found preserved in ice in Siberia. As a result the morphology is almost as well known as that of the modern *Elephas* and the presence of associated plant species characteristic of tundra indicate that when alive these animals did indeed occur under peri-glacial or at least cool openvegetational conditions.

Table 39. The temporal distribution of the elephantoids in the Dutch Pleistocene (after Vlerk and Florschütz, 1950)

	Archidiskodon planifrons Caut. & Falc.	*Archidiskodon meridionalis* arch. form. Nesti.	*Hesperoloxodon antiquus* Falc. & Caut.	*Parelephas trogontherii* Pohl.	*Mammonteus primigenius* Blum.
Tubantian					Found
Eemian					
Drenthian				?	Found
Needian			Found		
Taxandrian					
Tiglian		Found			
Pre-Tiglian	Found				

A succession comparable with that noted in European deposits by Vlerk and Florschütz (1950) also occurred in the New World. However, in this last-named region, where both mastodons and mammoths are now known to have persisted until at least 2,040 ± 90 B.P. (Martin, 1958), the mastodons seem to have always outnumbered the mammoths (Osborn, 1910).

12

PRIMATES

The primates have retained so many generalized mammalian characteristics that there is a considerable similarity between the tarsioids and lorisoids on the one hand and the tupaioid insectivores on the other. These three groups of animals presumably had a common ancestor at some time during the early Tertiary period when the tachytelic phase of post-Cretaceous mammalian evolution was taking place. It is not absolutely clear where the early primates evolved, but a primitive arboricolous, and in this case tupaioid form, the genus *Anagale*, is known from Mongolia. This has resulted in the suggestion that the Primates evolved in that region. In contradiction to this, the fossil is in fact of Oligocene age, and other older geological deposits contain primates. The earliest known genera are actually from the Middle Paleocene, and have occasionally been considered insectivores. They are in fact closely similar to insectivores. Hill (1953) considers that they represent at least three families, the Plesiadapidae, Apatemyidae and Carpolestidae. The relationship between these forms and the primitive modern species has varied according to the author considering them. Jepsen (1934) and Simpson (1940, 1945) consider that they are separate phyletic lines as early as the Upper Paleocene so that the primates must have evolved prior to that period, and perhaps in the late Cretaceous. Besides being independent of one another, these three prosimian fossil families also evolved independently from the modern tarsioid and strepsirhine stems, although classed together with them and the Tupaiidae in the Lemuriformes of Simpson (1945).

The characters of the modern primates are the result of Eutheria being adapted to an arboricolous life. The first digit of the pentadactyl limb is opposable, and there is a voluminous cranium in which the fully ossified orbits look to the front; the molars are multituberculate, and the movements of the jaw are essentially vertical. The fact that the radius and cubitus are not fused allows a considerable degree of supination and pronation. In the brain there is a progressive trend involving a relative decrease in the size of the rhinencephalon and a concomitant increase in the neopallium.

The literature on the primates, including that on man, is of course very extensive, and exceeds that on all other mammals. Nevertheless, prior to the as yet incomplete work of Hill (1953), there is no single all-embracing work. Most of the early literature on fossil forms was summarized by Abel (1931) whose work however contains some errors. Gregory (1915) gives a clear outline of the inter-relationships of the Prosimii of Simpson (1945), and Le Gros Clark (1954) summarizes the evolution of the primates, but numerous books, articles and papers relate to a variety of subjects. As the result of the different interests, abilities and qualifications of this last named myriad of authors, most primates have a series of alternative names. Many people entirely lose all sense of perspective when considering the primates, and more

175

especially man, so that almost all aspects of their biology are obscured by a tangle of often only at best half-correct pronouncements. Simpson (1945) and Hill (1953) are of course outstanding summaries of the relevant literature and one may cite further Broom (1939), Gregory (1916, 1920, 1922, 1934), Le Gros Clark (1934a, 1934b, 1954), Leakey (1953) and Matthew (1915), and also the extensive literature of both archeological and anthropological studies on man.

STREPSIRHINI

The modern strepsirhines differ from the tarsiers, monkeys, apes and man in having a philtrum joining the nostrils to the upper lip.

PLESIADAPIDAE

Many of the fossil animals classed in this primate family and occurring from Paleocene to Middle Eocene time are known only from their dentition. They are a group of primitive primate genera and possess many tupaioid-like insectivore characters. According to Lemoine (1881) these primitive characters are even suggestive of the marsupials, but the enlargement, elongation and specialization of the incisors suggest a close relationship with the Daubentoniidae (the modern aye-aye). The upper incisors have, in fact, an elongate main cusp together with one or two accessory cusps and a strong posterior basal spur. The upper molars are, however, unlike those of the aye-aye, and more similar to those of the generalized lemuroids. They are primitive, low-crowned, bunodont, and generally sub-quadrangular and tritubercular with accessory cusps.

The first specimen was found in the London Clay at Herne Bay, Kent. Nowadays 5 genera can definitely be placed in the family, these are *Chiromyoides*, *Megachiromyoides*, *Platychoerops*, *Plesiadapis* and *Pronothodectes*. There are also the 3 American trogolemurid genera *Phenacolemur*, *Trogolemur* and *Uintasorex* (Anthony and Caupin, 1931), which are probably closely related (Hill, 1953).

Of the 5 definitely plesiadapid genera, *Pronothodectes* represented by *P. matthewi* is the most ancient genus and is known by dentition from the Middle Paleocene of North America. These remains comprise mandibles with 6 teeth from the Crazy Mountain Field, Montana. They show that as in *Plesiadapis* and *Platychoerops* there were two functional lower premolars of small size; they differ from these genera in that there was no diastema between the second lower incisor and the cheek teeth. In all the later genera the dentition had undergone a further modification and in *Plesiadapis* and *Platychoerops* the diastema was present whilst *Phenacolemur* and *Megachiromyoides* had only one functional lower premolar.

The genus *Plesiadapis* is in fact the best known (Simpson, 1935) and many parts of the skeleton of *Plesiadapis gidleyi* are known. It is the only genus of the family which occurs in the deposits of both Europe and North America. It first appears in the Upper Paleocene and survived in the New World through to the Lower Eocene. There are in fact 7 species from deposits at Cernay in north-west France, and Tiffany, Fort Union, Bear Creek, Paskapoo and Clark Fork in the New World. It was very similar to *Chiromyoides* but in the remains of this last-named genus from the Upper Paleocene Thanetian

176

Beds, the incisors were even larger and the mandible was more like that of the modern aye-aye.

The two plesiadapids which occur in Eocene deposits are unequally known. The sole remains of *Megachiromyoides* is an imperfect skull which was discovered in Middle Eocene lignites near Halle, Germany (Weigelt, 1933). It had a long muzzle and consequently a longer diastema than the modern

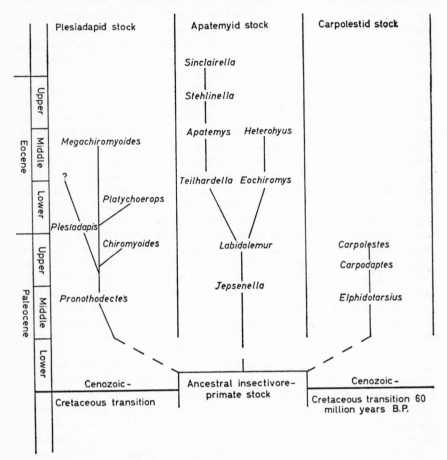

Figure 33. Diagram to illustrate the probable evolutionary inter-relationships of the plesiadapid, apatemyid and carpolestid genera (from Hill, 1953)

Daubentonia. The upper premolars were very simple and only consisted of a conical crown, a backwardly curved protocone, a deep crescentic groove behind it and a crescentic sharp-edged talon, whilst the third lower molar was very specialized.

APATEMYIDAE

Although the fossil remains of one genus, *Heterohyus*, were described as early as 1848 it was only when Teilhard (1922) associated them with the

177

cheiromyids that their probable identity became clear. This epitomizes the difficulties encountered by students of fossil primates and similar or related insectivore types. Simpson (1945), when considering the apatemyids, admits of a certain residual doubt about their relationships. Somewhat rodent-like in appearance, they were long associated with the Plesiadapidae until separated by Jepsen (1934) using improved methods including radiography. However, Simpson (1945) emphasizes that their primate nature is still not beyond doubt. Jepsen in fact pointed out that the only similarities between the Plesiadapidae and Apatemyidae are the basically primate molar structure and diprotodonty. Within his new family he included 7 genera to which Simpson (1940) added an eighth, *Jepsenella*. Hill (1953) suggests that in fact the apatemyid characteristics are best expressed in the two genera *Labidolemur* from the Upper Paleocene deposits of Colorado and Montana, and *Eochiromys* from the Lower Eocene of Europe. The former genus, of which two species are known, was originally considered to show affinities with the modern insectivores, and classed as a menotyphlous insectivore related to *Phenacolemur*. The principal characteristics are the short and moderately deep mandible with a posterior mental foramen beneath the first lower molar, a single enlarged procumbent incisor with enamelled trihedral crown and a large root which extends back beneath the cheek teeth, a reduction in the diastema by enlargement of the incisor, and molars with elongate subquadrate trigonids, the metaconid and protoconid sub-equal and the paraconid small but distinct and well removed from the metaconid. The principal difference between the type material of the two species of Hill (1953) is the deeper molar in *Labidolemur kayi* Simpson by comparison with that of *Labidolemur soricoides* Matthew and Granger, and the more distinct paraconid in the first-named species. The second genus, *Eochiromys*, which was recovered from the Lower Eocene Landenian deposits of Brabant, Belgium, comprises a right mandibular horizontal ramus with an incisor and molars one and two. Another mandible lacking any dentition was also recovered from the same site. In these remains the incisors were large, elongated and trihedral and there was no diastema. Other teeth found in the same locality may belong to the insectivores which are also known from the region. In fact the type genus of the family, *Apatemys*, which was recovered from the Middle Eocene Bridgerian deposits of North America, is, according to Hill, less certainly apatemyid in character than the foregoing genera. The genera *Stehlinella* from the Upper Eocene Uinta deposits of Utah, *Sinclairella*, represented by a single crushed skull and mandible from the Chadron formation of Washington County, Dakota, and *Apatemys*, seem to have replaced the Lower Eocene genus *Teilhardella* in North America. In the European region it seems probable that the variable *Heterohyus* replaced, and indeed evolved from, *Eochiromys*. These European genera appear to have persisted until the final phases of the Eocene, whilst in North America *Sinclairella* persisted until the Oligocene period, when it too seems to have become extinct.

CARPOLESTIDAE

Besides the two families discussed above, other insectivore/primate-like remains are also known from the lower Tertiary period. The Carpolestidae of Simpson (1935) comprise a small but very distinctive group with many insectivore and tarsioid affinities. As in the case of so many early primates they are only known from jaws and teeth. These latter organs were in fact characterized by the remarkable degree of specialization undergone by the premolars, and more especially the hind premolars, of both jaws. These teeth are quite different from those of all lower mammals and approach the conditions known elsewhere only amongst primitive primates. As both Simpson and Hill remark, this by no means indicates conclusively that the carpolestids are primates. Nevertheless, in the absence of further anatomical material, one must by definition classify them as such. In fact the molars suggest affinities with the fossil tarsioids noted below, but according to Hill these affinities are not very much greater than those with the Plesiadapidae, and the remains also suggest affinities with the adapid lemurs. Hill (1953) concludes that the Carpolestidae are a generalized group on the insectivore/primate boundary in which the known anatomical and dental characters foreshadow those of the later and undoubted primates.

The dental formula appears to have been $I_1^2:C_0^0:P_4^{12}:M_3^3$, and the upper dentition is very unusual. It is amongst the most peculiar in the Mammalia. An isolated upper premolar from Bear Creek, Montana, was originally considered by Simpson (1929) to be that of a multituberculate. Jepson (1930), in a consideration of an upper jaw, pointed out that this was not the case. In fact the hindmost upper premolars do resemble those of the multituberculates, but the molars do not. The premolars of *Carpodaptes* are simpler, and consequently it is suggested that the complex forms may have evolved from simpler ones similar to those known amongst the species of *Plesiadapis*.

Confined to the Middle and Upper Paleocene of North America, the family includes 3 known genera, namely *Carpodaptes*, *Carpolestes* and *Elphidotarsius*. Of these, *Elphidotarsius*, which was originally considered to be a tarsioid but removed to the Carpolestidae by Simpson (1937), appears to be the oldest. It consists of the species *Elphidotarsius florencae* Gidley, represented by a left mandibular fragment with the fourth premolar and third molar which was found at Gidley Quarry, Sweet Grass County, Montana. This fragment therefore occurs in the Fort Union Beds and is of Middle Paleocene age.

Carpodaptes, consisting of the two species *C. aulacodon* Matthew and Granger and *C. hazelae* Simpson, is probably the next oldest of the three genera. The genus is known from three mandibular fragments from the Tiffany Beds of south-west Colorado and the Fort Union Beds of the Crazy Mountain Field in Montana. *Carpolestes* is probably the most recent and highly evolved, as suggested above. It is distinguished from *Carpodaptes* by its generally larger size and the modified premolars. Three species of this more advanced genus are known and they occur in the Upper Paleocene deposits of Montana and Wyoming.

ADAPIDAE

Amongst the Strepsirhines, the lemurs are characterized by the pelvic limbs being longer than the pectoral ones and by the fact that in the ear the scapha, unlike that of the Lorisoidea, is incapable of folding. Generalized fossil forms which are probably true lemurs are represented by many remains, some of which are extraordinarily complete, known from the Tertiary

179

deposits of both North America and Europe. In fact the genera from these two regions are consistently different from each other so that Stehlin (1912, 1916) suggested that they should be classed in separate families. Hill (1953) relegates these differences to a sub-familial level, and classes all the fossil lemurs together as the Adapidae. These he defines as primitive and generalized forms with a small ovoid brain-case bearing a strong sagittal crest, a prominent and heavy facial region with smallish orbits and the dental formula $I_{\frac{2}{2}}:C_{\frac{1}{1}}:P_{\frac{4}{4}}:M_{\frac{3}{3}}$. The lower incisors are normal in shape and not modified as they are in the existing modern lemurs. The upper molars are trituber-cular and have large V-shaped protocones and small hypocones. The earliest discovery of such forms was made by Cuvier in the Paris gypsum. These skulls designated *Adapis* were originally thought to be ungulates. Only the work of Gaudry (1878) and also Filhol exemplified their primate status. Subsequently the works of Gregory (1915, 1920) on *Notharctus* and Matthew and Granger (1915) on the Lower Eocene Wasatch and Wind River faunas has increased our knowledge of the family. These conclusions are supplemented by Abel (1931), Gregory (1934), Heller (1930, 1935), Le Gros Clark (1934, 1954), Stehlin (1912, 1916), and Weigelt (1933).

In general these fossil forms differ from modern lemurs in their smaller brain-case and bulkier facial region of the skull. The conspicuous sagittal and lambdoidal crests suggest that there were well developed nuchal and temporal muscles. The cranial capacity is rather smaller than that of modern genera due to a sharp post-orbital constriction of the cranium. The bulla seems to have been less developed than in existing lemuroids, but the arterial foramina are exactly comparable (Hill, 1953).

The bulk of the axial and appendicular skeleton is known in detail for the genus *Notharctus* (Gregory, 1920). The vertebral column seems to have been held in the horizontal position. The bones of the limbs appear to be more primitive than those of the lemurs and the humerus is relatively short with a somewhat curved shaft, in contrast to the modern species. In the case of the central nervous system, endocranial casts show that there was a proportionately smaller and less advanced brain than amongst modern forms. In *Notharctus* the brain was more elongated than in *Adapis*, with large olfactory lobes which are joined to the cerebrum by long thick peduncles. The surface of the cerebral hemispheres seems to have been quite smooth and the cerebellum was exposed dorsally.

The chief distinctions between the North American and European fossil genera lie in the dentition. In the sub-family Adapinae the hypocones of the upper molars are true hypocones as in modern lemurs. The differences in the molars of the Notharctinae are correlated with the corresponding differences in the normal paths of the mandibular excursion during mastication. In the Adapinae the excursion remained more vertical than in the Notharctinae. The different movements reflect upon the form of the condyles which in the Adapinae resemble those of carnivores, being broad from side to side and narrow antero-posteriorly. These contrast with the more rounded condyles of the Notharctinae (Hill, 1953).

The European genera occur in the Eocene deposits of England, France, Germany and Switzerland. Simpson (1940) includes in the sub-family the genera *Adapis*, *Pronycticebus* and *Anchomys*. *Adapis* includes several species arranged by Stehlin (1912) in two groups corresponding to *Adapis parisiensis* and *Adapis (Leptadapis) magnus* from the Eocene deposits of France and southern England. Both species groups appear first of all in the Bartonian, and in the case of *Adapis parisiensis*, persisted until the end of the Eocene period. In contrast *Adapis magnus* seems to have become extinct somewhat earlier, namely prior to the Upper Ludian.

Anchomys includes 4 species differentiated by Hill (1953) on the tubercles of the first and second upper molars. They are small fossil primates recovered from the Eocene deposits of France and Switzerland and so named because of supposed similarities with the dentition of the American fossil tarsioid *Omomys*. On the basis of the adapine skull structure of the related *Pronycticebus* outlined by Le Gros Clark (1934), Simpson (1940) classes both genera as Adapinae.

Alongside the foregoing genera, Hill (1953) and Simpson (1940) place *Caenopithecus*, *Protoadapis*, *Europolemur* and *Amphilemur*. The first, *Caenopithecus*, occurs in deposits of Lower and Middle Lutetian age at Egerkingen, Switzerland, whilst *Protoadapis* is known from calcareous and conglomerate deposits of Thanetian age at Cernay near Rheims in France, and at Abbey Wood, Kent, in the United Kingdom. In this latter location it occurs alongside the pantodont genus *Coryphodon* and the tetradactylous hippomorph *Hyracotherium*. Both *Caenopithecus* and *Protoadapis* and the other two genera, *Europolemur* and *Amphilemur* from Upper Lutetian lignites at Halle, Germany, are of more or less doubtful affinities. They are often represented by only limited anatomical remains, in the case of *Europolemur* and *Amphilemur* these coming from a single site, and are apparently to be relegated to a single species within the genus. Of these additional genera *Protoadapis*, coming as it does from deposits of Paleocene age, is the oldest European lemuroid apart from the Plesiadapidae mentioned above. It persisted into post-Cuisian times according to Simpson (1929) and corresponds in the American fauna with *Pelycodus* from the Wasatch Beds of Mexico and Wyoming. Although an early genus, it was in fact originally raised to cover remains ascribable to the two species *Protoadapis cuspidens* and *Protoadapis recticuspidens* which, although only distinguishable with difficulty, are probably valid and separate species. A third species considered originally to be *Adapis* was added to these two species by Teilhard de Chardin, who is followed by Hill (1953).

The American fossils which are considered, as noted above, to constitute the related but separate sub-family Notharctinae, include the type genus *Notharctus* with some ten species, and also *Pelycodus*, a contemporary of the European Paleocene *Protoadapis*, and, in addition, the more questionable genus *Aphanolemur*. This last genus was created by Granger and Gregory (1917) for a single incomplete cranium from the Bridger formation of Wyoming. The shape of the skull is in fact suggestive of the tarsioids, but it agrees with *Notharctus* in its fundamental structure. The lachrymal bone lies within the orbit and has a wide contact with the frontalia. The form and relations of the post-orbital processes of the malar and frontal are similar to those of *Notharctus*, and the structure of the tympanic bulla and the course of the internal carotid are comparable. In addition to these three genera, Simpson (1940) suggested that *Caenopithecus*, considered above as a doubtful adapine, and *Protoadapis* of comparable status, should also be classed as notharctines.

However, Hill (1953) suggests that these are best left alongside the other European genera in the Adapinae. This seems a very sensible, if perhaps temporary, conclusion.

HAPLORHINI

In contrast to all the foregoing fossils which are broadly speaking related to the lemurs, lorises, pottos and aye-aye, all the remaining living and fossil forms are classed together as the Haplorhini. The principal characteristic which links all the living forms is the absence of a philtrum. That is to say there is no connection between the nose and the upper lip. Together with this character there occurs the presence of a post orbital partition and a discoidal or bi-discoidal placenta. Full details of the various organ systems are included in the immense work of Hill (1953). In general some degree of gregariousness is a constant feature in the life of Haplorhini. Most forms, like the living Strepsirhini, are fairly omnivorous. In contrast, however, some are highly specialized feeders. The omnivores tend to eat fruit, nuts, bark, leaves and seeds, whilst the specialized feeders are limited either to leaves or bark, or to certain types of these. These latter comprise the haplorhine counterparts to the strepsirhine indrises, and are represented by the Howler monkeys (*Alouatta*) of the neotropical regions, and the langurs and colobus monkeys of the paleotropics. Haplorhini also differ from the Strepsirhini in not using the teeth as a comb. Instead the hands and lips are used and characteristically there is a considerable degree of mutual toilet in which one individual cleans his fellows. This seems to play an important part in the social behaviour of the groups, which are organized on the basis of a dominance hierarchy amongst the adult males (Chance, 1953). The females menstruating, not having oestrus cycles like the remainder of the mammals, the social organization appears to be of two types. In the macaques the dominant male has access to the most receptive female, that is to say the one at the nearest point in the cycle to ovulation. Subordinate males have access to females progressively further removed in their cycle from ovulation, and less receptive. In contrast to this condition the social structure of baboons (Zuckermann, 1932, Hall, 1962) involves the dominant male having access to the largest actual number of females, irrespective of their phase in the menstrual cycle, and hence their receptivity. The net result of the female behaviour pattern is that she is sexually receptive for at least one-quarter of her fertile life instead of one-twelfth as in most mammals. Since the young are born at a relatively immature stage and mature sexually before they mature anatomically, young sexually mature males are in the presence of sexually receptive females before they are sufficiently developed themselves to be able to challenge and fight the dominant and anatomically mature males. Indeed when they initially attempt to assert their dominance they are driven from the family group. It seems highly probable that the overcoming of this conflict of motive in the young sexually mature males was the greatest single obstacle met in the psychological and neurological evolution to the complex social life of man.

The brain of the haplorhines is invariably large in proportion to the size of the body and, furthermore, in relation to the total head size, as compared

182

with that of the strepsirhines. Chance (1953) also suggests, with regard to the conflict situation outlined above, that the amygdaloid nucleus, associated with the control of temper in frustration situations, is also relatively larger in primates, and progressively more so in more man-like forms. In general, however, the enlargement of the brain involves only the cerebral hemispheres. The olfactory regions give way in size to the optic regions, which are progressively larger in the tarsioids, pongids and hominids. In all living primates above *Tarsius* the cerebrum in fact attains very voluminous proportions and even in the relatively primitive Cebidae it is larger proportionately than in man. Corresponding to the decrease in importance of olfaction, the size of the pyriform lobe is reduced and it is displaced downwards and finally on to the lower or even medial aspect of the hemisphere by the increasing size of the neopallium. The formation of gyri and sulci on this neopallium produces the complicated convolutional patterns on all primate brains above the South American Hapalidae (marmosets).

TARSIOIDEA

Following Hill (1953) one may consider the tarsiers as Haplorhini of small, or even minute, size with relatively enormous eyes. These overshadow and compress laterally the nasal region. The fully ossified orbits are separated by bone from the temporal fossa. About 30 fossil genera are currently allocated to the sub-order but many of these are only imperfectly known. All these Eocene forms are summarized by Gidley (1923). In view of the scarcity of our anatomical knowledge they are usually classed as Tarsioidea on the basis of their links with other genera of undoubted tarsioid affinities. Many of them would be equally satisfactorily classed within the lemuroid families of Hill (1953). All are true primates, and the nearctic genus *Tetonius* and the European genera *Necrolemur* and *Pseudoloris*, are conclusively tarsioid. However, they lack the specializations of the surviving species *Tarsius syrichta* Linn., *Tarsius bancanus* Hors and *Tarsius spectrum* Pallas. It would in fact be reasonable to consider the tarsioid forms of Eocene age as a generalized stock from which all the later primate genera, as well as the modern tarsioids, evolved.

The early tarsioids appear in Middle Paleocene deposits alongside the earliest strepsirhines. In North America they were represented by 4 genera as early as the Upper Paleocene and by the subsequent Lower Eocene, deposits show that this had been increased to 5 genera, of which only *Tetonius* was a relict genus already present in the Upper Paleocene. At this time fossil forms are already known to be present in Europe in the form of *Teilhardina*. The American genera persisted until the latest phase of the Middle Eocene with stragglers in the Upper Eocene and Lower Oligocene. In Europe the Upper Eocene seems to have seen a considerable flowering of the tarsioids. However, before the end of the subsequent Oligocene period all the tarsioids disappeared from the northern temperate region. It seems that at this period they were replaced by the more advanced haplorhines and retreated southwards either in the face of a deteriorating or changing climate, or because of competition from these self-same advanced haplorhine genera. Both reasons may explain the change in distribution.

All these fossil genera are usually classified separately from the living species in the Microchoeridae or Anaptomorphidae. Some authors also include them all in the Tarsiidae whilst others consider that there are sufficient differences between the American and European fossil genera for them to be classified in the separate families Necrolemuridae and Anaptomorphidae comparable with the lemuroid sub-families Adapinae and Notharctinae.

Hill (1953) follows the first suggestion and classes them all as Microchoeridae. In these Paleocene and Eocene tarsioids the orbits are less extravagantly enlarged than in the Tarsiidae and as a result the nasal region is less compressed. The dental formula is primitive but variable and in *Omomys belgicus* there are three pairs of lower incisors whilst *Pseudoloris* has three pairs of upper incisors. In *Hemiacodon*, *Washakius* and *Anaptomorphus* the lower incisors are reduced and they can be entirely lost as in *Necrolemur*. Similarly the premolars can be specialized and in *Tetonius* and *Absarokius* the upper ones are enlarged. All of the four lower incisors may be present, but there is a tendency for them to be reduced.

Although the genera are typically of Eocene and Paleocene age, and known from the European and American regions, there are, in the uppermost Eocene and early Oligocene deposits of Asia, remains which have been tentatively associated with the definitive forms of the family. According to Hill (1953) there are about thirty genera. The similarities between them are few and in fact they are associated largely on the basis of negative characteristics as is so often the case in the mammalian genera of early Tertiary age, and noted in the discussion of Condylarthra and Creodonta in Chapters 7 and 8.

On the basis of the dentition the Microchoeridae are further grouped into the 5 sub-families Paramomyinae, Microchoerinae, Omomyinae, Anaptomorphinae and Pseudolorisinae. The Paramomyinae are classified together on the basis of two pairs of enlarged anterior teeth and include the 4 genera *Palenochtha*, *Palechthon*, *Paromomys* and *Plesiolestes*, all of Middle Paleocene age. The Omomyinae is somewhat larger and includes some 10 genera, the Anaptomorphinae 6 genera, the Pseudolorisinae only 1 genus and the Microchoerinae 4 genera. These latter microchoerinine genera occur in the European strata of Middle to Upper Eocene age and have been arranged in an elaborate but speculative phylogenetic series by Hurzeler (1948). *Necrolemur filholi* Chantre and Gaillard is first recorded from Middle or Lower Lutetian deposits. In the Upper Lutetian it was replaced by *Necrolemur* cf. *zitteli* and in the Bartonian by *Necrolemur zitteli sensu stricto*. The group is thought to have originated from *Teilhardina* of Sparnacian deposits and *Necrolemur antiquus* of the Lower Ludian is represented as a direct descendant of this line. The group spans the Lower Lutetian to Upper Ludian phases of the Eocene period. As in the case of the independent hippomorph perissodactyl and lemuroid lines, these forms were contemporary with comparable North American genera. Gregory (1922) has suggested diphyletic evolution for the group as there is no genus common to Europe and America. However, if *Teilhardina* and *Omomys* are in fact one genus, as has been suggested, then this animal would have been common to the two areas in Sparnacian times. In any case the two genera are very closely related (Hill, 1953).

The forms classed together in the sub-order *Pithecoidea* of Pocock (1918) or Anthropoidea of Simpson (1945) are haplorhines which vary in size from small genera such as *Cebuella* to animals of very large size such as *Gorilla* or *Homo*. They are all distinguished from both fossil and living tarsioids by their relatively small eyes. Other distinguishing features are the almost complete separation between orbits and temporal fossa, by an inward extension of the malar meeting the alisphenoid, and the pentadactyl limbs with each digit bearing a nail. The single exception to this last is the Hapalidae which have claw-like structures on all digits except the hallux. There is a single pair of pectoral mammae, and, except in abnormal conditions, none on the abdomen, a single median uterus and a deciduate metadiscoidal placenta.

The classical concepts of the Pithecoidea divided them into platyrrhine and catarrhine stems which correspond to the neotropical and paleotropical genera respectively. However, following Simpson, one may note that there are more probably three natural groups:

I. The Ceboidea, corresponding to the classical Platyrrhini.

II. The Cercopithecoidea, which includes the fossil genus *Parapithecus* and related forms together with the Colobidae and Cercopithecidae.

III. The Hominoidea, which includes the Hylobatidae, Pongidae and the hominids.

Groups II and III are the equivalent of the Catarrhini of earlier authors and have many more anatomical similarities to each other than either has with the neotropical Platyrrhini.

Ceboidea

The platyrrhine monkeys have large oval nares which are directed laterally and, with the exception of the two genera *Aotes* and *Brachyteles*, are separated by a broad internarial septum. The pollex is not completely opposable and in the mouth there is an additional premolar by comparison with the condition in the paleotropical Catarrhini. So many and diverse are the evolutionary adaptations of these New World monkeys that a concise general account of their comparative anatomy and behaviour is virtually impossible. In view of this wide speciation and fascinating unsolved relationship with the Old World genera it is doubly unfortunate that very few fossil specimens are known. Those that are known are further scattered through a number of geological horizons and it is therefore difficult to reconstruct their geological history. In view of the numerous remains of the ungulates obtained from Patagonia one can only hope that in the future the discovery of Tertiary deposits with a jungle facies will help to elucidate these problems and place our knowledge of them upon a firm factual foundation.

In the absence of this irrefutable basis, Simpson has pointed out that their comparative anatomy and distribution show that there is little doubt that all the ceboid genera represent the radiation of a single evolutionary stock isolated within the neotropical region during Tertiary times. In view of the fact that these South American animals differ so markedly from the Old World Catarrhines, and also that these last were already separated into their major evolutionary lines by the Oligocene, it would seem highly probable that the Platyrrhini were separated from the Afrasian stock in Paleocene times. At that time they became isolated in South America along with the Notoungulates and Litopterns. In view of the scant nature of the fossil record no final decision can be made upon the validity of this theory.

Cercopithecoidea

As noted above many authors seem to lose all sense of perspective when they are dealing with man and as one approaches nearer to this genus the confusion bequeathed to us by the myriads of students becomes increasingly greater. Some idea of this web of inter-related fact, fiction and carelessness can be gained by noting that the macaques alone have been ascribed to some 27 different generic names besides having been included with other forms in broader genera.

The living cercopithecoids are typically arboricolous and have a quadrupedal plantigrade gait. The face is prominent and can be developed into a true muzzle. There are rudimentary auditory bullae and 19 dorso-lumbar vertebrae. The molars are bilophodont and have two transverse crests. The placenta is bidiscoidal and there is usually a penial bone. In spite of the profusion of the modern genera and species in the paleotropical region the number of fossil forms is again unfortunately small.

Mandibular remains of the early genera *Moeripithecus* and *Apidium* from the Lower Oligocene deposits of Egypt are of disputed taxonomic position but placed in association with the Cercopithecidae by Simpson (1945). This is also the case with the later remains which were ascribed to a genus *Oreopithecus* from the Italian Lower Pliocene. However, both the sub-families Cercopithecinae and Colobinae have authenticated fossil genera of Pliocene age. Those of the Cercopithecinae comprise *Simopithecus* from the Upper Pliocene or Lower Pleistocene in East Africa and *Lybipithecus* from the Middle Pliocene of Egypt. Of these *Simopithecus* is very similar to, and may well be the ancestor of, the modern Ethiopian *Theropithecus* from which it differs principally in having a shorter face. *Lybipithecus* possessed a strongly developed sagittal crest and a well-developed canine.

The Colobinae seem to have been well-distributed throughout Europe during the early Pliocene. *Mesopithecus pentelici* Wag. is represented by numerous examples in deposits of Upper Miocene age in Greece where it is included in the Pikermi fauna. Virtually complete skeletons are available which show that these animals were small monkeys of about 30 cm in height with a short muzzle. There appears to have been some degree of sexual dimorphism in the development of the canines since these appear to have been larger in the males. The limbs were approximately equal in length and there was a tail whose length exceeded that of the body. Similar species are also known from contemporaneous deposits in Czechoslovakia, Iran, and in the southern region of the U.S.S.R. Somewhat more primitive remains have also been reported from Kenya. During the Pliocene there were also other colobids in the Mediterranean region. In France both *Dolichopithecus* and

Semnopithecus occur in deposits of this age and seem to have persisted there to occur in the Villafranchian fauna at the beginning of the Quaternary.

Hominoidea

There are a large number of fossil remains of the Hominoidea contained within deposits situated at widespread localities throughout the Old World. These forms represent both modern sub-families of the Pongidae together with two entirely fossil sub-families the Dryopithecinae and the Australopithecinae. Together with these one must also of course cite the various genera of men Leakey (1953), Le Gros Clark (1954) and Oakley (1950).

In fact the earliest ape of which we have any remains is perhaps *Parapithecus*. This is sufficiently different from all the foregoing forms to be classed in the monogeneric fossil family Parapithecidae. It is known from a lower jaw which was discovered in the Oligocene deposits at Fayum in Egypt. Judging by its size it was a small animal and comparable in many respects to the physiognomy of the European squirrel. It had two incisors, a canine, two premolars and three molars. As a result we know that even by this relatively early Tertiary period the typical dental formula of the Old World monkeys and anthropoid apes had been attained. The canine was a relatively small tooth and was in fact very similar to the premolars in shape. These are themselves reminiscent of the teeth of the Eocene tarsioids as is the shape of the jaw fragment itself. In contrast, the structure of the molars resembles a somewhat simplified anthropoid pattern. Indeed, in view of this, what might be considered generalized pattern, it is conceivable that this genus may be close to the ancestry of all later anthropoid forms.

A contemporary of this small generalized genus which is also recorded from the same Lower Oligocene deposits in Egypt is the larger *Propliopithecus*. In size it is comparable to a small gibbon which it also resembles in its dentition. The teeth were, however, simpler in structure and the canine significantly less prominent than in the gibbons. Le Gros Clark (1954) suggests that *Propliopithecus* represents an evolutionary stage somewhat more advanced than that of *Parapithecus* along the evolutionary line leading to the later and living anthropoids. In any case it is clear from these very fragmentary remains that small primitive anthropoids were differentiated from the other Primate and more especially catarrhine stock at least by the Oligocene. Indeed Le Gros Clark suggests that these records are of such an early date that they indicate that the anthropoid apes have evolved from Eocene tarsioid ancestors without the separate intervention of a cercopithecid phase. In agreement with the suggestions of Simpson (1945) this would therefore indicate that the three major haplorhine groups, the Ceboidea, Cercopithecoidae and Hominoidea, were well differentiated as long ago as the Lower Oligocene.

In contrast to these sparse remains of Oligocene age there are a considerable number of hominoid fossils of Miocene age. These represent a very varied fauna which existed in the central regions of Africa and occur as fossils in deposits situated around Lake Victoria. These animals ranged in size from small animals, comparable to the Oligocene *Propliopithecus*, to large apes the size of the modern gorillas. The small forms are classified together with the gibbons and *Propliopithecus* in the Hylobatidae, since one of them,

187

Limnopithecus, must have been closely similar to the Asiatic gibbon genera of today.

The larger remains of Kenyan Miocene apes are ascribed to a separate fossil sub-family. This includes some 8 genera which are known from 500 specimens in the Miocene of Kenya and from others from Europe and India. The Miocene genus *Proconsul* is in fact suggested as an ancestor of the chimpanzee by Le Gros Clark (1954) and others. If this were the case it would suggest that the entirely fossil Dryopithecinae are in fact late Tertiary forms ancestral to at least certain of the Pleistocene and living Ponginae.

Most of the Kenyan remains are, as in the case of the Egyptian Oligocene remains, only fragmentary collections of teeth and incomplete jaws. However, in 1948 the greater part of a skull of *Proconsul* was recovered. Several of the features of this skull, such as the smooth forehead, small size of the neuro-cranium by comparison with the jaws, and the form of the nasal apertures, suggest that it is much more primitive than the modern African apes. In fact these characters would rather suggest affinities with the catarrhine monkeys.

The few and incomplete skeletal remains of the early Miocene apes which have so far been found indicate that the larger types were of a much lighter build than the modern apes. Le Gros Clark suggests that in association with this they were more agile and active. He bases these conclusions on the slender character of the humerus and femur and the characteristics of the ankles. He also suggested in this context that they were less specialized for brachiating through the trees than modern apes. The limb bones of the gibbon-like *Limnopithecus* also show that they had not developed the excessively long arms which are so characteristic of the living Hylobatidae.

The structure of the jaws and dentition lacks the specializations which are characteristic of the modern paleotropical anthropoid apes. In this respect it appears that in terms of their relationships within the temporo-spatial distribution of Primate evolution they were more closely allied to the various genera of sub-men, and indeed to man himself, than are the modern anthropoids. An example of such generalized traits lies in the absence of a simian shelf. This last-named structure is characteristic of the modern anthropoids and results from the great enlargement of the incisor teeth together with an increase in the width of the anterior end of the jaw. It is absent from man and its absence from the skulls of these Miocene genera shows that it is an adaptation which has probably taken place during Pliocene or Quaternary time.

By the end of the Miocene, if not actually at the time during which *Limnopithecus* and *Proconsul* were living in Kenya, similar genera were sufficiently widespread to occur as fossils in the European region. *Dryopithecus* itself, which gives its name to the sub-family, is known from western and central Europe in deposits of Upper Miocene and Lower Pliocene age. Numerous specimens of this genus have been described, they possess a simian shelf in their jaw and show a considerable amount of variation in their dentition. These variations can be variously interpreted but, in corroboration of the suggestion made in connection with *Proconsul*, they do appear to represent possible ancestral stages leading to the chimpanzees, gorillas and orang-utans. With the exception of a humerus and a femur few other skeletal remains of these species of *Dryopithecus* are known. Both these limb bones were discovered in Europe and were ascribed to a giant gibbon designated *Paido-pithex*, (Simpson, 1945) within the Hylobatinae. However, Le Gros Clark (1954), Leakey (1953) and others consider that this is not the case and that the remains are of a large species of *Dryopithecus*. This suggestion is supported by the similarity between the shape of the femur and those of the early Miocene apes. The humerus is a slender bone and lacks the well-developed

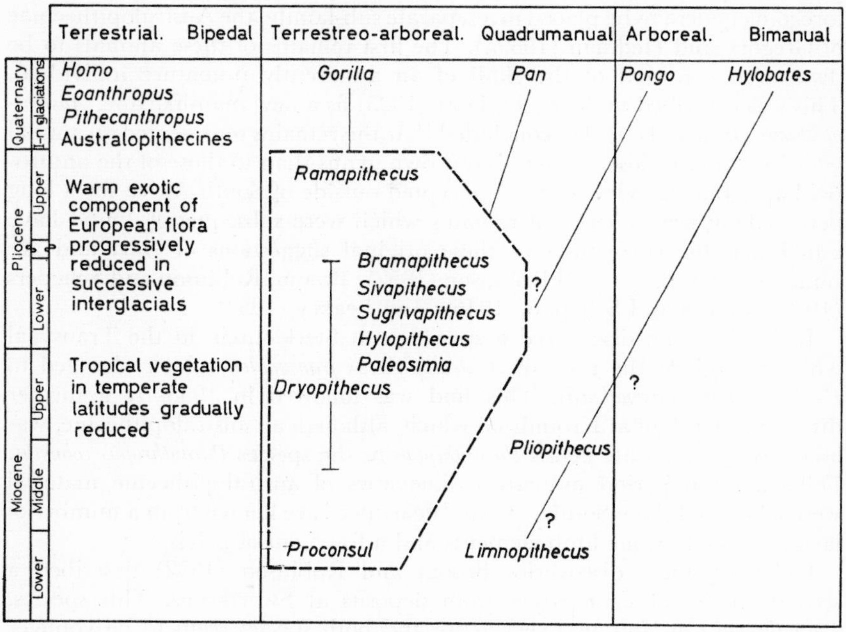

		Terrestrial. Bipedal	Terrestreo-arboreal. Quadrumanual	Arboreal. Bimanual
Quaternary (n glaciations)		Homo Eoanthropus Pithecanthropus Australopithecines	Gorilla Pan	Pongo Hylobates
Pliocene	Upper	Warm exotic component of European flora progressively reduced in successive interglacials	Ramapithecus	
Pliocene	Lower		Bramapithecus Sivapithecus ? Sugrivapithecus Hylopithecus Paleosimia	
Miocene	Upper	Tropical vegetation in temperate latitudes gradually reduced	Dryopithecus	?
Miocene	Middle			Pliopithecus
Miocene	Lower		Proconsul Limnopithecus	?

Figure 34. Diagram illustrating the possible evolutionary relationships of some of the late Tertiary and Recent Primates together with their ecological characteristics

ridges for the insertion of the powerful arm muscles which occur in the gorillas and chimpanzees. This suggests that the arms of *Dryopithecus* had not undergone the increase in length of the modern anthropoids.

In fact *Dryopithecus* seems to have been more widespread than even the last few paragraphs would suggest. During the Pliocene there seems to have been an endemic primate fauna in India comparable with the endemic ungulate fauna known from the Siwaliks. Within this fauna occurred forms similar to *Dryopithecus* and *Proconsul*. However, these appear to have been sufficiently different from the African and European genera to be ascribed to separate genera. Of these *Sivapithecus, Hylopithecus, Paleosimia, Sugrivapithecus* and *Bramapithecus* are from deposits which are thought to be of Lower Pliocene age, whilst *Ramapithecus* of the Upper Pliocene is perhaps a descendant form. Since recent information on the age of the nut-cracker man *Zinjanthropus* would place this early tool-maker well back towards the late Pliocene, it is possible that more detailed information on these Indian Pliocene anthropoids might well provide sensational revelations of the degree and nature of the speciation of hominid-like Primates. Unfortunately the information which is available consists of scattered finds of scanty remains and it is difficult to draw conclusions from them. In spite of these difficulties, Leakey (1953) concludes that although the majority of the remains are close to those of *Dryopithecus* in form, *Ramapithecus* and *Sivapithecus* are somewhat different and might well repay further study.

Another line of evolution which has become of immense interest in recent years comprises fossil remains sufficiently different from those of all the foregoing genera to be placed in a separate sub-family, the Australopithecinae of Gregory and Hellman (1939a). The first remains of these animals to be discovered consisted of the skull of an apparently immature individual. This was described in *Nature* by Dart (1925) as a new man-like ape, *Australopithecus africanus* Dart. He concluded that the remains represented an animal which was more closely allied to our own genus than to those of the anthropoid apes but this view was not accepted outside of South Africa for a long period. However, a series of remains which were subsequently found have established the correctness of these original suggestions of Dart and are summarized in Broom and Robinson (1952); Broom, Robinson and Schepers (1950); Broom and Schepers (1946); and Leakey (1953).

In 1936 Broom discovered a specimen at Sterkfontein in the Transvaal which was given the rank of *Australopithecus transvaalensis* later changed to *Plesianthropus transvaalensis*. This find was followed in 1938 by a further discovery of a skull at Kromdraai which, although an australopithecine, was ascribed to a separate genus *Paranthropus* as the species *Paranthropus robustus*. Following this period numerous discoveries of australopithecine material were made and these South African 'near-men' are known from a number of jaws and skulls, some limb elements and a fragment of pelvis.

Following these discoveries Broom and Robinson (1952) described a second species of *Paranthropus* from deposits at Swartkrans. This species, *Paranthropus crassidens*, was very large and both species seem to be younger than *Plesianthropus transvaalensis*. Leakey (1953) indeed suggested that the age of the various remains was such that the original *Australopithecus* find was the oldest and the two genera *Plesianthropus* and *Paranthropus* were of progressively more recent date. A second species *Australopithecus prometheus* is probably younger than *Australopithecus africanus* and contemporary with the later *Plesianthropus*.

Following this early work Leakey (1959) reported a new fossil australopithecine skull from the Olduvai Gorge in Tanganyika. Remains of *Hipparion*, *Dinotherium* and a chalicothere skull had also been found in this deposit. The australopithecine remains were in the process of being eroded out of the sides of the gorge and were therefore partially exposed. It was in fact an almost complete skull and in its stratigraphical position was associated with a well-defined floor of the Olduwan, pre-Chelles-Acheul culture. Upon the floor there were Olduwan tools and waste flakes together with the fossil remains of splintered bones of birds, amphibians and reptiles which had presumably constituted the hominids' diet. In certain respects the skull recalls that of *Parapithecus*, particularly in the presence of a sagittal crest, reduced size of the canines and incisors, the position of the nasal spines and the flatness of the frontalia. In other characters it resembles *Australopithecus*, for example it has a high cranial vault, a deep palate, which is in fact very similar to that of man, and M³ is smaller than M². However, Leakey (1959) considers that the remains differ from those of these genera more than they differ between themselves. As a result he places the new finds in a separate genus *Zinjanthropus*.

The type specimen consists of a young male with the sutures relatively open. The faunal remains led Leakey to equate the level with the upper half of the Villafranchian and not the lower part of the Middle Quaternary. Dated by potassium/argon analysis at 1·5 million years B.P. it therefore represents the oldest known hominoid associated with artefacts, and also suggests that if the equation of the strata with the Quaternary is correct then this latter represents a period of 1·5 million years not, as previously defined, the last million years.

Subsequently more recent work has resulted in the discovery of further skull fragments, dentition, a nearly complete tibia and fibula, as well as what appear to be the remains of a pelvic girdle, left foot, six carpals and two ribs. Associated with these was a bone tool which Leakey (1960) suggests may have been used for scraping leather.

The general features of the skull of the australopithecines other than *Zinjanthropus* are as follows. In absolute size the neurocranium compares with that of the living apes, and reached a volume of 600 c.c. or larger, and as such had a cranial capacity equal to about half that of man. Le Gros Clark (1954) suggested that this represents a proportionally larger brain in relation to body size than occurs in the chimpanzee and gorilla. Endocranial studies also suggest that the pattern of the cerebral convolutions might have been more complicated than in those animals. The jaws were massive and projecting and had large molar teeth. In the particularly well-preserved skull from Sterkfontein the muscular ridges, characteristic of the anthropoid apes, are less developed. The nuchal crest which serves for the attachment of the trapezius and neck muscles generally is at a level more coincident with that of fossil human skulls. In relation to this the forehead is also rather similar to that of *Homo* but retains heavily built supra-orbital ridges although the latter do not project in the form of a torus or supra-orbital shelf as they do in the African apes today. As the braincase is set higher in relation to the face than is the case in the apes the orbital region and zygomatic arch have a remarkably human appearance. Le Gros Clark suggests that this is related to the bending upward of the basal axis of the skull, a feature characterizing the human skull in contrast to that of the apes.

The foramen magnum of the australopithecines is of particular interest. In at least 5 skulls this has been sufficiently well preserved to be investigated and the results show that the occipital condyles are further forward than in the dryopithecines or apes. Together with the low nuchal crest this forward position of the condyles suggests an upright posture and a terrestrial bipedal gait in which the skull is balanced on the top of the vertebral column. This suggestion is further supported by the human form of the ilium although this posture and gait could not have been so well developed as in ourselves.

From the foregoing paragraphs it is clear that the Hominoidea appeared in the early Oligocene and that by the end of the Pliocene the evolutionary line had resulted in the australopithecine forms whose degree of behaviouristic complexity enabled them to use tools. In terms of classical anthropology such tool-makers were by definition men. This being the case the early ideas of Le Gros Clark (1954) and others that the australopithecines were pre-hominid is clearly an overstatement. If they were responsible for the pro-duction and use of the Olduwan tools they may perhaps represent a com-parable stage to the Asiatic species *Pithecanthropus erectus*. Remains of this species were originally discovered by the Dutch anthropologist Dubois in central Java over 50 years ago. The remains included fragmentary parietalia and a femur. The capacity of the neurocranium is thought to have been about 900 c.c. and as such to represent an intermediate stage between the Dryopi-thecinae, Ponginae and Australopithecinae on the one hand and man on the other. Further discoveries made during the period 1936–1939 produced the remains of a massive lower jaw, an adult skull, the posterior region and roof of a third skull and also that of an infant. This had a small cranial capacity by comparison with that of European children, it being *ca.* 700 instead of 1,000 c.c., and even at the young age of approximately one year there were prominent supra-orbital ridges, and the forehead, which is prominent in the young of both apes and man, is retreating. A further find which was made in Java in 1941 comprised an enormous jaw whose size resulted in its being relegated to a separate genus *Meganthropus*. This is, however, still the subject of controversy and one must await the discovery of more complete remains before its precise relationships can be decided.

In contrast to the doubtful nature of these more recent Javanese remains, other fossil localities in the Asiatic region have provided undoubted skeletons of *Pithecanthropus*. The skulls of 14, and fragmentary remains of 40 individuals in all, including femora, a humerus, and scapulae, are known from China. These remains are so markedly distinct from the Javanese ones that they were originally designated *Sinanthropus* and are today considered to be a separate species within the Javanese genus, *Pithecanthropus pekinensis*. If the two species are considered together there is a considerable variation in endocranial parameters. In five of the Chinese skulls the neurocranial volume seems to vary between 850 and 1,300 c.c., in contrast to the *ca.* 750–900 c.c. of the Javanese specimens. Although this would suggest that *Pithecanthropus erectus* had the relatively smaller brain of the two, the overall size of the species was also small. However, no artefacts have been discovered in association with these Javanese remains although beds of a slightly more recent date contain the Patjitanian industry. This industry is similar in appearance to the roughly broken pieces of quartz, crudely flaked pebbles of greensand, quartzite and cherty rocks which constitute the Choukoutien industry associated with *Pithecanthropus pekinensis*. These results suggest that the genus was an early member of the stock to which the chopper tool and flake tool peoples of Eurasia belong (Oakley, 1950).

The fossil human jaw which was found in interglacial sands at Mauer, near Heidelberg, Germany, probably represents an almost contemporary but somewhat more evolved variant of the same stock. It was found in a riverine deposit associated with *Rhinoceros etruscus* and the proboscidean *Hesperoloxodon antiquus*. No flint implements were associated with it so that its generic status of *Homo heidelbergensis* is based entirely upon anatomical considerations. The jaw is of massive build and in the complete absence of a chin eminence has a somewhat simian appearance. The width of the vertical ramus and the shallowness of the notch on its upper border are also primitive features and indicate the presence of powerful masseter muscles. In contrast the dentition is fundamentally similar to that of man although relatively larger than in the case of European man.

The find of the incomplete skull at Swanscombe, Kent, consisted of a well-preserved occipital and parietal bone. As in the case of *Homo heidelbergensis* these were again found in association with remains of the proboscidean *Hesperoloxodon antiquus*. The presence of flint implements of the Acheulian culture is now further understood as an indicator of considerable behavioural complexity in view of West's work at Hoxne which was discussed in Chapter 4. This culture occurred at the last-named site during the latter phase of the Hoxnian (cf. Mindel/Riss) interglacial. Pollen-analytical results indicate that the culture was associated with a considerable amount of forest clearance and primitive agriculture, probably comparable to that carried out by the aborigines in the Indo-Malayan region today.

This early horticultural Acheulian industry was replaced in the subsequent interglacial period by the Mousterian culture and *Homo neanderthalensis*. This last appears to have persisted to the last glaciation and is known from remains at Dusseldorf, from Spy near Namur, Belgium, from La-Chapelle-aux-Saints in south-west France and at numerous other sites in Europe and elsewhere. These include Krapina, Croatia, where some twenty individuals were found, St. Brelade's Bay, Jersey; Italy, Palestine, Siberia, southern U.S.S.R. and north Africa. The main anatomical characteristics of this widespread species comprise the large skull with thick cranial walls and massive supra-orbital ridges, the retreating forehead, the characteristically flattened cranium and the large superior nuchal lines for the insertion of the trapezius. There are large orbita and nasal apertures and a prominent upper jaw with large air sinuses and a consequently inflated appearance. The plane of the foramen magnum is inclined somewhat backwards and gives a more forward tilt to the head when compared with *Homo sapiens*.

As in the case of the Heidelberg jaw there is a receding chin and a broad ramus for the attachment of the masseter muscles. In the axial and limb skeletons the cervical vertebrae have spinous processes for the insertion of the cervical muscles and there are thick curved shafts and large extremities to the limb bones. *Homo neanderthalensis* therefore seems to have differed from his successor *Homo sapiens* in having a stooping posture, perhaps a lumbering gait, and, although only 5 feet in height, was very muscular.

It seems that the replacement by *Homo sapiens* took place during the last glaciation and was complete by the Late-glacial Upper Paleolithic phase. As a result, the invasion of Europe from Eurasia gave rise to the tall Cro-Magnon race and its associated Aurignacian culture, the Predmostian race and associated Gravettian culture, and the rather Eskimo-like Chancelade race associated with the Magdalenian culture. Subsequently the cultures of the Mesolithic and Neolithic phases replaced these Paleolithic cultures. These occurred during the final Post-glacial climatic amelioration and afforestation. As a result the requirements of agriculture resulted in the widespread forest clearance already discussed in Chapter 5 (Oakley, 1950).

13

SYNTHESIS

Following the climatic deterioration which occurred in the final phases of the Cretaceous there was a marked improvement which resulted in the tropical conditions of the early Tertiary and more especially the Eocene. These conditions persisted until the Miocene when an overall deterioration seems to have begun which culminated in the final deterioration which caused the southward extension of the polar ice at the end of the Pliocene. This advance of the polar ice heralded in the Quaternary Period which is characterized by a series of alternating glacial and interglacial periods. During these glaciations the southward extension of the polar ice in the northern hemisphere, coupled with the advance of glaciers in the Alpine, Himalayan and North American arenas, brought peri-glacial conditions far south into those regions which are today the north temperate latitudes or to the lower altitudes of the tropical latitudes. Precise investigations of the limits of the New Drift show that at their maximum extent these polar ice sheets reached south to the south Wales coast and the Wash in the British Isles and to comparable latitudes elsewhere.

The results of Van der Hammen, Gignoux, and others suggest that this major cycle of climatic events, which lasted the entire length of the Tertiary and gave way to 5 or 6 shorter and more extreme climatic oscillations during the Quaternary, may be further divisible. The overall cycle of 60–70 million years may include some 10 shorter cycles of say 6 million years which are themselves divisible into three minor cycles of 2 million years.

In relation to this major 60–70 million year cycle the known variations of the Cretaceous climate are of considerable interest. Isotopic assays show that this earlier period of geological time lasted a total of about 70 million years. During this period it would seem, from the determinations of Lowenstam and Epstein, there was at least one major climatic cycle. In view of this, it appears that we are confronted with a series of major climatic cycles lasting 30 and 60 million years. The extent to which the events of the Quaternary may be compared with those which occurred at the end of the Cretaceous Period is as yet unknown. Lasting a total overall period of some 2 million years up until the present, the short-term climatic oscillations of the various glacial and interglacial periods may perhaps compare with short-term climatic variations at the Cretaceous/Cenozoic transition. In view of the earlier Pre-Cambrian and Carboniferous glaciations (Lacey, 1962), and the vegetational cycles reported from the Carboniferous by Dybova and Jachovicz (1957), they may also represent a further component in a far longer climatic cycle, or, alternatively, bear little or no relation to the foregoing glaciations. Whatever the answer to these stimulating and important questions may prove to be, it is clear that during and just prior to the Cenozoic Era there were major cycles of variation in the physical environment of the world. These resulted in a progressive deterioration in the climate during the later Tertiary and culminated in the alternating glacial and interglacial periods of the Quaternary.

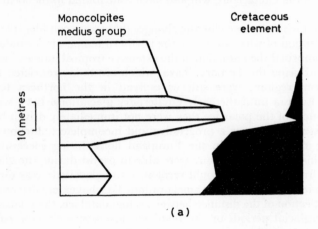

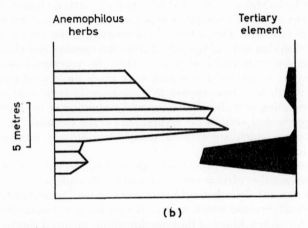

Figure 35. Pollen diagrams illustrating the changes of vegetation and presumably climate (a) at the Cretaceous/Tertiary transition; (b) at the Tertiary/Quaternary transition (simplified from van der Hammen, 1961)

Further modifications of the climates at particular parts of the world were caused by differences in their topography from one period to another during the Cenozoic. An example of these differences is provided by the conditions in the Panamanian region. No connection existed between North and South America throughout the majority of the Tertiary. The absence of this central American land-bridge resulted in considerable mixing of the waters of the Atlantic and Pacific Oceans. This intercommunication would have modified the climate of the neighbourhood in a manner similar to that suggested by Emiliani (1956). Since the orogenesis in the Californian and Himalayan regions is of relatively recent occurrence, tectonic activity of this kind, over and above that which occurred during the Laramide revolution at the end of the Cretaceous, will also have contributed to the local climatic variations.

Associated with all these climatic changes there were considerable changes in the vegetation of what are today the northern temperate latitudes. These changes comprised the reduction of the extensive tropical jungles which were widespread during the Tertiary. Taxa, which are today restricted to warm or American regions, were still widespread in the northern temperate regions of Eurasia until the early Quaternary glaciations. Even with these early advances of the polar ice they were not immediately driven from this region. Instead there was a progressive and incomplete reduction of their percentage representation in the European flora during successive inter-glacials. This suggests that many were able to persist during the glaciations in regions from which they could recolonize the glaciated areas during the subsequent interglacial climatic amelioration. To what extent this recoloniza-tion is a reflection of the distance between refugia and ice, the relative length of the interglacial periods or the relatively less severe climatic conditions during the early glaciations, it is not yet possible to say.

Aside from this reduction in the area of distribution of the components of the modern Indo-Malayan flora there is another marked change. This is the increase in the observed frequencies of occurrence of the herbaceous species in temperate latitudes. This tendency culminated in the extensive areas of open vegetation that were widespread during the opening and closing phases of each Quaternary interglacial period. Thus the vegetation in which the principal events of placental evolution took place underwent considerable changes. Nevertheless these appear to have been in large part a complex series of alternating periods of extension and restriction of the species limits. It would appear that even in the earliest part of the Cenozoic the genera of the angiosperms which are existing today were already present in some regions of the world.

Within the environment provided by these changing climatic and vegeta-tional conditions the various orders of placentals underwent an extensive evolution. From the deltatherioid insectivores of the Djadochta Cretaceous deposits, animals evolved which were suited for life in the numerous special-ized ecological niches. Many of these modifications involved similar anatom-ical changes in only distantly related genera.

This parallel evolution is, of course, an outstanding characteristic of zoology and we need not discuss it in any further detail. Similarly the known methods by which viable forms within the varied populations of a species are selected by natural selection and the methods by which particular character-istics are distributed through populations in time and space have been sum-marized by numerous authors, notably Carter (1954), Dobzhansky (1937), Mayr (1942), Sheppard (1958) and Simpson (1944).

Simpson has pointed out that the rates of evolution are not identical in all taxa of animals. Some taxa remain relatively unchanged over long periods of time whilst, on the contrary, others change with rapidity, and yet others at a rate intermediate between that of these two. The slow evolution he termed bradytely, the fast tachytely and the 'normal' or intermediate rate horotely. In his terminology the outstanding representatives of the slow rate would be the lamellibranch genera *Lima*, *Ostrea* and *Nucula* and the brachiopod *Lingula*. All these genera have remained unchanged in their anatomical characteristics since the Paleozoic. In these terms none of the mammalian genera or evolutionary lines can represent anything slower than horotely. Indeed the equid hippomorphs, the brontotherioids and elephantoids, together with all the actively radiating lines of mammals, are horotelic. Tachytelic evolution may strictly be exemplified by the change from browsing to grazing amongst the equids. In a more general sense there was, however, a tachytelic phase of evolution amongst all the placental mammals during the early phases of the Cenozoic.

Simpson has, in fact, justifiably suggested that bradytely is the result of an adaptation by a widespread population, tolerant of considerable environmental variation, to a relatively homogeneous environment. In the classical case of the lamellibranch and brachiopod genera cited above, this temporo-spatially homogeneous environment is the sea. The complementary situation under which tachytely occurs involves an explosive response to a change in the physical or biotic environment. After such an environmental change the selective value of many characters will be modified. Some which were previously selected will be excluded and others, previously excluded, will be favoured. Under these conditions the genotype of the population will therefore move to a new optimum in response to the changed selection pressure.

It is, of course, clear that the tachytelic phase during which the placental stock occupied the ecological niches left vacant at the end of the Cretaceous accords with Simpson's view. With the extinction of the reptiles and the majority of the advanced multituberculates during the climatic deterioration and Laramide revolution in the final phases of the Cretaceous, the ancestral placentals and marsupials came into contact with numerous unfilled niches. Thus a combination of physical and biotic environmental changes resulted in the evolution of the archaic Paleocene placentals. The persistence of relatively unmodified tapiroid-, lemuroid- and tarsioid-like forms from a slightly more recent date until the present day in the tropical jungles is also illustrative of Simpson's general thesis. This relatively bradytelic situation occurred within the homogeneous environment of the Cenozoic tropical vegetation.

There is, however, an interesting contrast between the relative stability of the plant genera, perhaps throughout the Cenozoic and certainly during the Quaternary, and the complex evolution of the placentals during these periods. Clearly the evolution of the mammals can lead to scansorial, cursorial, saltatorial and subterranean species of both herbivores and carnivores within a single vegetational complex. A single habitat, therefore, offers greater opportunities for the evolution of mammals than angiosperms. However, the predominant feature of this mammalian evolution, and more especially the succession of comparable and related genera, is the interaction of predator and prey. As emphasized in the relevant chapters, the evolution of the anatomy and nervous system of carnivores is intimately related to that of the herbivores upon which they prey. This situation will result in a more or less constant change in the characters of both. These considerations show that the marked difference between the degree of evolution which the plants and mammals underwent during the Cenozoic are the result of the greater instability of the factors influencing the latter. Both are subject to the multi-factorial variation of the environment during major climatic cycles but the mammals further influence each other.

With respect to these climatic cycles the results of Van Hammen are of considerable importance. Both carnivore and herbivore faunas undergo marked changes at the end of the Paleocene, Eocene, Oligocene etc. If the results of the analysis of *Monocolpites* pollen are of general application it would appear that these mammalian faunas replace each other at, or just subsequent to, periods of climatic deterioration. The faunal succession in which the dominant carnivore groups are the Procreodi, Acreodi and Pseudocreodi, Eucreodi and finally Fissipedia, would therefore be correlated on the one hand with changing prey, as suggested by many authors, and on the other with the rather more fundamental factor of periodic climatic change. Following each climatic cycle, the deterioration of the climate resulted in the extinction of certain components of the world mammal fauna. With the subsequent climatic amelioration this would result in the residual forms undergoing a brief tachytelic phase, refilling the now empty ecological niches, and therefore becoming the dominant component.

Unfortunately it is not at all clear in the present state of our knowledge to what extent the *Monocolpites* data from Columbia tie in with the periodical marine transgressions in the Paris Basin. Nor is it clear to what extent they are of application outside Columbia. Should they be of more general application there would, however, then be two principal effects of climatic influence on mammalian evolution during the Tertiary. The overall climatic deterioration during the latter phases of the period led to a progressive increase in the percentage representation of the herbaceous species in the vegetation. Culminating in the open vegetation of the opening and closing phases of the Quaternary interglacials, this resulted in extensive open vegetation in what had been areas of tropical jungle during, for example, the Eocene. This was probably of paramount importance in the evolution of the cursorial carnivores and herbivores and the bipedal and cursorial anthropoids. On the other hand, the cyclical climatic effects noted above, caused the continual replacement of the dominant forms within these faunas, this replacement finally resulting in a considerable increase in the temperate species at the expense of the tropical ones.

Darwin (1906) emphasized that extinction is one of the natural consequences of evolution. Thus, as outlined above, the interrelationships of the carnivores and herbivores, together with the effects upon both of the vegetation and climate, produced a succession of analogous faunas filling comparable niches during the Cenozoic. In North America the results of ^{14}C assay have shown that in a number of cases species only became extinct relatively recently by comparison with their time of extinction in the Old World (Martin, 1958). As an example of this, one may cite the mammalian fauna from St. Petersburg, Florida (Martin, 1958). This included a mastodon, camelid, ursid, sloth, horse and mammoth and was dated at 2,040 ± 90 years B.P. by the Lamonte geological observatory. Similar recent dates were

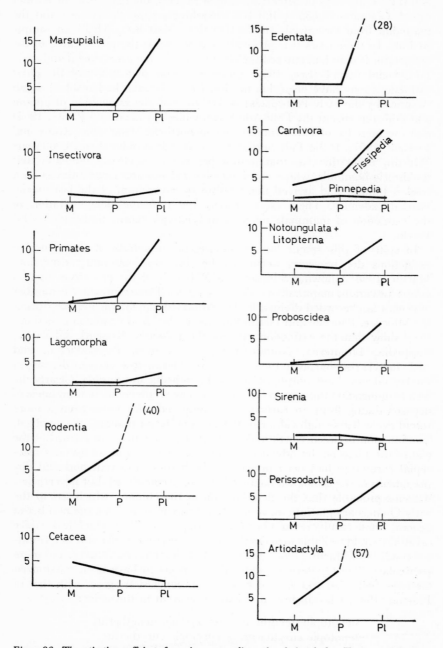

Figure 36. The extinction coefficients for various mammalian orders during the late Tertiary and Quaternary. The coefficients were obtained by dividing the number of genera by the supposed length of the period involved (from Martin, 1958 after Simpson, 1945)

199

obtained for the giant ursid at Lagoa Funda, Minais Gerais, Brazil (3,000 ± 300 B.P., University of Michigan sample M.354), the mammoth at Kassler Quad, Colorado (4,885 ± 160 B.P., Washington sample W.288) and the mastodon from Cromwell, Indiana (5,300 ± 400 B.P., Michigan sample M.138). In these cases it is probable that man was the prime cause of the extinction. If man had entered the New World by the Late-glacial and early Post-glacial period (Lee, 1957; Quimpy, 1958) then many of the older extinctions may have been due to him. Certainly man had reached South America by the early Post-glacial, as is shown by the association of human and sloth remains at the Palli Aiki Cave, Chile (Cruxent and Rouse, 1956) and the presence of Paleo-Indian sites in northern Venezuela (Rouse and Cruxent, 1957). If the Tule Spring site in Nevada is older than 23,000 years (Martin, 1958) then, as that author points out, it clearly indicates that prehistoric hominids, whose economy involved hunting large animals on a treeless tundra, had arrived there before the maximum of the last glacial (stadial) advance. These facts support the immense documentation of the extinction of mammals by man in relatively recent time in the Old World.

In spite of this recent human interference the bulk of the Cenozoic extinctions do, however, occur at the Tertiary/Quaternary transition. Martin (1958) following Simpson (1945) has listed the generic extinction curves for various mammalian orders (*Figure 36*). These represent the number of genera last recorded divided by the estimated age for each epoch during the Miocene, Pliocene and Pleistocene. As implied in the foregoing sections, these show that the extinction rates of the Primates, Rodents, Edentates, Fissipedia, Litopterna, Notoungulata, Proboscidea, Perissodactyla and Artiodactyla rise sharply in the Quaternary. This is, however, not the case in the Insectivora, Lagomorpha, Cetacea, Pinnepedia and Sirenia. Clearly the factors influencing these curves are varied. The relatively high abundance of deposits dating from an early age as compared with those from a more recent age will give high values for the fauna of the particular facies involved. The junction between North and South America, which was formed at the end of the Pliocene, let advanced placental carnivores in where only marsupial carnivores had been previously. Both these apparent and real displacements of the ecological balance have to be considered, but nevertheless it seems probable that the deterioration of the climate, which led to the early Quaternary glaciations, resulted in the extinction of a large number of genera. Those carnivores and herbivores adapted for life on the late Tertiary savannas would be liable to extinction as these were reduced in the deteriorating conditions. Martin (1958), indeed, concludes that Quaternary, and more particularly late Quaternary, extinction appears to have been maximized for large body-size and limited range. This conclusion agrees with that of Pearson (1963) who suggests that extinction went in the order:

Stenotopic stenotherms > eurytopic stenotherms > stenotopic eurytherms > eurytopic eurytherms

and these tendencies were enhanced by the activities of man in the most recent period.

REFERENCES

ABEL, O. (1910). Kritisches Untersuchungen uber die paläogenen Rhinocerotiden Europas. *Abh. Geol. Reichsanst., Wien,* **20**, 1–52

ABEL, O. (1931). *Die Stellung des Menschen in Rahmen der Wirbeltiere.* Gustav Fischer. Jena

ABRARD, R. (1925). *Le Lutetien du Bassin de Paris.* Dissertation, Paris

ABRARD, R. (1941). Les lambeaux éocène des côtes meridionales de Bretagne. *Bull. Mus. Hist. nat., Paris,* **13**, 3

AHRENS, L. H. (1948). A summary of the use of the Rb/Sr method for the determination of geologic age. *Rep. Comm. Meas. geol., Washington,* 1946–47, 47–54

ALDRICH, L. T. AND WETHERILL, G. W. (1958). Geochronology by radio-active dating. *Ann. Rev. Nuclear Sci.,* **8**, 257–298

ALLISON, J., GODWIN, H. AND WARREN, S. H. (1952). Late-glacial deposits at Nazeing in the Lea Valley, North London. *Phil. Trans.,* **B236**, 169–240

AMEGHINO, F. (1902). Linea filogenetica de los proboscideos. *An. Mus. Nac. B. Aires,* **8**, 19–43

AMEGHINO, F. (1904). Nuevas especies de mamiferos cretaceos y terciarios de la Republica Argentina. *An. Soc. Cient. argent.,* **56, 57, 58,** 1–142

AMEGHINO, F. (1906). Les formations sédimentaires du Crétacé superieur et du tertiaire de Patagonie. *An. Mus. Nac. B. Aires.* (3rd ser.), **15**, 1–568

AMEGHINO, F. (1936). *Obras completas.* La Plata. Government Press, Argentina

AMIRKHANOFF, K. I., BRANDT, S. B. AND BARNITSKY, E. N. (1961). Radiogenic argon in minerals and its migration. *Ann. N.Y. Acad. Sci.,* **91**, 235–275

AMIRKHANOFF, K. I., MAGATAYEV, K. S. AND BRANDT, S. B. (1957). Determination of the absolute age of sedimentary rocks by radiological methods. *Dokl. Akad. Nauk. U.S.S.R.,* **117**, 4

AMIRKHANOFF, K. I., MAGATAYEV, K. S. AND TIMOFEYAVA, G. I. (1957). Results of the absolute age determinations on sedimentary rocks of the oil-bearing provinces of Daghestan. *Trans. 5th. Sess. C.A.D.G.F.* Acad. Press, Moscow

ANDREWS, C. W. (1906). *A Descriptive Catalogue of the Tertiary Vertebrata of the Fayum, Egypt.* British Museum (Nat. Hist.), London

ANTHONY, H. E. (1924). A new fossil perissodactyl from Peru. *Amer. Mus. Novit.,* **111,** 1–3

ANTHONY, R. AND CAUPIN, F. (1931). Tableau résumé d'une classification generique des Primates fossiles et actuels. *Bull. Mus. Hist. nat. Paris,* **2**, 566–569

AXELROD, D. I. (1937). A Pliocene flora from the Mount Eden beds, Southern California. *Carnegie Inst. Wash. Publ.,* **476**, 125–183

AXELROD, D. I. (1949). Discussion of the sedimentary facies in geologic history. *Mem. geol. Soc. Amer.,* **39**, 155–164

BADER, R. S. (1954). Variability and evolutionary rate in the Oreodonta. *Evolution,* **4**, 119–140

BECKER, C. J. (1948). *Mosefundne Lerkar fra Yngre Stenalder.* Dissertation, Copenhagen *(vide* Iversen, 1960)

BEETS, C. (1946). The Pliocene and Lower Pleistocene gastropods in the collections of the geological foundation in the Netherlands. *Meded. geol. Sticht. N.S.,* **C4**, 1–6

BERRY, E. W. (1916). *U.S. geol. Surv. Profess. Pap.,* **91**, 138

BLACKBURN, K. B. (1952). The dating of a deposit containing an elk skeleton at Neasham, near Darlington, County Durham. *New Phytol.,* **51**, 364

BLAINVILLE, H. M. D. de (1816). Prodrome d'une nouvelle distribution systematique du regne animal. *Bull. Soc. phil. Paris.* (ser. 3), **3**, 105–124

REFERENCES

BOGOLEPOV, K. V. (1955). Stages in the development of the Tertiary vegetation in Angara region of the Jenisei ridge. *Dokl. Akad. Nauk. U.S.S.R.*, **100**, 985–988

BOHLIN, B. (1926). Die Familie Giraffidae mit besonderer Berucksichtigung der fossilen Formen aus China. *Pal. Sinica.* (ser. C), **4**, 179

BOHLIN, B. (1938). Einiger jungtertiarer und pleistozaner Cavicorner aus Nord-China. *Nova Acta Soc. Sci. upsal.* (ser. 4), **11**, 1–54

BOSWELL, P. G. H. (1952). The Plio-Pleistocene boundary in the east of England. *Proc. geol. Ass.*, **63**, 301–312

BOWLE, J. (1962). *A New Outline of World History.* Allen and Unwin

BREUNING, S. (1923). Einige Worte zur Stammesgeschichte der Familie Rhinocerotidae. *Paleont. Z.*, **5**, 118–121

BROCKMANN-JEROSCH, H. (1936). Futterlaubbaume und Speiselaubbaume. *Ber. Schweiz. bot. Ges.*, **46**

BROECKER, W. S., KULP, J. L. AND TUCEK, C. S. (1956). Lamonte natural radiocarbon dates III. *Science.*, **124**, 154–165

BROOKS, C. E. P. (1949). *Climate Through the Ages.* McGraw-Hill, New York

BROOKS, C. E. P. (1951). Geological and historical aspects of climatic change. *Compend. meteor.* 1004–1023

BROOM, R. (1939). The dentition of the Transvaal Pleistocene anthropoids, *Plesianthropus* and *Paranthropus*. *Ann. Transvaal Mus.*, **19**, 303–314

BROOM, R. AND ROBINSON, J. T. (1952). The Swartkrans ape-man, *Paranthropus crassidens*. *Mem. Transvaal Mus.*, **6**, 123

BROOM, R., ROBINSON, J. T. AND SCHEPERS, G. W. H. (1950). The Sterkfontein ape-man, *Plesianthropus*. *Mem. Transvaal Mus.*, **4**, 97–117

BURGL, H. (1959). Quoted by van der Hammen, 1961

BURESCH, F. C., FLORSCHÜTZ, F. AND VLERK, J. M. VAN DER (1938). An early Paleolithic site on the northern Veluwe. *Proc. Kon. Ak. v. Wetensch.*, **41**, 909–920

CABRERA, A. (1939). Los generos de la familia Typotheriidae. *Physis.* Buenos Aires, **14**, 359–372

CABRERA, A. (1941). Cranial and dental characters of some South American Cervidae. *Publ. Field. Mus. Nat. Hist.* (zool), **27**, 125–135

CARLSSON, A. (1926). Ueber die Tragulidae und ihre Beziehungen zu den ubrigen Artiodactyla. *Acta Zool.* Stockholm., **7**, 69–100

CARTER, G. S. (1954). *Animal Evolution.* Sidgwick and Jackson. London

CHANCE, M. R. A. AND MEAD, A. P. (1953). Social behaviour and Primate evolution. *S.E.B. symposia*, **7**, *Evolution*, 395–439

CHANDLER, M. E. J. (1921). The arctic flora of the Cam Valley at Barnwell, Cambridge. *Quart. J. geol. Soc. London*, **77**, 4

CHANDLER, M. E. J. (1923). Geological history of the genus *Stratiotes*. *Quart. J. Geol. Soc.*, **79**, 117

CHANDLER, M. E. J. (1961). *The Lower Tertiary floras of southern England.* British Museum (Nat. Hist.), London, 2 vols.

CHANEY, R. W. (1924). Quantitative studies on the Bridge Creek flora. *Amer. J. Sci.* (ser. 5) **8**, 127–144

CHANEY, R. W. (1938). Paleo-ecological interpretations of Cenozoic plants in western North America. *Bot. Rev.*, **9**, 371–396

CHANEY, R. W. (1940). Tertiary forests and continental history. *Bull. geol. Soc. Amer.*, **51**, 469–488

CHANEY, R. W. (1947). Tertiary centres and migration routes. *Ecol. monogr.*, **17**, 139–148

CHANEY, R. W. (1951). A revision of fossil *Sequoia* and *Taxodium* in western North America. *Trans. Amer. Phil. Soc.* New series, **40**, 3

CHANEY, R. W. AND AXELROD, D. I. (1959). Miocene floras of the Columbia Plateau. *Carnegie Inst. Washington Publ.*, **617**, 237

REFERENCES

CHANEY, R. W. AND SANBORN, E. I. (1933). The Goshen flora of west central Oregon. *Carnegie Inst. Washington Publ.*, **439**, 103

TEILHARD DE CHARDIN, P. (1916–1922). Les mammiferes de l'Eocene inferieur et leurs gisements. *Ann. Paléont. Paris*, **10**, 171–176; **11**, 1–116

TEILHARD DE CHARDIN, P. (1939). The Miocene cervids from Shantung. *Bull. geol. Soc. China*, **19**, 269–278

CHARLESWORTH, J. K. (1956). *The Quaternary Era*. Arnold, London. 2 vols.

CLAPHAM, A. R., TUTIN, T. G. AND WARBURG, E. F. (1952). *Flora of the British Isles*. Cambridge

CLARK, B. L. (1932). Fauna of the Poul and Yakataga formations (Upper Oligocene) of southern Alaska. *Bull. geol. Soc. Amer.*, **43**, 797–846

CLARK, B. L. AND WOODFORD, A. O. (1927). Geology and paleontology of the type section of the Meganos formation of California. *Bull. geol. Soc. Amer.*, **17**, 63–142

CLARK, J. G. D. (1952). *Prehistoric Europe*. Methuen, London

CLARK, J. G. D. (1954). *Excavations at Star Carr*. Cambridge University Press

CLEMENTS, F. (1916). Plant succession. *Carnegie Inst. Washington Publ.*, **290**

COLBERT, E. H. (1933). The skull of *Dissopsalis carnifex* Pilgrim, a Miocene creodont from India. *Amer. Mus. Novit.*, **603**, 1–8

COLBERT, E. H. (1935a). Distribution and phylogenetic studies on Indian fossil mammals. 3; A classification of the Chalicotherioidea. *Amer. Mus. Novit.*, **798**, 1–16

COLBERT, E. H. (1935b). Siwalik mammals in the American Museum of Natural History. *Trans. Amer. phil. Soc.* (new ser.), **26**, 1–401

COLBERT, E. H. (1936) Tertiary deer discovered by the American museum Asiatic expeditions. *Amer. Mus. Novit.*, **854**, 1–21

COLBERT, E. H. (1938a). *Brachyhyops*, a new bunodont artiodactyl from the Beaver Divide, Wyoming. *Ann. Carnegie Mus.*, **27**, 87–108

COLBERT, E. H. (1938b). Fossil mammals from Burma in the American Natural History Museum. *Bull. Amer. Mus. Nat. Hist.*, **74**, 255–436

COLBERT, E. H. (1939). Carnivora of the Tung Gur formation of Mongolia. *Bull. Amer. Mus. Nat. Hist.*, **76**, 47–81

COLBERT, E. H. (1941). The osteology and relationships of *Archeomeryx*, an ancestral ruminant. *Amer. Mus. Novit.*, **1135**, 1–24

COLBERT, E. H. AND CHAFFEE, R. G. (1939). A study of *Tetrameryx* and associated fossils. *Amer. Mus. Novit.*, **1034**, 1–21

COMPSTON, W. AND JEFFERY, P. M. (1961). Metamorphic chronology by the Rubidium-Strontium method. *Ann. N.Y. Acad. Sci.*, **91**. (Kulp ed.), 185–191

CONDIT, C. (1938). The San Pablo flora of west central California. *Carnegie Inst. Washington Publ.*, **476**, 217–268

CONNOLLY, A., GODWIN, H. AND MEGAW, E. M. (1950). Studies in the Post-glacial history of the British vegetation. XI; Late-glacial deposits in Cornwall. *Phil. Trans.*, **B234**, 397

CONWAY, V. M. (1942). Biological flora of the British Isles; *Cladium mariscus* L. *J. Ecol.*, **30**, 211

COOPE, G. R. (1959). A late Pleistocene insect fauna from Chelford, Cheshire. *Proc. Roy. Soc.*, **B151**, 70–86

COOPE, G. R., SHOTTON, F. W. AND STRACHAN, I. (1961). A late Pleistocene fauna and flora from Upton Warren, Worcestershire. *Phil. Trans.*, **B244**, 379–421

COPE, E. D. (1880). On the genera of the Creodonta. *Proc. Amer. phil. Soc.*, **19**, 76

COUTO, C. DE PAULO. (1952). Fossil mammals from the beginning of the Cenozoic in Brazil. *Bull. Amer. Mus. Nat. Hist.*, **99**, 355–394

COUTOURIER, M. (1953). *L'ours brun*. Grenoble

CRUSAFONT, P. M. (1952). Los Jirafidos fosiles de España. *Mem. Communic. Inst. Geol. Barc.*, **8**, 1–240

REFERENCES

DAL PIAZ, G. (1930). Creodonta dell' Oligoceno Veneto. *Mem. Inst. geol. Univ. Padua.*, **8**, 3–14

DAM, A. TEN AND REINHOLD, T. (1941). Die stratigraphische Gliederung des nieder-landischen Plio-Plistozäns nach Foraminifera. *Med. Geol. Sticht.*, **C5**, 1 (Oligo-cene–Miocene, 1942, **C5**, 2)

DARLINGTON, P. J. (1957). *Zoogeography.* Wiley and Sons, New York

DAVIS, M. B. (1961). Pollen-diagrams as evidence of Late-glacial climatic changes in southern New England. *Ann. N.Y. Acad. Sci.*, **95**, 623–631

DEEVEY, E. S. JR. (1949). Biogeography of the Pleistocene. *Bull. geol. Soc. Amer.*, **60**, 1315–1416

DEEVEY, E. S. JR. (1951). Late-glacial and Post-glacial pollen diagrams from Maine. *Amer. J. Sci.*, **249**, 177–207

DEGERBØL, M. AND IVERSEN, J. (1945). The bison in Denmark. A geological and zoological investigation of the finds in the Danish Pleistocene deposits. *Danm. geol. Unders.*, **11**, 1–59

DENNISON, R. H. (1938). The broad-skulled Pseudocreodi. *Ann. N.Y. Acad. Sci.*, **37**, 163–256

DEPERET, C. (1908). L'histoire geologique et la phylogenie des anthracotherides. *C.R. Acad. Sci. Paris*, **146**, 158–162

DOBZHANSKY, T. (1927). *Genetics and the origin of species.* New York

DONNER, J. (1957). The geology and vegetation of the Late-glacial retreat stages in Scotland. *Trans. Roy. Soc. Edin.*, **63**, 221–264

DUIGAN, S. (1957). *The vegetational history of the English interglacial deposits.* Dissertation, Cambridge

DURHAM, J. W. (1942). Eocene and Oligocene coral formations from Washington. *J. Paleont.*, **16**, 84–104

DURHAM, J. W. (1950). Cenozoic marine climates of the Pacific coast. *Bull. geol. Soc. Amer.*, **61**, 1243–1264

DYBOVA, S. AND JACHOWICZ, A. (1957). Microspores of the Upper Silesian coal measures. *Inst. geol. Warsaw*, **23**

EDWARDS, A. H. (1874). *Récherches pour servir a l'histoire naturelle des mammifères com-prenant des considerations sur la classification.* Masson, Paris

EMILIANI, C. (1954). Temperatures of the Pacific bottom waters during the Tertiary. *Science*, **119**, 853–855

EMILIANI, C. (1955). Pleistocene temperatures. *J. Geol.*, **63**, 538–573

EMILIANI, C. (1956). Oligocene and Miocene temperatures of the equatorial and sub-tropical Atlantic Ocean. *J. Geol.*, **64**, 281–288

EMILIANI, C. (1961). Cenozoic climatic changes as indicated by the stratigraphy and chronology of deep sea cores of Globigerina ooze facies. *Ann. N.Y. Acad. Sci.*, **95**, 521–536

EPSTEIN, S. (1959). The variation in the O^{18}/O^{16} ratio in nature and some geologic implications. In *Researches in Geochemistry* (Abelson ed.) Wiley and Sons. 217–240

EPSTEIN, S., BUCHSBAUM, R., LOWENSTAM, H. AND UREY, H. C. (1951). Carbonate water isotopic temperature scale. *Bull. geol. Soc. Amer.*, **62**, 417–425

EPSTEIN, S. AND MAYEDA, T. (1953). Variation of the O^{18} content of waters from natural sources. *Geochim. et Cosmochim. Acta*, **4**, 213–224

ERDBRINK, D. P. (1953). *A Review of the Fossil and Recent Bears of the Old World.* Deventer. Press J. Lange

ERDTMANN, G. (1952). *Pollen Morphology and Taxonomy.* Waltham, Mass. In progress

ERICSON, D. B., EWING, M. AND WOLLIN, Q. Pliocene/Pleistocene boundary in marine deposits. *Science*, **139**, 727–737

FAEGRI, K. (1944). On the introduction of agriculture to western Norway. *Geol. Foren. Stockholm. Forh.*, **66**, 449–462

REFERENCES

FAEGRI, K. AND IVERSEN, J. (1950). *Textbook of Modern Pollen-Analysis*. Munksgaard, Copenhagen

FARRINGTON, A. (1947). Unglaciated areas in southern Ireland. *Irish geog.*, **1**, 89

FIRBAS, F. (1949). *Spät- und Nacheiszeitliche Waldgeschichte Mitteleuropas nordlich der Alpen.* vol. 1. Jena

FLEROW, C. (1931). On the generic characters of the family Tragulidae. *C.R. Acad. Sci. U.S.S.R.*, 75–79

FLINT, R. F. (1957). *Glacial geology and the Pleistocene Epoch*. Revised edition

FLINT, R. F. *et al.* (1949). Pleistocene Research. *Bull. geol. Soc. Amer.*, **60**, 1305–1525

FLORSCHÜTZ, F. (1925). On *Pseudolarix kaempferi* Gord. from the clay of Reuver. *Rec. d. Trav. Bot. Néerl.*, **22**, 269–273

FLORSCHÜTZ, F. (1928). Fossiele *Azolla* in Nederland. *Ned. Kruidk. Arch.*, **38**, 75–81

FLORSCHÜTZ, F. (1930a). Fossiele overblijfselen van een toendravegetatie in Nederland. *Proc. Kon. Ak. Wetensch.*, **33**, 137

FLORSCHÜTZ, F. (1930b). Fossiele overblijfselen van den plantengroei tijdens en het Riss-Wurm interglaciaal in Nederland. *Proc. Kon. Ak. Wetensch.*, **33**, 1043–1044

FLORSCHÜTZ, F. (1945). *Azolla* uit het Nederlandsche Palaeoceen en Pleistoceen. *Verh. Geol. Mijn. gen. geol.*, **14**, 191–198

FLORSCHÜTZ, F. (1958). Steppen und salzsumpfelemente aus den Floren der letzten und vorletzten Eiszeit in den Niederlanden. *Flora*, **146**, 489

FLORSCHÜTZ, F. AND JONKER J. P. (1942). Ueber der Flora des Mindel-Riss Interglazial in der Niederlanden. *Rec. Trav. Bot. Néerl.*, **34**, 176

FLORSCHÜTZ, F. AND SOMEREN, A. VAN (1948). Microbotanische verschillen tussen de klei van Reuver en de klei van Tegelen. *Geol. en Mijnb.*, **10**, 68

FOSTER-COOPER, C. (1934). The extinct rhinoceroses of Baluchistan. *Phil. Trans.*, **B223**, 569–616

FRECHKOP, S. (1955). Super-ordre des Ongulés. *Traité de Zoologie*, **17**, 484–667

FRENZEL, B. AND TROLL, C. (1952). Die Vegetationszonen des nordlichen Eurasiens wahrend der letzten Eiszeit. *Eiszeitalter und Gegenwart.*, **2**, 154–167

FREY, D. G. (1953). Regional aspects of the Late-glacial and Post-glacial forest succession of south eastern North Carolina. *Ecol. monogr.*, **23**, 289–313

FRICK, C. (1921). Vertebrates from the Mount Eden formation. *Univ. Calif. Pub. Bull. Geol.*, **12**, 338

FRICK, C. (1926). The Hemicyoninae and an American Tertiary bear. *Amer. Mus. Nat. Hist. Bull.*, **56**, 1–119

FRICK, C. (1937). Horned ruminants of North America. *Bull. Amer. Mus. Nat. Hist.*, **69**

FRYE, J. C. AND LEONARD, A. B. (1957). Ecological interpretations of the Pliocene and Pleistocene stratigraphy in the Great Plains area. *Amer. J. Sci.*, **225**, 1–11

FUNNELL, B. M. (1961). The Paleogene and early Pleistocene of Norfolk. *Trans. Norfolk Norw. Nat. Soc.*, **19**, 340–364

GAST, P. W. (1961). The rubidium/strontium method. *Ann. N.Y. Acad. Sci.*, **91** (Kulp ed.), 181–184

GAUDRY, A. (1878). *Les enchainements du monde animale dans les temps geologiques*. Mammifères tertiaires. Paris

GAUDRY, A. (1906). Fossiles de Patagonia. Etudes sur une protion du monde antarctique. *Ann. Paleont.*, **1**, 101–143

GAZIN, C. L. (1941). The mammalian faunas of the Paleocene of central Utah. *Proc. U.S. Nat. Mus.*, **91**, 3121; 1–53

GAZIN, C. L. (1946). *Machaeroides eotheri* Matt. the sabre-tooth creodont of the Bridger Eocene. *Proc. U.S. Nat. Mus.*, **96**, 335–347

GAZIN, C. L. (1953). The Tillodontia—an early Tertiary order of Mammals. *Smithsonian misc. coll.*, **121**, 1–110

205

REFERENCES

GERLING, E. K., MOROZOVA, I. M. AND KURBATOV, V. V. (1961). The retentivity of radiogenic argon in ground micas. *Ann. N.Y. Acad. Sci.*, **91** (Kulp ed.), 227–234

GIDLEY, J. W. (1923). Paleocene Primates of the Fort Union with a discussion of the relationships of Eocene Primates. *Proc. U.S. Nat. Mus.*, **63**, 1–38

GIGNOUX, M. (1955). *Stratigraphic Geology.* Freeman, San Francisco

GLENDENNING, L. (1961). The present status of decay constants. *Ann. N.Y. Acad. Sci.*, **91** (Kulp ed.), 161–180

GODWIN, H. (1940a) Pollen analysis and forest history of England and Wales. *New Phytol.*, **39**, 370

GODWIN, H. (1940b). Studies on the Post-glacial history of the British vegetation. III. Fenland pollen diagrams. *Phil. Trans.*, **B230**, 239

GODWIN, H. (1949). The spreading of the British flora in relation to the Late-glacial period. *J. Ecol.*, **37**, 140–147

GODWIN, H. (1956). *The History of the British flora.* Cambridge University Press

GODWIN, H. (1960). The Croonian lecture. *Proc. Roy. Soc.*, **B153**, 287–320

GODWIN, H. (1962). The half-life of radio-carbon. *Nature, Lond.*, **195**, 984

GODWIN, H., SUGGATE, R. P. AND WILLIS, E. H. (1958). Radio-carbon dating and the eustatic rise in ocean-level. *Nature, Lond.*, **181**, 1518

GODWIN, H., WALKER, D. AND WILLIS, E. H. (1957). Radio-carbon dating and Post-glacial vegetational history. Scaleby Moss. *Proc. Roy. Soc.*, **B147**, 352–266

GODWIN, H. AND WILLIS, E. H. (1958). Radiocarbon dating of the Late-glacial period in Britain. *Proc. Roy. Soc.*, **B150**, 199

GODWIN, H. AND WILLIS, E. H. (1960). Cambridge natural radio-carbon dates II. *Amer. J. Sci.* Radio-carbon suppl., **2**, 62–72

GRANGER, W. (1915). A revision of the Lower Eocene Wasatch and Wind-River faunas. Part 3. Condylarthra. *Bull. Amer. Mus. Nat. Hist.*, **34**, 329–361

GRANGER, W. AND GREGORY, W. K. (1936). Further notes on the gigantic extinct rhinoceros *Baluchitherium*, from the Mongolian Oligocene. *Bull. Amer. Mus. Nat. Hist.*, **72**, 1–73

GRANGER, W. AND GREGORY, W. K. (1943). A revision of the Mongolian Titanotheres. *Bull. Amer. Mus. Nat. Hist.*, **80**, 349–389

GRANGER, W. AND SIMPSON, G. G. (1929). A revision of the Tertiary multituberculata. *Bull. Amer. Mus. Nat. Hist.*, **56**, 601–676

GREGORY, W. K. (1915). On the classification and phylogeny of the Lemuroidea. *Bull. geol. Soc. Amer.*, **26**, 426–446

GREGORY, W. K. (1916). Studies on the evolution of the Primates. *Bull. Amer. Mus. Nat. Hist.*, **35**, 239–355

GREGORY, W. K. (1920). On the structure and relations of *Notharctus*, an American Eocene Primate. *Mem. Amer. Mus. Nat. Hist.*, **3**, 49–243

GREGORY, W. K. (1922). *The Origin and Evolution of Human Dentition.* Williams and Wilkins, Baltimore

GREGORY, W. K. (1934). *Man's Place amongst the Anthropoids.* Clarendon Press, Oxford

GREGORY, W. K. AND HELLMAN, M. (1939a). The dentition of the extinct South African man-ape *Australopithecus* (*Plesianthropus*) *transvaalensis* Broom. *Ann. Transvaal Mus.*, **19**, 339–373

GREGORY, W. K. AND HELLMAN, M. (1939b). On the evolution and major classification of the civets (Viverridae) and allied fossil and recent Carnivora. *Proc. Amer. phil. Soc.*, **81**, 309–392

GROSS, H. (1954). Das Allerød-Interstadial als Leithorizont der letzten Vereisung in Europa und Amerika. *Eiszeitalter u. Gegenwart.*, **4/5**, 189

GROSS, H. (1955). Weitere Beitrage zur Kenntnis der Spätglazials. *ibid.*, **6**, 110

206

HALL, K. R. L. (1962). The sexual, agonistic, and derived social behaviour patterns of the wild chacma baboon, *Papio ursinus. Proc. Zool. Soc. Lond.*, **139**, 283–327

HAMMEN, T. VAN DER (1949). De Allerød oscillatie in Nederland. *Proc. Kon. Akad. Wetensch.*, **52**, 169–176

HAMMEN, T. VAN DER (1957). Climatic periodicity and evolution of the South American Maestrichtian and Tertiary floras. *Bogotá Bol. Geol.*, **5**, 49–91

HAMMEN, T. VAN DER (1961). Upper Cretaceous and Tertiary climatic periodicities and their causes. *Ann. N.Y. Acad. Sci.*, **95**, 440–448

HARTZ, N. AND MILTHERS, V. (1901). Det senglaciale ler i Allerød Teglvaerksgrav. *Medd. Dansk geol. Foren.*, **8**, 31–60

HATCHER, J. B. (1896). Recent and fossil tapirs. *Amer. J. Sci.*, **1**, 161–180

HATCHER, J. B. (1902). Oligocene Canidae. *Mem. Carnegie Mus.*, **1**, 65–108

HAUGHTON, S. H. (1931). The fossil equidae of South Africa. *Ann. South African Mus.*, **28**, 407–427

HAY, O. P. (1929–30). Second bibliography and catalogue of the fossil vertebrata of North America. *Carnegie Inst. Wash. Publ.*, **390**, 1–916

HELLER, F. (1935). *Amphilemur eocaenicus* ein primitiver Primate aus dem Mitteleozän des Geisaltales bei Halle. *Nova Acta Leo. Carol. Halle.*, **2**, 293–300

HILL, W. C. O. (1953). *The Primates.* 4 vols, in progress. University Edinburgh Press

HOLLAND, W. J. AND PETERSEN, O. A. (1913). The osteology of the Chalicotherioidea with special reference to a mounted skeleton of *Moropus elatus* Marsh. *Mem. Carnegie Mus.*, **3**, 189–406

HOLMES, A. (1947). The construction of a geological time scale. *Trans. Geol. Soc. Glasgow*, **21**, 117–152

HOUTEN, F. B. VAN (1945). Review of the latest Paleocene and early Eocene mammalian faunas. *J. Paleont.*, **19**, 421–461

HULTÉN, E. (1950). *Atlas of the Distribution of Vascular Plants.* Stockholm

HURLEY, P. M. (1961). Glauconite as a possible means of measuring the age of sediments. *Ann. N.Y. Acad. Sci.*, **91**, (Kulp ed.), 294–297

HURZELER, J. (1936). Osteologie und Odontologie der Caenotheriden. *Mem. Soc. Paleont. Suisse*, **58**; 1–89. **59**; 90–112

INQUA (1956). Fourth International Quaternary Conference. Subdivisions of the Pleistocene. *Quaternaria*, **3**, 205

INTERNATIONAL GEOLOGICAL CONGRESS (1950). Recommendations of the commission appointed to report on the definition of the Plio-Pleistocene boundary. 18th session. 1948. *Report*, part 9, 6

ISBERG, O. (1949). Visenten—*Bison bonasus arbustotundrarum*—i Sverige jamte ett bidrag til dennes invandringshistorie. *Acta Univ. Lunds. (N.F.)*, **45**, 1–7

IVERSEN, J. (1941). Landnam i Danmarks Stenalder. En pollenanalytisk Undersøgelse over det første Landbrugs Indvirkning paa Vegetationsudvikling. *Danm. geol. Unders.* Rk. 11, 66

IVERSEN, J. (1944). *Viscum, Hedera* and *Ilex* as climate indicators. *Geol. Foren. Stockholm*, **66**, 463–483

IVERSEN, J. (1947). Plantevaekst, Dyreliv og Klima i det senglaciale Danmark. *Geol. Foren. Stockholm*, **69**, 67

IVERSEN, J. (1954). The Late-glacial flora of Denmark and its relation to climate and soil. *Danm. Geol. Unders.* II, **80**, 87–114

IVERSEN, J. (1960). Problems of the Post-glacial forest development of Denmark. *Danm. geol. Unders.*, 4, **3**, 1–32

JENSEN, P. B. (1929). Studier ofer skovtraeernes Forhold til Lyset. *Dansk Skovfor. Tid.* 1929

REFERENCES

Jepsen, G. L. (1930). New Vertebrate fossils from the Lower Eocene of the Bighorn Basin, Wyoming. *Proc. Amer. phil. Soc.*, **69**, 117–131

Jessen, K. (1935). The composition of the forests in northern Europe in Epipaleo-lithic time. *Kgl. Danske Vidensk. Selsk. Biol. Meddel.*, **12**, 1

Jessen, K. (1949). Studies in the Late-Quaternary deposits and floral history of Ireland. *Proc. Roy. Irish Acad.*, **52B**, 85

Jessen, K. and Milthers, V. (1928). Stratigraphical and paleontological studies of interglacial fresh-water deposits in Jutland, and north-west Germany. *Danm. geol. Unders.*, **2**, 48

Kazakow, G. A. and Polevaya, N. I. (1958). Some preliminary data on the development of a post Pre-cambrian scale of absolute chronology based on glauconites. *Geokhimyia*, **4**

Kirkham, V. R. D. (1931). Revision of the Payette and Idaho formations. *J. Geol.*, **39**, 193–239

Kraglievich, L. (1928). Sobre el supuesto *Astrapotherium christi* Steh., descubierto en Venezuela. *La editorial Franco.* Buenos Aires, 1–6

Kraglievich, L. (1932). Contribucion al conocimento de los ciervos fosiles del Uruguay. *Ann. Mus. Nat. Hist. Montevid.* (2nd. ser.), **3**, 257–321

Kraglievich, L. (1934). La antiquedad pliocena de la faunas Monte Hermoso y Chapadmalal, deducidas de su comparacion con las que le precedieron y sucedieron. Montevideo. *El siglo illustrado*, **938**, 136

Kryshtofovich, A. N. (1927). Evolution of the Tertiary flora of Asia. *New Phytol.*, **28**, 303–312

Kryshtofovich, A. N. (1936). Development of the geographical provinces in the northern hemisphere since the late Cretaceous. *Zool. Inst. Akad. Nauk. U.S.S.R. Report*

Kryshtofovich, A. N. (1938). *Miocene Flora of the Ukraine and its Correlation with the Tertiary of Asia.* Acad. Press, Moscow

Lambert, C. A., Pearson, R. G. and Sparks, B. W. (1963). A late-Pleistocene fauna and flora from Sidgwick Avenue, Cambridge. *Proc. Linn. Soc. Lond.*, **174**, 13–29

La Motte, R. S. (1936). The Upper Cedarville flora of north western Nevada and adjacent California. *Carnegie Inst. Washington. Publ.*, **455**, 57–142

Laurent, L. (1919). Les Liquidambars. *Ann. Mus. d'Hist. Nat.*, **17**, 9–27

Laurent, L. and Marty, P. (1923). Flore pliocène des argiles de Reuver. *Meded s'Rijks Geol. Dienst.* ser B, 1

Lavocat, R. (1955). Ongulés fossiles. *Traité de Zoologie*, **17**, 668–693; 1126–1162

Leakey, L. S. B. (1953). *Adam's Ancestors.* 4th ed. Methuen, London

Leakey, L. S. B. (1959). A new fossil skull from Olduvai. *Nature, Lond.*, **184**, 491

Leakey, L. S. B. (1960). The affinities of the new Olduvai Australopithecine. *Nature, Lond.*, **186**, 458

Lee, T. E. (1957). The antiquity of the Shequiandah site. *Canad. Field Nat.*, **71**, 117–137

Le Gros Clark, W. (1934a). *Early Fore-runners of Man.* London and Baltimore

Le Gros Clark, W. (1934b). On the structure of *Pronycticebus gaudryi. Proc. Linn. Soc. Lond.*, 19–27

Le Gros Clark, W. (1954). *History of the Primates.* 4th ed. British Museum (Nat. Hist.)

Libby, W. F. (1951). Radio-carbon dates, II. *Science*, **114**, 291

Libby, W. F. (1955). Radio-carbon dating. University of Chicago Press

Libby, W. F. (1963). Accuracy of radio-carbon dates. *Science*, **140**, 278

Lipson, J. (1958). Potassium–argon dating of sedimentary rocks. *Bull. geol. Soc. Amer.*, **69**, 2

Loomis, F. B. (1914). *The Deseado Formation of Patagonia.* Amherst College, Mass.

Loomis, F. B. (1926). *The Evolution of the Horse.* Jones, Boston

REFERENCES

LORTET, D. AND CHANTRE, E. (1879). Récherches sur les Mastodontes et les faunes mammalogiques qui les accompagnent. *Arch. Mus. d'hist. Nat. Lyon.*, **2**, 285–311

LOWENSTAM, H. A. AND EPSTEIN, S. (1954). Paleotemperatures as measured by the oxygen isotope method. *J. Geol.*, **62**, 207–248

LYDEKKER, R. (1894). Contributions to the knowledge of fossil Vertebrates of Argentina. 3. Ungulata. *An. Mus. La Plata. Argent.*, **2**, 1–91

MACGINITIE, H. D. (1937). The flora of the Weaverville beds of Trinity County, California. *Carnegie Inst. Wash. Publ.*, **465**, 83–151

MACGINITIE, H. D. (1953). Fossil plants of the Florissant beds, Colorado. *Carnegie Inst. Wash. Publ.*, **599**, 198

MACGINITIE, H. D. (1933). The Trout Creek flora of south eastern Oregon. *Carnegie Inst. Wash. Publ.*, **416**, 21–68

MACGINITIE, H. D. (1958). Climate since the late Cretaceous. *Zoogeography*. A Darwin/Wallace memorial volume. *Amer. Ass. Adv. Sci.*, 61–80

MARTIN, R. (1906). Revision der obereocänen und unteroligocänen Creodonten Europas. *Rev. Suisse Zool.*, **14**, 405–598

MARTIN, P. S. (1958). Taiga-tundra and the Full-glacial period in Chester County, Pennsylvania. *Amer. J. Sci.*, **256**, 470–502

MARTIN, P. S. (1959). Pleistocene ecology and biogeography. In *Zoogeography*, Darwin/Wallace Memorial volume, *Amer. Ass. Adv. Sci.*, 375–420

MATTHEW, W. D. (1901). Additional observations on the Creodonta. *Bull. Amer. Mus. Nat. Hist.*, **14**, 1–38

MATTHEW, W. D. (1906). The osteology of *Sinopa*, a creodont carnivore of the Middle Eocene. *Proc. U.S. Nat. Mus.* **30**, 203–233

MATTHEW, W. D. (1908). Osteology of *Blastomeryx* and the phylogeny of the American Cervidae. *Bull. Amer. Mus. Nat. Hist.*, **12**, 19–75

MATTHEW, W. D. (1909). The Carnivora and Insectivora of the Bridger Basin, Middle Eocene. *Mem. Amer. Mus. Nat. Hist.*, **9**, 289–257

MATTHEW, W. D. (1915). A revision of the Lower Eocene Wasatch and Wind River faunas. Part. 1. Ferae. sub-order Creodonta. *Bull. Amer. Mus. Nat. Hist.*, **34**, 4–103

MATTHEW, W. D. (1924). Third contribution to the Snake Creek fauna. *Amer. Mus. Novit.*, **50**, 59–210

MATTHEW, W. D. (1926). The evolution of the horse. *Quart. Rev. Biol.*, **1**, 139–185

MATTHEW, W. D. (1929). Reclassification of the artiodactyl families. *Bull. geol. Soc. Amer.*, **40**, 403–408

MATTHEW, W. D. (1931). Critical observations on the phylogeny of rhinoceroses. *Univ. Calif. Publ. Bull. geol. Sci.*, **20**, 1–9

MATTHEW, W. D. (1932). A review of the rhinoceroses with a description of *Aphelops* material from the Pliocene of Texas. *Univ. Calif. Publ. Bull. geol. Sci.*, **20**, 411–480

MATTHEW, W. D. (1934). A phylogenetic chart of the Artiodactyla. *J. Mammal.*, **15**, 207–209

MATTHEW, W. D. (1937). Paleocene faunas of the San Juan basin, New Mexico. *Trans. Amer. phil. Soc.*, **30**, 14–103

MATTHEW, W. D. AND GRANGER, W. (1925). New ungulates from the Ardyn Obo formation of Mongolia. *Amer. Mus. Novitates*, **195**, 1–12

MATTHEW, W. D. AND STIRTON, R. A. (1930). Equidae from the Pliocene of Texas. *Univ. Calif. Publ. Bull. geol. Sci.*, **29**, 171–216

MAYR, E. (1942). *Systematics and the Origin of Species.* New York

McCREA, J. M. (1950). On the isotope chemistry of carbonates and a paleotemperature scale. *J. chem. Phys.*, **18**, 849–857

REFERENCES

McKinney, C. R., McCrea, J. M., Epstein, S., Allen, H. A. and Urey, H. C. (1950). Improvements in mass spectrometers for the measurement of small differences in isotope abundance ratios. *Rev. Sci. Instrum.*, **21**, 724–730

Milankovitch, M. (1930). *Théorie mathématique des phenomènes produit par la radiation solaire.* Gauthier, Paris

Milankovitch, M. (1938). Astronomische Mittel zur Erforschung der erdesgeschichtlichen Klimate. *Handb. Geophysik.*, **9**, 593

Mitchell, G. F. (1951). Studies in the Irish Quaternary deposits 7. *Proc. Roy. Irish Acad.*, **53B**, II, III

Mitchell, G. F. and Parkes, H. M. (1949). The giant deer in Ireland. *Proc. Roy. Irish. Acad.*, **52B**, 291–314

Moseley, H. N. (1892). *Notes by a Naturalist on the Challenger Expedition.* 2nd ed.

Nordhagen, R. (1954). Om barkebrød og treslaget alm i kulturhistorisk belysning. *Danm. geol. Unders.*, 2nd. ser., **80**

Oakley, K. (1950). *Man the Tool-maker.* British Museum (Nat. Hist.)

Oldfield, F. (1961). The Full- and Late-glacial in the south of France. *Proc. Linn. Soc. Lond.*, **172**, 49–53

Oostingh, C. H. and Florschütz, F. (1928). Bijdrage tot de kennis van de fossiele fauna en flora van Neede. *Versl. afd. Nat. Kon. Akad. Wetensch.*, **37**, 69–75

Osborn, H. F. (1906). The causes of the extinction of the Mammalia. *Amer. Naturalist*, **40**, 769–795, 829–859

Osborn, H. F. (1910). *The Age of Mammals in Europe and North America.* Macmillan, New York

Osborn, H. F. (1918). Equidae of the Oligocene, Miocene and Pliocene of North America. *Mem. Amer. Mus. Nat. Hist.* (new ser.), **2**, 330

Osborn, H. F. (1923). *Baluchitherium grangeri.* A giant hornless rhinoceros from Mongolia. *Amer. Mus. Novitates.*, **78**, 1–15

Osborn, H. F. (1929). The Titanotheres of ancient Wyoming, Dakota and Nebraska. *Monogr. U.S. Geol. Surv.*, **55**, 1–953

Osborn, H. F. (1936). *The Proboscidea. A monograph of the discovery, evolution, migration and extinction of the mastodonts and elephants.* 2 vols. Amer. Mus. Nat. Hist.

Pannekoek, A. J. (ed.) (1956). *The Geological History of the Netherlands.* State Press

Patterson, B. (1932). The auditory region of the Toxodonta. *Publ. Field. Mus. Nat. Hist. (geol.),* **6**, 1–27

Patterson, B. (1934a). Upper premolar structure in the Notoungulata, with notes on their taxonomy. *Publ. Field. Mus. Nat. Hist. (geol.),* **6**, 91–111

Patterson, B. (1934b). *Trachytherus,* a typotheriid from the Deseado beds of Patagonia. *Publ. Field. Mus. Nat. Hist. (geol.),* **6**, 119–139

Patterson, B. (1936). The internal structure of the ear in some Notoungulates. *Publ. Field. Mus. Nat. Hist. (geol.),* **6**, 199–227

Patterson, B. (1937). Some notoungulate braincasts. *Publ. Field. Mus. Nat. Hist. (geol.),* **6**, 273–301

Patterson, B. (1942). Two Tertiary mammals from northern South America. *Amer. Mus. Novit.,* **1173**, 1–7

Pearson, H. S. (1927). On the skulls of the early Suidae together with an account of the otic region in some other primitive Artiodactyla. *Phil. Trans.,* **B215**, 389–460

Pearson, R. G. (1961). *Chlaenius tristis* Sch. (*holosericeus* F.) Coleoptera Carabidae, from an interglacial deposit at Selsey Bill. *Ent. mon. mag.* (4th ser.), **21**

Pearson, R. G. (1962a). The Coleoptera from a detritus-mud erratic of Full-glacial age at Colney Heath, St. Albans. *Proc. Linn. Soc. London,* **173**, 38–55

Pearson, R. G. (1962b). The Coleoptera from a Late-glacial deposit at St. Bees, West Cumberland. *J. Anim. Ecol.,* **31**, 129–150

REFERENCES

PEARSON, R. G. (1963). Coleopteran associations in the British Isles during the late Quaternary period. *Biol. Rev.*, **38**, 334–363

PENCK, A. AND BRÜCKNER, E. (1901–1909). *Die Alpen im Eiszeitalter*. Tauschnitz, Leipzig

PENNINGTON, W. (1947). Studies on the history of the British vegetation, VII. Lake sediments. *Phil. Trans.*, **B233**, 137–175

PETERSON, O. A. (1919). Report on the material discovered in the Upper Eocene of the Vinta Basin by Earl Douglas. *Ann. Carnegie Mus.*, **12**, 40–168

PILGRIM, G. E. (1926). The fossil Suidae of India. *Pal. Indica.* (new ser.), **8**, 1–65

PILGRIM, G. E. (1939). The fossil Bovidae of India. *Pal. Indica.* (new ser)., **26D** 1–356

PILGRIM, G. E. (1940). Middle Eocene mammals from north west India. *Proc. Zool. Soc. Lond.*, **110**, 127–152

PILGRIM, G. E. (1941). The dispersal of the Artiodactyla. *Biol. Rev.*, **16**, 134–163

PILGRIM, G. E. (1944). The lower limit of the Pleistocene in Europe. *Geol. Mag.*, **81**, 28–38

PILGRIM, G. E. (1946). The evolution of the buffaloes, oxen, sheep and goats. *J. Linn. Soc. Zool.*, **41**, 272–286

PILGRIM, G. E. AND HOPWOOD, A. T. (1928). *Catalogue of the Pontian Bovidae of Europe*. British Museum (Nat. Hist.)

PILGRIM, G. E. AND SCHAUB, S. S. (1939). Die schraubenhornige Antilope des europäischen Oberpliocaens. *Abh. Schweiz. Paleont. Ges. Basel.*, **62**, 1–30

PIVETEAU, J. (1955). Les mammifères mesozoiques. *Traité de Zoologie*, **17**, 27–46

POCOCK, R. I. (1919). On the external characters of the existing chevrotains. *Proc. Zool. Soc. Lond.*, 1–11

POST, L. VAN (1946). The prospect of pollen-analysis in the study of the earths climatic history. *New Phytol.*, **45**, 193–217

POTBURY, S. S. (1935). The La Porte flora of Plumas County, California. *Carnegie Inst. Washington. Publ.*, **465**, 29–81

PRESTWICH, J. (1854). On the thickness of the London Clay. *Quart. J. geol. Soc. Lond.*, **10**, 401–419

QUIMPY, G. I. (1958). Fluted points and geo-chronology of the Lake Michigan basin. *Amer. Antiquity*, **23**, 247–254

REID, C. AND REID, E. M. (1915). The Pliocene floras of the Dutch–Prussian border. *Meded. Rijksopsporing v. Delftstoffen.*, **6**, 178

REID, E. M. (1920). A comparative review of Pliocene floras based on the study of fossil seeds. *Quart. J. geol. Soc. Lond.*, **76**, 145–161

REID, E. M. (1949). The late-glacial flora of the Lea Valley. *New Phytol.*, **48**, 245

REID, E. M. AND CHANDLER, M. E. J. (1923). The fossil flora of Clacton-on-sea. *Quart. J. geol. Soc.*, **79**, 619

REID, E. M. AND CHANDLER, M. E. J. (1933). *The Flora of the London Clay*. British Museum (Nat. Hist.)

RIGGS, E. (1935). A skeleton of *Astrapotherium*. *Publ. Field. Mus. Nat. Hist. (geol.)*, **6**, 167–177

RINGSTROM, T. (1927). Uber quartare und jungtertiare Rhinocerotiden aus China und Mongolei. *Pal. Sinica.* (ser. C), **4**, 1–21

ROBINSON, J. T. (1958). Prehominid and hominid evolution. *Evolution*, **8**, 324–334

ROMAN, M. F. (1911). Les rhinocérides de l'Oligocene d'Europe. *Arch. Mus. Hist. Nat. Lyon.*, **11**, 1–92

ROMER, A. S. (1945). *Vertebrate Paleontology*. Chicago University Press

ROTH, S. (1903). Los ungulados sudamericanos. *An. Mus. La Plata Paleont. Argent.*, **5**, 1–36

ROTH, S. (1927). La differenciacion del sistema dentario en los ungulados notoungulados y primates. *Rev. Mus. La Plata*, **30**, 172–255

REFERENCES

SANBORN, E. I. (1935). The Comstock flora of west central Oregon. *Carnegie Inst. Washington Publ.*, **465**, 1–28

SCHAUB, S. (1928). Die Tapirschädel von Haslen. *Abh. Schweiz. Paleont. Ges. Basel.*, **47**, 1–28

SCHLAIJKER, E. M. (1937). A new tapir from the Miocene of Wyoming. *Bull. Mus. Comp. Zool. Harvard*, **76**, 1–27

SCHLOSSER, M. (1904). Die fossilen Cavicornis von Samos. *Beitrag. Geol. Osterreich-Ungarns.*, **17**, 21–118

SCHLOSSER, M. (1924). Uber die systematische Stellung jungtertiarer Cerviden *Centralbl. Min. Geol. Paläont.*, **20**, 634–640

SCHULTZ, C. B. AND FALKENBACH, C. H. (1940). Merycochoerinae, a new sub-family of oreodonts, *Bull. Amer. Mus. Nat. Hist.*, **77**, 213–306

SCHULTZ, C. B. (1941). Ticholeptinae, a new sub-family of oreodonts. *ibid.*, **79**, 1–105

SCHUTRUMPF, R. (1943). Paleobotanisch-pollenanalytische Untersuchungen der palaolithischen Rentierjagerfundstatte von Meiendorf bei Hamburg. *Veröff. Archäolog. Reichsinst.*, 1

SCHWARZ, E. (1937). Die fossilen Antilopen von Oldoway. *Wiss. Ergebn. Oldoway. Exp. 1913*, **4**, 7–90

SCOTT, W. B. (1910). Mammalia of the Santa Cruz beds. Pt. 1. Litopterna. *Rept. Princeton Univ. Exp. Patagonia*, **7**, 1–156

SCOTT, W. B. (1913). *A History of the Land Mammals of the Western Hemisphere*. Macmillan, New York

SCOTT, W. B. (1928). Mammalia of the Santa Cruz beds. Pt. 4. Astrapotheria. *Rept. Princeton Univ. Exp. Patagonia*, **6**, 301–342

SCOTT, W. B. (1937). *A History of the Land Mammals of the Western Hemisphere*. 2nd format. Macmillan, New York

SCOTT, W. B. (1941). Artiodactyla. Pt. 4. Of the mammalian fauna of the White River Oligocene. *Trans. Amer. phil. Soc. (new ser.)*, **28**, 155–269

SCOTT, W. B. (1940b). Perissodactyla. *Ibid.* Pt. 5

SEDDON, B. (1957). Late-glacial cwm glaciers in Wales. *J. glaciol.*, **3**, 94–99

SEFVE, I. (1912). Die fossilen pferde sudamerikas. *K. Svensk. Vetens. Handl. Stockholm*, **48**, 1–185

SELLARDS, E. H. (1952). *Early Man in America*. University of Texas Press

SEWARDS, A. C. (1926). The Cretaceous plant-bearing rocks of western Greenland. *Phil. Trans.*, **B115**, 57–175

SEWARDS, A. C. AND HOLTTUM, R. E. (1924). Tertiary plants from Mull. *Mem. Geol. Surv. Scotland*, 67–90

SHEPPARD, P. M. (1958). *Natural Selection and Heredity*. Hutchinson, London

SIMPSON, G. G. (1929). Paleocene and Lower Eocene mammals of Europe. *Amer. Mus. Novit.*, **354**, 1–17

SIMPSON, G. G. (1933a). Structure and affinities of Trigonostylops. *Amer. Mus. Novit.*, **608**, 1–28

SIMPSON, G. G. (1933b). Brain casts of two typotheres and a litoptern. *Amer. Mus. Novit.*, **629**, 1–18

SIMPSON, G. G. (1934). Provisional classification of extinct South American mammals. *Amer. Mus. Novit.*, **750**, 1–21

SIMPSON, G. G. (1935a). Descriptions of the oldest known South American mammals from the Rio Chico formation. *Amer. Mus. Novit.*, **793**, 1–25

SIMPSON, G. G. (1935b). The first mammals. *Rev. Biol.*, **10**, 154–180

SIMPSON, G. G. (1936). Additions to the Puerco fauna, Lower Paleocene. *Amer. Mus. Novit.*, **849**, 1–11

SIMPSON, G. G. (1937). The Fort Union of the Crazy Mountain Field, Montana, and its mammalian fauna. *Bull. U.S. Nat. Mus.*, **169**, 1–287

REFERENCES

SIMPSON, G. G. (1940). Studies on the earliest Primates. *Bull. Amer. Mus. Nat. Hist.*, **77**, 185–212

SIMPSON, G. G. (1944). *Tempo and Mode in Evolution.* Columbia University Press

SIMPSON, G. G. (1945). The principles of the classification of mammals. *Bull. Amer. Mus. Nat. Hist.*, **85**, 1–350

SIMPSON, G. G. (1945). A review of some Pleistocene and Recent tapirs. *Bull. Amer. Mus. Nat. Hist.*, **86**, 40–81

SIMPSON, G. G. (1948). The beginning of the age of mammals in South America. *Bull. Amer. Mus. Nat. Hist.*, **91**, 1–230

SINCLAIR, W. J. (1909). Mammalia of the Santa Cruz beds. Typotheria. *Rept. Princeton Univ. exp. Patagonia*, **6**, 1–110

SINNOTT, E. W., AND BAILEY, I. W. (1915). Investigations on the phylogeny of the Angiosperms. *Amer. J. Bot.*, **2**, 1–22

SINNOTT, E. W AND BAILEY, I. W. (1916). The climatic distribution of certain types of angiosperm leaves. *Amer. J. Bot.*, **3**, 23–39

SMITH, A. G. (1958). The lacustrine deposits in the south of the English Lake district. *New Phytol.*, **57**, 363

SODAY, F. J. (1954). The Quad site, a paleo-indian village in northern Alabama. *Tenn. Archeol.*, **10**, 1–20

SOKOLOV, I. I. (1954). Natural classification of the Bovidae. *Trav. Inst. Zool. Akad. Nauk. U.S.S.R.*, **14**, 3–295

ŚRODON, A. (1952). Pózno-glacjalny flora z dziadowych Kątow koło grywaldu. *Panst. inst. geol. Warsaw. Bull.*, **67**, 77–97

STEENHUIS, J. F. (1937). Bijdrage tot de kennis van het kwartsgehalte der grind-houdende zandlagen aan de oppervlakt en in de ondergrond van Nederland. *Verh. Geol. Mijnb. gen. geol.*, **12**, 1–40

STEHLIN, H. G. (1900). Ueber die Geschichte des Suiden-Gebisses. *Abh. Schweiz. Paleont. Ges. Basel.*, **27**, 337–527

STEHLIN, H. G. (1903–1916). Saugetiere des schweizerischen Eocaens. *Ibid.* Final contribution, **41**, 1299–1552

STEHLIN, H. G. (1928). Bemerkungen uber die Hirsche von Steinheim am Aalbach. *Eclog. Geol. Helvetiae*, **21**, 245–256

STEHLIN, H. G. (1937). Bemerkungen uber die miocänen Hirschgenera *Stephan-ocnemas* und *Lagomeryx*. *Verh. Naturf. Ges. Basel*, **48**, 193–214

STIRTON, R. A. (1938). Notes on some late Tertiary and Pleistocene antilocaprids. *J. mammal.*, **19**, 366–370

STIRTON, R. A. (1940). Phylogeny of North American Equidae. *Univ. Calif. Publ. Bull. Geol. Sci.*, **25**, 165–198

SUGGATE, R. P. AND WEST, R. G. (1959). On the extent of the last glaciation in eastern England. *Proc. Roy. Soc.*, **B150**, 263–283

SZAFER, W. (1946). The Pliocene flora of Krościenko, in Poland. *Rozpr. Wydz. mat. przy. Akad. Um.*, **72** (2 vols.)

TANSLEY, A. G. (1949). *The British Islands and their Vegetation.* 2nd ed. Cambridge

TESCH, P. (1942). De Noordzee van historisch-geologisch standpunt. *Mededeel. s'Rijks Geol. Dienst*, **A9**

THORPE, M. R. (1937). The primitive and carnivore like characters of the Mery-coidodontidae. *Amer. J. Sci.*, **6**, 239–246

TROELS-SMITH, J. (1954). Ertebøllekultur–Bondebøllekultur. *Arb. Nordisk. Oldkyndig og hist.*

TROELS-SMITH, J. (1955). Pollenanalytische Untersuchungen zu einigen schweizer-ischen Pfahlbauproblemen. *Das Pfahlbau-problem.* Schaffhausen

TROELS-SMITH, J. (1960). Ivy, mistletoe and elm. Climate indicators—Fodder, plants. *Danm. geol. Unders.* IV, **4**, 1–32

REFERENCES

UMBGROVE, J. H. F. (1942). *The Pulse of the Earth.* Martinus Nyhoff, The Hague

VAUFREY, R. (1955). Proboscidiens fossiles. *Traité de Zoologie,* **17,** 784–875

VAUFREY, R. (1957). Proboscidiens fossiles. *Traité de Paléontologie.* Masson, Paris

VIRET, J. (1955). Ordre des Créodontes. *Traité de Zoologie.* Masson, Paris, **17,** 188–193

VLERK, I. VAN DER (1959). Problems and principles of Tertiary and Quaternary stratigraphy. *Quart. J. geol. Soc. Lond.,* **115,** 49

VLERK, I. VAN DER, AND FLORSCHÜTZ, R. (1950). *Nederland in het Ijstijdvak.* de Haan, Utrecht

DE VRIES, H. AND BARENDSON, G. W. (1954). Measurements of age by the radio carbon technique. *Nature, Lond.,* **1745,** 1138

WASSENBERG, G. I., HAYDEN, R. I. AND IENSEN, F. (1956). Ar⁴⁰ and K⁴⁰ dating of igneous rocks and sediments. *Geochim. Cosmochim. Acta.,* **10,** 153

WALKER, D. (1955a). Studies in the Post-glacial history of the British vegetation, XIV; Skelsmergh Tarn and Kentmere, Westmorland. *New Phytol.,* **54,** 222–254

WALKER, D. (1955b). Late-glacial deposits at Lunds, Yorkshire. *New Phytol.,* **54,** 343–349

WALKER, D. (1956). A Late-glacial deposit at St. Bees, West Cumberland. *Quart. J. geol. Soc. Lond.,* **112,** 93–101

WEAVER, C. E. (1943). Paleontology of the marine Tertiary of Oregon and Washington. *Univ. Wash. Publ. Geol.,* **5,** 1–789

WEBER, M. (1928). *Die Saugetiere.* Gustav Fischer, Jena

WEIGELT, J. (1933). Neue Primaten aus der mitteleozänen (oberlutetischen) Braunköhle des Geisaltales. *Nova. Acta. Leo. Carol.* (new ser.), **1,** 97–156

WEST, R. G. (1955). The glacial and interglacial deposits of East Anglia. *Quaternaria,* **2,** 45–52

WEST, R. G. (1956). The Quaternary deposits at Hoxne, Suffolk. *Phil. Trans.,* **B239,** 265–356

WEST, R. G. (1957). The interglacial deposits at Bobbitshole, Ipswich. *Phil. Trans.,* **B241,** 1–31

WEST, R. G. (1958). The Pleistocene Epoch in East Anglia. *J. Glaciol.,* **3,** 211

WEST, R. G. (1961a). Interglacial and interstadial vegetation. *Proc. Linn. Soc. Lond.,* **172,** 81–89

WEST, R. G. (1961b). Vegetational history of the early Pleistocene of The Royal Society investigations at Ludham. *Proc. Roy. Soc.,* **B154,** 437–453

WEST, R. G. AND GODWIN, H. (1958). The Cromerian interglacial. *Nature, Lond.,* **181,** 1554

WEST, R. G. AND SPARKS, B. W. (1960). Coastal interglacial deposits of the English Channel. *Phil. Trans.,* **B243,** 95–133

WINGE, H. (1924). *Patterdyr-Slaegter.* Copenhagen

WITTHOFT, J. (1952). A paleo-indian site in eastern Pennsylvania. *Proc. Amer. Phil. Soc.,* **96,** 464–495

WOERKOM, A. J. J. VAN (1953). The astronomical theory of climate changes. In Shapley, H. *Climatic Change.* Harvard University Press, 147–157

WOLDSTEDT, P. (1956). Das vereisungsgebiet der Britischen Inseln. *Geol. Jahr.,* **65,** 621–640

WOOD, H. E. (1934). Revision of the Hyrachyidae. *Amer. Mus. Nat. Hist. Bull.,* **67,** 181–295

WOOD, H. E. (1937). Perissodactyl suborders. *J. Mammal.,* **18,** 106

WOOD, H. E. (1941). Trends in rhinoceros evolution. *Trans. N.Y. Acad. Sci.* (ser. 2), **3,** 83–96

WORMINGTON, H. M. (1957). Ancient Man in North America. 4th ed. *Denver Mus. Nat. Hist. Colorado*

ZAGWIJN, W. H. (1957). Vegetation, climate and time correlations in the early Pleistocene of Europe. *Geol. en Mijnb.* 19 Jaarg, **7,** 233–244

REFERENCES

ZAGWIJN, W. H. (1960). Aspects of the Pliocene and early Pleistocene vegetation in the Netherlands. *Meded. Geol. Sticht.*, **C3, 1,** 1–78

ZDANSKY, O. (1925). Fossile Hirsche Chinas. *Pal. Sinica* (ser. C), **2,** 1–90

ZEUNER, F. E. (1945). *The Pleistocene Period,* Ray Soc. Publ., London. New edition, Hutchinson, 1959

ZEUNER, F. E. (1952). *Dating the Past.* 3rd ed. Methuen, London

ZUCKERMAN, S. (1932). *The Social Life of Monkeys and Apes.* Kegan Paul

INDEX

15   217

227